LANDSCAPE

CAMBRIDGE
UNIVERSITY PRESS
LONDON: BENTLEY HOUSE
NEW YORK, TORONTO, BOMBAY
CALCUTTA, MADRAS: MACMILLAN
TOKYO: MARUZEN COMPANY LTD

Alluvial fans built upon the margin of the Canterbury piedmont alluvial plain, New Zealand, which is here trenched to a depth of 600 ft. by the terraced valley of the Rakaia River.

LANDSCAPE

AS DEVELOPED BY THE PROCESSES OF
NORMAL EROSION

by

C. A. COTTON

Professor of Geology
Victoria University College, Wellington, N.Z.

CAMBRIDGE
AT THE UNIVERSITY PRESS
1941

PRINTED IN GREAT BRITAIN

To the memory of
the illustrious

GILBERT, POWELL & DAVIS

Explanatory concepts are known through and through, fore and aft: the farther side of the concept of a ridge is seen just as well as the near side, by the eye of the imagination, which takes any point of view that it desires; the inside of the ridge is seen as well as the outside, the past and future forms of the ridge as well as the present form, for all these concepts are avowedly mental concepts only and not matters of fact.

W. M. DAVIS

CONTENTS

Chapter X. Homoclinal Features and Structural Benches

Homoclinal ridges. Structural escarpments. Hogbacks. Cuestas. Homoclinal shifting. Mesas and buttes. Structural plateaux. Structural benches and terraces.

Chapter XI. Transverse Valleys; Superposed and Antecedent Gorges

Transverse gorges. Antecedent rivers. Anteconsequent gorges. Gorges of superposed rivers. Superposed subsequents.

Chapter XII. Lateral Corrasion and Meandering Rivers

Lateral corrasion. Flood plains. Spur trimming. Cut-off and narrowed spurs. Meanders. Misfit rivers. Lateral planation. Wide valley plains. Braided river courses.

Chapter XIII. River Terraces

Terraces due to lateral corrasion. Valley-plain terraces. Slip-off slope terraces. Rock-defended terraces. Terraces of continuous valley excavation during restrained down-cutting. Causes of terracing. Slopes of terraces.

Chapter XIV. Maturity of the Landscape; Subdued Relief-forms

Grading of slopes. Subdued hill forms. Granite domes. Convex profiles. Concave valley sides. Razor-back ridges. Theory of waxing and waning valley development. Mature-born landscapes.

Chapter XV. Constructional Land Forms; Aggraded Plains

Talus slopes. Graded land slopes. Reversion after deforestation. Aggraded plains. Aggradation in the Glacial Period. Ponding by aggradation and diversion of rivers by alluviation.

Chapter XVI. Fans; Bahadas; Basin Plains; and Deltas

Alluvial fans. Piedmont alluvial plains or bahadas. Basin plains. Deltas. Delta plains.

Chapter XVII. Peneplains

Old age of the landscape. Peneplanation. Monadnocks. Old-from-birth peneplains. Infantile features of uplifted peneplains. European, Asiatic, and American peneplains. The great Australian peneplain. Peneplanation in New Zealand. Late geological date of most peneplanation. Accordance of summit levels.

Chapter XVIII. Resurrected Fossil Land Surfaces

Fossil erosion surfaces. Fossil peneplains. Resurrected surfaces. Conditions of survival. Proofs of origin. Intersecting peneplains.

PLATES

x

VIII

1. V-shaped young valley of the Ngahauranga, New Zealand

2. Winding valley forms in the young Ngahauranga Valley, Wellington, New Zealand, where curves have been enlarged by lateral corrasion accompanying incision of the valley. At the right the neck of a valley-side spur is narrowed, and almost cut through, by intersection of undercut slopes

IX

1. A stream infantile in the post-Glacial cycle of normal erosion plunges at the Stirling Falls from the lip of a hanging valley, dropping 500 ft. into a fiord, Milford Sound, New Zealand
   Photo. by H. C. Peart

2. Halawa Falls, Molokai, Hawaiian Islands, illustrating plunge-pool back-scour
   Photo. by U.S. 18th Air Base Photo. Lab.

X

1. The Wairua Falls, North Auckland, New Zealand

2. Stoneybyres Falls, Lanark, Scotland, showing development of a canyon below the falls
   Photo. by H.M. Geol. Survey. By permission Controller H.M. Stationery Office

XI

1. Lakelets on an ice-scoured upland in Switzerland

2. The English Lake Ullswater, of Glacial origin

XII

Waikaremoana, a landslide lake. The outlet gorge (left) through a homoclinal ridge of sandstone, the escarpment of which defines the skyline, has been blocked by an enormous rock slide, and this dams the lake to a high level in a branching valley-system
   Photo. by *Wellington Evening Post*

XIII

1. Lake Rotoaira, New Zealand, impounded by the more distant lava-flows descending northward (right to left in this view) from the volcano Tongariro
   Photo. by Professor Douglas Johnson

2. A small lake in a valley blocked by a wandering dune, near Auckland, New Zealand
   Photo. by T. L. Lancaster

XIV

1. Youthful dissection of an uplifted peneplain, Southern Tableland, New South Wales ("Shoalhaven Lookover")
   Photo. by Eric Merton

2. Consequent drainage on a volcanic "shower" deposit spread over a hilly surface near Lake Rotomahana, New Zealand, by the explosive eruption of 1886.

PLATES

XV

1. Homoclinal ridge, Marlborough, New Zealand, showing contrast between escarpment and dip-slope
2. Full-face view of the escarpment in a continuation of the ridge shown in Fig. 1

XVI

1. Serrate hogback ridges, Marlborough, New Zealand
2. A rapidly retreating escarpment of limestone in the Broken River intermont basin, New Zealand

XVII

1. A scalloped escarpment of the Carboniferous limestone, Eglwyseg Mountain, Denbighshire
   Photo. by H.M. Geol. Survey. By permission Controller H.M. Stationery Office
2. Butte near Ficksburg, Orange Free State
   Photo. by L. C. King

XVIII

1. The Vermilion Cliffs escarpment separating broad structural benches, in the Colorado Plateau province of the Western United States
   Photo. by Professor Douglas Johnson
2. Structural terraces and dissected valley-side spurs projecting into the Grand Canyon of the Colorado River, Arizona
   Photo. by Professor Douglas Johnson

XIX

1. The Rakaia Gorge, Canterbury, New Zealand
2. Lodore Canyon, part of the gorge of the Green River through the Uinta Mountains, which was formerly regarded as of antecedent origin, but now explained as superposed
   Photo. by Geo. A. Grant

XX

1. Flood-plain scrolls, an early stage of flood-plain development, in the valley of the Waimana River, Urewera, New Zealand
2. The Rainbow Natural Bridge, Utah
   Photo. by Professor H. E. Gregory

XXI

1. Meanders on a continuous flood plain in the upper valley of the Cobb River, Nelson, New Zealand
   Photo. by A. R. Kingsford
2. Valley-floor features in the beheaded valley of the Karori stream, Wellington, New Zealand, which is now occupied only by an underfit rivulet

XXII

1. Braided channels of the Waimakariri River, New Zealand
2. "Rock terrace", Wairoa River, Nelson, New Zealand

PLATES

XXX

1. An aggraded valley-plain, which is an up-valley extension of the delta of the Clarence River, New Zealand

2. Horizontal sky-line of a level-topped block mountain, Mount Pisa, Otago, New Zealand, which may be a remnant of an extensive late-Tertiary peneplain

XXXI

1. The Gouland Downs plateau, New Zealand. The plateau is a resurrected fossil plain, and the same surface, slightly dissected, is warped up over the mountains at the rear

2. A narrow tilted strip of resurrected fossil plain, showing the bottle-neck valleys of superposed consequent streams incised to a shallow depth below the surface, near St Bathans, New Zealand

XXXII

1. Sarsen stones lying on the little-dissected tilted surface of Rough Ridge, New Zealand
   Photo. by Professor Douglas Johnson

2. Dissected margin of the undulating plateau of south-eastern Otago, at Hillend, New Zealand

XXXIII

1. Shoulders separating fully mature upper valley-side slopes from steep young lower slopes, Haywards, Wellington, New Zealand

2. Valley-in-valley form of the Shotover Valley, New Zealand

XXXIV

1. Incised ("ingrown") meanders in a rejuvenated landscape, Hawke's Bay, New Zealand
   Photo. by V. C. Browne

2. Headwater tributaries of the Wainui-o-mata system aggraded so as to form extensive swampy flats as a result of strong headward tilting, Wellington, New Zealand

XXXV

1. Youthfully dissected fault scarp, with blunt-ended spurs strictly in line, Wellington, New Zealand

2. Young fault scarp of a granitic mountain block south-east of Deep Springs Valley, eastern California, "Narrow V-shaped canyons have abnormally small alluvial fans at their mouths. Also the lowest part of the valley...is situated at the base of the scarp instead of in the middle of the basin" (Blackwelder)
   Photo. by Professor Eliot Blackwelder

PLATES

XXXVI

1. Maturely-dissected fault scarp of the Inyo Mountains (of Palaeozoic rocks with granite intrusions) north of Lone Pine, California
   Photo. by Professor Eliot Blackwelder

2. Facetted spur-ends along part of the western base of the Wasatch Range, Utah
   Photo. by Professor Douglas Johnson

XXXVII

1. Facets of the Wellington fault scarp at Petone, New Zealand

2. Scarplet along the west base of the Sonoma Range, Nevada, formed at the time of the earthquake in 1915. It extends for about 40 miles across both spur-ends and alluvial fans, and is from 10 ft. to 20 ft. high
   Photo. by Professor Eliot Blackwelder

XXXVIII

1. "Earthquake rent" tracing the line of outcrop of a great thrust fault which bounds the tectonic block of the Seaward Kaikoura Range, New Zealand, on the south-east side
   Photo. by W. A. McKay

2. Wharf at Napier, New Zealand, uplifted 6 ft. in 1931. Former and present high-water marks are at the upper edges of two dark bands of marine growth on the piles

XXXIX

1. Fault-line scarp. Ruakokopatuna Valley, Wairarapa district, New Zealand. Deformed Mesozoic rocks are separated by a fault at the base of the scarp from Pliocene limestone (foreground), from above which a great thickness of weak beds has been eroded

2. West base of the Baldwin Range, New South Wales, which, as described by W. N. Benson, is a fault-line scarp exposed by the removal of soft mudstone of late Upper Devonian age along a fault contact with resistant agglomerate beds (early Upper Devonian). Relief, 1000 ft.

XL

1. Fault-line or composite scarp, Cave, South Canterbury, New Zealand. Subdued forms developed by erosion on soft covering strata are seen in front of the scarp

2. Rejuvenated outlet gorge from the Hanmer intermont basin, New Zealand, which has been in part re-excavated, with resurrection of fault scarp bounding it

XLI

1. Splinter of the scarp forming the north wall of the Waitaki Valley graben, New Zealand

2. A fault-scarp facing Death Valley, California, showing structural bands of rock-outcrops running obliquely down the scarp

PLATES

XLII

1. Karrenfeld, Punakaiki, New Zealand
   Photo. by W. A. Scott

2. A stream emerges at water-level from an underground course through a tunnel due to solution of limestone, Broken River, New Zealand
   Photo. by Professor R. Speight

XLIII

1. Sinkholes in a limestone surface, South Canterbury, New Zealand
   Photo. by M. C. Gudex

2. One of a series of sinkholes aligned along an underground drainage channel, Nelson province, New Zealand

XLIV

1. Limestone arches, Jenolan Caves, New South Wales

2. A wasting outcrop (a small "hum") of limestone, showing lapiés, Whangarei district, New Zealand

PREFACE

NOTWITHSTANDING the close relation of the study and description of the natural landscape to geography, I trust that geologists will accept this modest exposition of the elementary principles of geomorphology as a contribution to the literature of their science. Not only has the development of geomorphic forms followed as a corollary of prior geological events, but a reasoned understanding of the working out of geomorphic processes is also a necessary part of the equipment required for the interpretation of geological history. So geologists must do their part in the elucidation of geomorphic problems and the development of the science of systematic geomorphology.

The book has been inspired by the writings of the master geomorphologist William Morris Davis, and to a smaller but by no means negligible extent by his oral teaching. I need make no apology, therefore, for raiding the treasure house of ideas and illustrative examples which are available to all who will read his works. My indebtedness to this great teacher and leader in his science was acknowledged long before his lamented death.

I need not apologise either for adopting the method of deductive analysis so effectively used by Davis, wherever it seems it can be safely applied to the description and classification of land forms on the basis of what may be termed the Davisian cycle. As is stated in Chapter IV, features can be found in actual landscapes to match *practically every one* of a deduced series worked out on the assumption of the essential correctness of the concept of the cycle of erosion. If asked why *every* one cannot actually be so matched, and whether some appearance of inconsistency, or lack of completeness, in nature can be reconciled with a belief in the efficacy of the cycle method of treatment of geomorphology, I should reply with this parable: Once there was staged an elaborate pageant of many acts and scenes. Some of the scenes were long, requiring from ten to fifteen minutes for their presentation, but others were so short as to require but a rise and fall of the curtain. An unenthusiastic spectator, spending only an occasional few minutes in the auditorium, could not fail to see something of the longer scenes, but some of the shorter he might miss altogether. So with landscape stages. Some are essential links in a deductive chain, but have been run through in nature in a flash (if we think in terms of geological time), and examples illustrative of such stages must necessarily be very rare in the landscapes of to-day. Others that require perhaps thousands of times as long for their enactment are responsible for the development of relatively stable (in the sense of long-lived) types of land forms with which we are familiar in many landscapes. A stock example of the former is the elusive stage of "cuesta-bridges" several times referred to by Davis in philosophical discussions of the explanatory description of land forms (see Fig. 37, p. 66).

This preface would be incomplete without some further acknow-ledgments, for my net has been widely spread for illustrative examples and it has been necessary for me to go considerably beyond the range of my own observations. I have tried to acknow-ledge fully in the appropriate places my indebtedness both to the writers on whose descriptions of typical landscape forms I have drawn and to those correspondents who have most generously supplied photographic illustrations, and I trust that any omissions inadvertently made will be charitably forgiven.

C. A. C.

Postscript. It has been said that every text-book is out of date before it is printed. I believe this is an exaggeration; but, if a great lag in publication can be detected in the case of this book, some excuse for it may be found in the troublous times in which we live and in the long sea route by way of which manuscript and proofs must pass to and fro between Cambridge and the antipodes.

WELLINGTON, N.Z.
September 1940

CHAPTER I

Introduction

THE student of geomorphology is so often confronted with the results of atmospheric weathering, predominantly chemical, combined with downhill transportation of rock debris, largely facilitated by rain and running water, that he tends to separate these processes from all others. He is accustomed to think of them as "normal" as compared with others, which he places in a "special" category. These latter include the climate-controlled agencies, active in arid deserts, also glacial erosion, active at the present day only in restricted areas, and marine erosion, important only around the margin of the land. It is noteworthy that though certain commonly observed processes are termed "normal", it is not implied that others are "abnormal". As Fenneman observes, "The term 'normal erosion' is plainly open to criticism on the ground that one mode is just as normal as another, but no other satisfactory term has been proposed."

Normal processes develop normal landscapes, most of which present to the eye a succession of hill-and-valley or ridge-and-valley forms, and it is now universally recognised and regarded as a truism that the valleys have for the most part been excavated by streams of water that still flow through them. This explanation of the origin of valleys (and also of hills and ridges, which are merely the residual portions of the rock mass sculptured by erosion) gained acceptance, however, only in the nineteenth century. The arguments in favour of it were first clearly stated in 1802 by Playfair. Playfair relied for proof on what Davis has termed the *law of accordant junctions*, the principle of the adjustment of the gradients of tributaries so that they make accordant junctions with the main valley—so "that none of them join the principal valley either on too high or too low a level".[1] Though exceptions to Playfair's law of accordant junctions may be found, they are all capable of explanation in such a way as not to contradict the principle.

Many rivers are guided, as will be shown in later chapters, by

[1] J. Playfair, *Illustrations of the Huttonian Theory of the Earth*, p. 102 (1802).

depressions of tectonic origin, that is to say, due to earth movements. Thus guided they proceed to erode valleys for themselves, and a tectonic depression after it has been modified in form by a river flowing through it is often called the valley of the river. Such valleys are not wholly the work of rivers, and some geomorphologists try to restrict the application of the term "valley" to the portion that is really the result of river erosion. Neighbouring mountain masses also are not wholly residual in that they do not owe their full heights to the excavation of valleys by erosion. These, however, are the major landscape features, and even where such forms are dominant there can be no doubt regarding the erosional origin of all the smaller valleys and the residual character of the hills, ridges, and spurs that separate them.

It was not until the 'seventies of the nineteenth century, the heroic period of scientific exploration of the American West, that a corollary to Playfair's law sometimes known as "Powell's law of base-levelling" gained acceptance.[1] If sufficient time is allowed, the slopes of valley sides become more and more gentle, valley floors become broader and broader, and the intervening ridges and spurs become lower and lower, and, as the material of the land above sea-level is gradually carried away, particle by particle, the whole surface is eventually reduced to very faint relief.

When the enormous age of the earth is taken into account, the fact that the land surface is not a continuous plain sloping gently to sea-level seems to contradict Powell's principle, but the explanation is that, from time to time, parts of the surface have been uplifted, so that the work of erosion has had to be begun afresh on them. Some parts of the earth's surface have been worn down almost to sea-level over and over again in the course of "geological time".

In studying land forms one must bear in mind that no feature of the surface is a finished product. The agencies that effect changes of form are everywhere at work: every part of the surface is even now undergoing change, and its future forms will differ from the present as the present differ from the past.

The flowing landscapes of geologic time may be likened to a kinetoscope panorama. The scenes transform from age to age, as from act to

---

[1] J. W. Powell, *Report on the Colorado River of the West*, p. 204 (1875); *Report on the...Uinta Mountains*, pp. 27, 32, 196 (1876).

act; seas and plains and mountains follow and replace each other through time, as the traveller sees them replace each other in space....Science demonstrates that mountains are transient forms, but the eye of man through all his lifetime sees no change, and his reason is appalled at the thought of duration so vast that the millenniums of written history have not recorded the shifting of even one of the fleeting views whose blendings make the moving picture. (BARRELL.)

Little is known of the absolute rate at which landscape changes due to erosion proceed. It is certain, however, that the rate varies within very wide limits—to some degree with different conditions of climate, and to a far greater extent with the varying degree of weakness of, or of resistance to erosion offered by, the rocks of the terrain.

CHAPTER II

Mass Movement of Waste

THE waste produced by weathering, more especially that resulting from chemical weathering, or "rock decay", accumulates on all surfaces except the steepest and forms the waste-mantle of soil and subsoil, the latter consisting of residual clay and partly disintegrated and decayed rock fragments. It is the presence of the waste-mantle that allows of growth of vegetation; and vegetation, when present, does its part in turn by helping to bind the waste, and by thus retarding its removal increases the thickness of the accumulation and makes possible the rounding and smoothing of hilltops and slopes of moderate steepness (Chapter XIV).

Though rock decay continues, the thickness of the waste-mantle does not increase indefinitely, for the waste, or, at least, its upper layer, is continually being removed by rain-wash and downhill creep, starting thus on its long journey towards the sea or some other resting-place, where it will sooner or later come to rest as sediment.

More spectacular results are produced when gravity induces the sudden, or very rapid, precipitation of masses of waste and loosened rocks down slopes as *landslides*. These, though sporadic in occurrence and spasmodic in development, claim first attention as large-scale phenomena, and also because they are the direct and obvious causes of the formation of conspicuous land forms both in the scars left on the sides of hills and mountains and in the accumulation forms which result where the sliding, slumping, or streaming waste comes to rest. Into the scheme of the cycle of erosion, which will be developed in later chapters, these forms may be fitted as local and minor interruptions, and must be further regarded as locally developed initial forms on which the work of erosion must begin anew.

In *rock falls* and *rock slides* the displaced material consists almost wholly of loosened blocks of fresh or only slightly weathered rock, but more frequently landslide or "slip" material consists in great part of the debris of rock decay. It may be relatively dry, but often contains much water, which, acting as a lubricant, facilitates the downhill movement. Saturation by unusually heavy rain, indeed, lubricating the material of the waste-mantle so as to overcome the friction that has been holding it in place on a slope against the pull of gravity is the commonest cause of initiation of movement. With complete saturation, sliding movement may be replaced by flow. Support at the toe of a slope having been removed by active erosion of some kind, downhill movement takes place when friction has been reduced to such an extent that it is no longer competent to hold the material, the trigger effect that sets a slip in motion being produced by unusually heavy rain, or perhaps by an earthquake.

In a *rock slide* (as defined by Sharpe)[1] the surface on which movement takes place is a bedding plane, major joint, or other plane of separation existing in the rocks, and is generally inclined somewhat less steeply than the average slope of the ground. The great rock slide known as the "fall of the Rossberg", a major disaster, which caused much loss of life and property in Switzerland in 1806, took place along a bedding plane in the rocks of the Rossberg mountain, and resulted in spreading a collection of huge blocks of rock over the Goldau lowland several miles away.

Usually on a smaller scale a *debris slide* (Sharpe) is a similar movement of the waste-mantle, which separates itself from a lubricated surface of bedrock.

[1] C. F. S. Sharpe, *Landslides and Related Phenomena* (New York, 1938).

4

Rock falls (Sharpe), as their name indicates, are precipitated from cliffs or valley sides when these are sapped at the base by an

Fig. 1. Landslide-scarred mountain side, Karamea gorge, West Nelson, New Zealand. (Drawn by Dr J. Marwick.)

undercutting agent such as a river (Pl. I, 1) or the sea, or when an earthquake occurs. They obviously do not depend on lubrication to the same extent as slides, nor is movement guided by an under-lying slip plane.

5

Great rock falls, very extensive rock slides, and innumerable debris slides were set in motion by the New Zealand earthquakes of 1929 and 1931 in the West Nelson and Hawke's Bay districts. Every mountain side in the former district is now marked by numerous scars, where the waste-mantle and with it the forest covering have slipped away (Fig. 1). Similar scars have survived on the Rimutaka Range, near Wellington, since the earthquake of 1855.

In landslides of a *slump* character (Pl. I, 2), as distinguished from "slides", movement takes place on a *slip surface*, which is "typically deep-reaching and is a spoon-shaped surface or zone concave towards the slip" (Sharpe). The material moves "as a unit or as several subsidiary units, usually with backward rotation". This movement is of the nature of superficial gravity faulting. Curved branches from the slip surface commonly extend upwards, and so the slumped ground exhibits a terraced or stepped effect, with backward tilting of the steps that are formed at the surface where slumped strips have rotated somewhat as they have moved down the curved branches of the slip surface (Fig. 2 and Pl. II, 1). Slump movement may result in exposure of a great amphitheatre-shaped (or "spoon-shaped") scar in the landscape.

In some cases slumping that extends only to a shallow depth is indicated at the surface only by a series of slightly rotated narrow strips, termed *terracettes* (Sharpe). These are formed on slopes of 20° and even less of material that is thoroughly shattered and self-lubricated—like the "hydraulic limestone" of northern New Zealand, for example. This material is so unstable that the opening of road and railway cuttings is sufficient to cause whole hillsides to slump, even though the relief is small and all slopes are gentle.

Slump movement involves a forward horizontal thrust as an accompaniment of the subsidence at the rear, and, consequently, an upthrust or upwarped zone is found in some cases instead of heaped or streaming debris in front of the slumped ground. A striking example of this is afforded by the Whitecliffs slide,[1] which developed in front of a collapsing sea cliff, 1200 ft. high, on the west coast of Nelson, New Zealand, as a result of the great earthquake of 1929. A part of the marginal sea floor 50 acres in extent,

---

[1] As interpreted by J. Henderson, The West Nelson Earthquakes of 1929, *N.Z. Dep. Sci. Indust. Res. Bull.* 55, pp. 132–5 (1937).

with its population of marine organisms, was thrust up to heights varying up to 100 ft. above the sea (Pl. II, 2).

The displaced material of a rock slide, even though dry, may be shot forward with such momentum as to spread it over a large area, burying vegetation, the habitations of men, and even pre-existing features of surface relief to a great depth, as in the case of the Rossberg-Goldau slide. In numerous places in the West Nelson

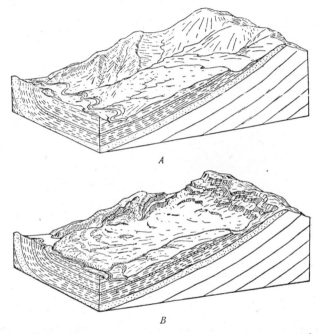

Fig. 2. Diagram of the Gros Ventre slide, Wyoming. *A* is a restoration of the former landscape; *B* exhibits slump and "earth-flow" features. (After Blackwelder.)

district of New Zealand burial to a depth of 100–200 ft. is recorded at distances up to a mile from the sources of the 1929 earthquake slides.

In the case of a slide of debris or of unconsolidated material saturated with water, the mobility may be sufficiently great to allow of flow down quite gentle slopes. The debris stream moves forward with a rolling motion and sometimes with considerable velocity, spreads over low-lying and perhaps level ground far from

7

its source, and comes to rest as a concourse of irregular ridges and hummocks somewhat resembling glacial moraines. Undrained hollows among the hummocks may form tarns or small lakes (Pl. I, 2 and Pl. III, 1).

Larger lakes are formed when landslides block valleys and pond rivers (Fig. 3). Lakes held up by dams of loose debris are short-lived, for their overflow streams scour channels through the dams very soon after overflow takes place. Such bursting of landslide dams has been a frequent cause of disastrous floods in lower valleys. In the case of the Gohna landslide and temporary lake, formed in a Himalayan tributary of the Ganges in 1893, a barrier of debris 2 miles long and 800–900 ft. high blocked the mountain valley in

Fig. 3. A landslide lake in a mountain valley. (After W. M. Davis.)

such a way as to form a lake in it 3 miles long. Though the river took eight months to fill the lake basin so formed, when it became full to overflowing the outgoing stream cut a trench 400 ft. deep through the dam in a few hours.

Numerous lakes were formed as a result of the rock falls and rock slides brought down by the 1929 earthquake in New Zealand. One, in the Matakitaki valley is 3 miles long, and took four days to fill. Others, in the Maruia, Buller, and Mohikinui valleys had only short lives. The last-named was impounded by a dam 75 ft. high and lasted seventeen days.

Some large lakes are held up by dams formed by ancient rock falls or rock slides blocking gorges. These accumulations consist of boulders and great blocks of hard rock, and have greater strength to resist scouring by river erosion than have those composed of weathered debris or other loose material. Such is the origin ascribed to the large and beautiful New Zealand lake Waikaremoana, 2015 ft. above sea-level (Pl. XII). The overflow channel from this lake descends 1200 ft. in about 2 miles by the side of a great rockslide dam of sandstone blocks, which has closed a gorge through a sandstone ridge. Water leaks through and gushes from many chinks in the dam.

Earth flows (Sharpe) are landslides in which movement is so slow that the time occupied in attaining a new equilibrium may range from hours to years. An example is the Gros Ventre slide, in Wyoming (Fig. 2). Such movement takes place down gentle slopes. Superficial layers of waterlogged material may flow completely away from considerable areas—in some cases, as in examples in the St Lawrence Valley, in Canada, through bottle-neck outlets —to come to rest on adjacent valley bottoms, leaving extensive scarp-bounded scars. Incomplete outflow leaves slump features, including terracettes, within the scar boundaries.

Rapid and far-extending *mud flows* take the easiest courses down gullies and river valleys. They may travel many miles, temporarily filling the channels they follow to great depths with debris, though the flow passes on, and eventually comes to rest many miles from the source. They occur on steep slopes in Alpine districts and, rather commonly, in semi-arid regions, where the surface is not bound and protected by vegetation. Mud flows also characterise some phases of volcanic activity. Originating at or near the summits of high cones, these carry down the lower slopes not only volcanic mud but also great quantities of rock fragments, including some blocks of large size, and so mounds of volcanic boulders of all sizes may remain as hillocks, irregularly scattered or more regularly aligned in the direction of flow, after the finer material of the mud flow has been washed away (Pl. III, 2).

Less obvious than landsliding, but at the same time far more general, indeed almost universal, is an imperceptible downhill movement of the waste-mantle of slopes that is continuously in progress. Working along with surface wash, which is effective during heavy rains, this movement, termed *creep* by W. M. Davis, is the cause of migration of much waste to lower levels before it is eventually carried off by permanent running streams. The agency at work promoting creep is gravity, but creep has little else in common with flow, though the one may grade into the other. Small to-and-fro movements of rock and soil fragments in the waste-mantle are always taking place as the result of alternate heating and cooling, wetting and drying, freezing and thawing. Owing to the constant pull of gravity, there is a preponderance of downhill over uphill movement, and slow downhill creep results.

If expansion were equal in all directions, and extended indefinitely downward, the arrangement of the particles—or the structure of the formation—would not be affected; but dilatation is resisted in all directions except outward, and expansion in a single direction modifies the structure. The structure is again modified during the ensuing contraction, and during both changes gravity enters as a constant factor tending downhill. (GILBERT.)

Evidence of creep may be seen in the downhill sag of the edges of layers of partially weathered rocks, which is sometimes termed "outcrop curvature". Further positive evidence is found in the bending of tree trunks away from the vertical and the canting over of fence posts (Pl. IV, 1), the partial closing of artificial trenches that contour a slope, and the sometimes obvious migration of rock fragments away from outcrops of the parent rock (Fig. 4).

Fig. 4. Diagram of downhill creep of waste. (After Davis.)

Observers in regions with cold winters, who are familiar with the heaving of soil and subsoil due to frost, may be inclined to ascribe to frost action the chief role in promoting soil creep, but it cannot be the sole, and is perhaps not even the dominant, agency, as is witnessed by the evidence that creep is in progress in places where the soil is never frozen, as is the case in most parts of New Zealand.

Originating in association with soil creep there may be systems of small-scale terracettes, which may be taken advantage of by grazing animals and used by them as paths. It has been suggested that development of all "sheep track" patterns (such as those illustrated in Plate IV, 2) is controlled by backward tilting or rotation of small turf-covered soil blocks along curved surfaces.[1] Most sheep tracks, however, are worn paths of bare ground cut by the hooves of grazing animals and scoured to some extent by rain wash. To what extent "the continued walking of cattle [or sheep] on hillside paths will aid the development of small slip planes", as Sharpe suggests, and so assist the mass movement of waste remains problematical.

Downhill movement on screes or talus slopes takes place in part by creep (*talus creep* or *rock creep*), but there may be also much streaming and rolling of material down the surface slope as down a chute. The source of supply of the usually angular scree material is most often a bare-rock cliff or sharp mountain crest that is undergoing mechanical weathering of the spauling type, or perhaps exfoliation.[2] The supply may be limited, if the outcrop from which it is derived is small, or may be almost inexhaustible. Being built by constant addition to its surface of rock waste glissading or streaming down, a talus slope may grow to such dimensions that its base covers all the available ground. If it is still abundantly fed from above, it will serve thereafter as a chute, delivering waste at the toe of the slope for transportation by a river or glacier or to be broken up and removed by the waves of the sea. "Unless constantly fed from above," however, "the angle of slope of the talus will fall below the maximum angle of rest[3] as a result of the combined work of weathering and creep" (Sharpe). Weathering then

---

[1] H. Ødum, On the Nature of so-called Sheep Tracks, *Dansk. Geol. Fören. Medd.* 6, pp. 1–29 (1922).

[2] Phases of mechanical disintegration recognised by A. C. Lawson are: "(1) Development of joints; (2) exfoliation in broad slabs...; (3) spauling, due to ruptures necessary for the relief of strain; (4) granulation, particularly exemplified in certain coarse-grained granites; and (5) slacking, as exemplified by shale." *Bull. Geol. Soc. Am.* 43, pp. 704–5 (1932).

[3] "The angle of slope of a talus is determined in part by the kind, shape, and size of the rock fragments of which it is composed. If there is a constant and abundant 'dribble' of rock from above, the upper part of the slope will stand at the maximum angle of repose for the given conditions—usually between 26 and 36°. The term *angle of repose*, or *angle of rest*, however, is ambiguous because it has been used to mean not only the angle at which a stable mass of unconsolidated material will begin to move but also the somewhat lower angle at which such a mass in motion will come to rest. The angle at which rock waste accumulates on a talus approaches the higher of the two." Sharpe, *loc. cit.* p. 30.

begins on the surface and some soil is formed, the slope becomes (under favourable conditions of climate) more or less completely covered with vegetation, and future downhill movement is of a similar nature to that on slopes of weathered waste overlying bedrock.

In climates so cold that freezing and thawing of the ground occur frequently, rock rubble creeps more rapidly down even quite moderate slopes. In winter the ground is hard-frozen in Arctic lands, and in summer it remains frozen at some depth, but in a superficial layer saturated with water supplied by the melting of winter snows frequent freezings cause frost heaving. On quite horizontal ground, notably in Spitsbergen, polygonal patterns result, the larger stones being apparently thrust outward from evenly spaced centres to form ridges (*stone rings*) that arrange themselves so as to enclose circular or roughly hexagonal areas. These are flat or slightly domed and are paved with smaller rock fragments. Where the material is coarse the polygons are large, having diameters up to 12 ft., but in fine material they are as small as 3 ft. in diameter. Where there is any slope, however, frost heaving under these Arctic conditions induces *solifluction*, a rapid downhill creep that affects especially rubble with fine material in the interstices. Such material moves down slopes as low as 2 or 3°. Rock rubble moving by solifluction develops *stone stripes*, which are bands of alternately coarse and fine stones aligned in the direction of steepest slope.

The boulders of a *felsenmeer*, which is a field of angular blocks on a flat-topped mountain in a temperate region, or perhaps on a lowland in the frigid zone (e.g. on Bear Island in the Arctic Ocean), are subject to creep of the nature of solifluction down very gentle slopes, and the "stone rivers" of the Falkland Islands, which are boulder fields occupying valley floors, are believed to be in transit down the valleys under the influence of a similar mechanism.

In *rock glaciers* (Capps)—so-called because of a resemblance in form to the tongues of true glaciers—the tongue is thrusting slowly forward and developing wrinkles of the surface parallel to its front and sides. This movement, which takes place down gentle slopes, is attributed to frost heaving.

CHAPTER III

Rain and Rivers

RUNNING water is the most important of the agents responsible for the shaping of the land surface by erosion[1] under "normal"— that is to say, humid and warm or temperate—climatic conditions. Streams and rivers transport seaward the debris from the whole landscape and, at the same time, do an important share of the work of valley excavation, while the run-off of newly fallen heavy rain as rills and flowing films of water removes fine soil particles, co-operating thus, as *rain-wash*, with other agencies in the general wastage and lowering of the land surface.

Heavy raindrops as they fall loosen particles of fine waste and take the material into suspension as mud: they thus facilitate its removal by rain-wash. Especially when the soil and subsoil are already saturated by continued heavy rain, a network of rills or a continuous water film, or sheet flood, may develop even on convex upper slopes, picking up and carrying off fine soil particles, delivering them presently into more concentrated though ephemeral streams in the gullies, which are the feeders of more continuously flowing rivers. Raindrop impact is effective only on bare ground, but the rills and sheet floods formed during heavy rain may rob soil particles even from ground with a protective covering of vegetation, and this type of erosion of the waste-mantle must be at work over a great proportion of the land surface. It is not easy, however, to find positive evidence in demonstration of the process, and the argument for its universality depends on the prevalence of con-vexity of summit forms in most landscapes, in the development of which this process, according to Lawson's hypothesis,[2] plays an important part.

The effects of raindrop impact and of scouring by concentrated wash in places where the run-off is gathered quickly into definite

---

[1] Most English and American writers use "erosion" as an inclusive term, for which "denudation" is a synonym. Some geomorphologists of the German school attempt to distinguish between "denudation", defined as "degradation by surficially extensive mass movements" (C. Sauer), and "linear erosion" (corrasion).

[2] See Chapter XIV.

streams are more easily demonstrated. Both are conspicuous on outcrops of sandy clay where these are bare or only sparsely protected by vegetation, as is the case in semi-arid regions, in the vast areas of "bad-lands", for example, in the western interior of North America. *Bad-land* erosion is rare in the natural landscape under normal humid conditions, however, though it may appear as a result of deforestation or of overstocking on hilly pasture land. The close texture of clay causes an immediate run-off of nearly all the water that falls upon it as heavy rain. Gathering in close-set rills this water scours channels, especially if some sand particles are present mixed with the clay to act as cutting tools, and a miniature landscape of innumerable closely spaced steep-sided valleys and ridges is thus developed by stream sculpture. The conditions for development of bad-land forms may vary considerably, as is shown by the fact that they are not confined to sandy clay terrains but make their appearance occasionally also on surfaces underlain by gravel. Bad-land erosion is seen even on an extensive outcrop of fault-crushed rock at Palliser Bay, New Zealand (Pl. V, 1).

Some land surfaces from which rain-wash (assisted by raindrop impact) is engaged in removing fine soil particles are littered with residual boulders, small or large. Most of these have been rounded by *spheroidal weathering* before becoming exposed at the surface as a result of removal of the surrounding finely weathered waste, but still retain hard cores that are in many cases scarcely affected as yet by rock decay. Their rounding has been an effect of truncation of the edges and angles of subsurface joint-bounded blocks as the processes of chemical decay have worked inwards towards the core of each block from intersecting flat-joint surfaces. Once the original corners have been rounded off in this way, successive concentric layers have been shed by exfoliation due mainly perhaps to volume changes accompanying hydration of silicate minerals in the process of chemical weathering, and thus the dwindling cores of still unweathered rock may have become almost spherical.[1] Igneous rocks with abundant silicate minerals are perhaps the most susceptible to spheroidal weathering (Pl. V, 2), but feldspathic sandstones are also frequently affected. Accumulations of boulders of this origin on upland surfaces have often been mistaken for

[1] E. Blackwelder, Exfoliation as a Phase of Rock Weathering, *Jour. Geol.* 33, pp. 793–806 (1925).

alluvial deposits of water-worn cobbles or coarse gravel, and even for glacial moraines.

Tors on peneplains and uplands on granite terrains (Pl. VI, 1) are scattered or piled boulders of similar origin but of large size. In some cases the boulders have been very incompletely rounded by subsurface weathering, though undergoing further rounding and reduction in size by physical weathering after exposure. The cores of the great granite blocks appear to have lain between joints in a widely spaced pattern. The well-known tors of Dartmoor take the form of piled groups of boulders with horizontal extension that suggest architectural effects; and rectangular tors, still attached to bedrock, occur at very frequent intervals all over those parts of the flat-lying mica-schist terrain of the South Island of New Zealand that are situated in the semi-arid inland district, where, apparently, the finely disintegrated soil in intervening areas has been removed by rain-wash.[1]

Parts of the central African plateaux that are underlain by granite rocks are heavily encumbered with huge boulders disrupted and exposed by weathering and rain-wash; and unglaciated parts of the granitic highland surface of the Sierra Nevada of California are completely covered by a "veneer of loose blocks" so thick that it swallows all surface water and prevents the formation of running streams.[2] This constitutes a *felsenmeer*.

Raindrop impact is effective on all unprotected surfaces of weathered or unconsolidated fine material, but only rarely is a yardstick available to make possible an estimate of the rate at which material has been loosened by this agency and removed. Certain textures and structures in the materials undergoing erosion, however, favour the survival of residual forms that give some idea of the depth of erosion, though rather exceptional conditions are required for the perfect development of these. The picturesque minor surface-relief forms termed *hoodoo columns* and *earth pillars* are slender residual columns of unconsolidated sediment or waste of a kind susceptible to rapid erosion by rain, which are capped or roofed by slabs or boulders of resistant material in such a way that

[1] C. A. Cotton, Block Mountains in New Zealand, *Am. Jour. Sci.* 44, pp. 287–9, and Fig. 25 (1917).
[2] A. C. Lawson, The Geomorphogeny of the Upper Kern Basin, *Univ. Cal. Publ. Bull. Dep. Geol.* 3, pp. 313–14 (1904).

they have escaped the effects of general lowering of the ground-level by erosion. Hoodoo columns are capped by surviving relics of thin hard layers in horizontally bedded formations. Some such features no doubt originate also by processes of stream erosion, and they grade into the larger table-topped forms developed in the course of the cycle of erosion in such materials and structures.

Typical earth pillars, such as those in upland valleys near Bozen (Bolzano), in South Tyrol, are capped by boulders. In the Tyrolese examples the material composing them is a glacial deposit consisting of rock fragments, with a clay matrix, and containing scattered boulders, some of which are of considerable size (Pl. VII, 1). High columns can be developed only in windless situations, for wind-driven rain would undercut and destroy them. Indeed, the stronger the wind the more effective is raindrop impact. An illustration of the efficiency of erosion by wind-driven rain is afforded by nearly horizontal "earth fingers", as they may be called, near the "windy city" of Wellington, New Zealand (Pl. VI, 2). The material which locally favours their formation, and which is exposed in a road cutting that acts as a wind funnel, is a sandy clay derived by weathering from feldspathic blown sand, and there is an admixture with this of small rock fragments derived from adjacent outcrops, which protect the "finger tips".

Wet-weather rills and sheet floods, constituting the *run-off* from the surface, feed the ephemeral streams that flow in gullies, and these are tributary to more permanent streams or rivers and furnish a part of their flow. Permanent streams, however, draw a great part of their supply of water from the ground. The greater part of the water that falls as rain, but, of course, a very variable proportion of it, does not run off immediately, but sinks into the ground. A certain amount of this water is returned to the surface by capillarity, and evaporates either directly or through the leaves of plants, but much of it, after sinking through the unsaturated and generally weathered surface material, joins a continuous body of *ground water*. This ground water is the sole source of supply of water to permanent streams in dry weather, and some streams are drawing from it at all times, though leakage of water through stream beds to join the ground water takes place also under certain conditions.

The ground water has a definite upper surface, the *ground-water level*, or *water table*, which rises and sinks in wet and dry seasons, and may reach the land surface after a prolonged spell of wet weather. Its lowest position sets a limit to the depth of chemical weathering. On the banks of permanent streams the water table reaches the land surface and coincides with the surface of the flowing water (Fig. 5). The ground water moves slowly through the pore spaces between the grains of open-textured rocks, and through fissures in more compact and impermeable rocks, seeking an outlet at a lower level. Barriers of impermeable rock may cause the water table to intersect the land surface on hillsides, so that springs result, but this is rather exceptional, and normally the water finds a way of escape by seepage along the beds and sides of streams below the level of the running water. Owing to friction of the narrow passages through which ground water makes its way,

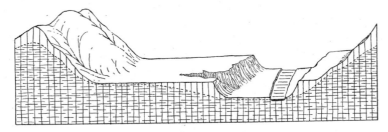

Fig. 5. Diagram showing the ground water (shaded), and the water table (the broken line).

retarding its rate of flow, it does not get away quickly, but remains heaped, with an irregularly convex water table, under ridges (Fig. 5). This heaped water flowing out gradually into rivers—the water table meanwhile slowly sinking—during a dry period maintains the flow of the rivers.

Not all the water with which rivers are thus fed reaches the sea. Evaporation goes on from the free surface, and this loss may lead to a serious shrinkage in volume—serious, that is to say, in that it will impair a river's ability to perform the tasks of transportation and erosion we are expecting of it—in arid regions where rivers receive no tributaries, as in the case, for example, of the Nile flowing through Egypt. Rivers lose volume also owing to soakage from their beds into alluvium, especially in deserts but wherever the water table is below the floor of the river channel. Many rivers in arid climates dwindle, therefore, to mere threads or chains of water holes, and finally disappear altogether, as in the interior of Australia. Other rivers debouch into lakes that do not overflow, as inflow is balanced by evaporation from the lake surface—the Jordan, for example, flowing into the Dead Sea. Under normal humid climatic conditions, however, rivers flow to the sea; lakes into and out of which rivers may flow can be regarded as locally expanded portions of river courses; and rivers, as they receive tributaries and are fed by ground-water seepage, increase progressively in volume of flow from source to sea.

All flowing streams take part in the task of transportation of waste to lower levels and generally in a seaward direction. In addition, many rivers are assisting in the general lowering of the land surface by actively abrading the bedrock. Others have, at least temporarily, suspended this activity, and are depositing a portion of their load, while continuing in most cases to transport another portion. The deposited material builds land forms, and so such rivers are doing their part in shaping the landscape. Rivers that erode are engaged in excavating or in modifying the forms of already excavated valleys.

In so far as rivers may enlarge their channels by solution their work is in part chemical (*corrosion*); but such work is hard to gauge. Quite a large part of the load carried down by rivers is, indeed, in solution (in the case of the Mississippi about a quarter of the total load), but most of the dissolved salts in river water are supplied to it already in solution by ground-water seepage, and, though they must be taken into account in estimates of the lowering of the general level of the land, they have their origin in surface weathering, not river corrosion.

River *corrasion*, the mechanical cutting and scouring work of rivers, is largely responsible for the deepening and widening of valleys. The stream that does this work is a stream of water and waste, for rock fragments and coarse sand particles in suspension, of such size as to be able to strike an effective blow, are the tools without which a water stream is inefficient as an agent of corrasion. In addition to the fine solid material carried into streams by rainwash, coarser fragments of all sizes are derived from talus slopes and landslides and the more general process of soil creep. Rock fragments in a running stream soon become converted into rounded pebbles by mutual abrasion as they are swept downstream. While gravel, sand, and mud are all carried by rivers, it has been noted that gravel-bearing streams carry but little sand. Sand grains and also small rock fragments are crushed between the larger pebbles and cobbles and reduced to mud,[1] and so the river load comes to consist mainly of gravel of somewhat even grade together with mud.

A river, the bed of which is covered by a thick layer of waste in transit, expends most of its corrasive energy in grinding the waste, but also scours and abrades outcrops of bedrock where these are exposed on its banks. It is thus able to widen its channel by *lateral corrasion*. *Vertical corrasion* is possible only where the layer of waste in transit on the floor of a river channel is thin and discontinuous. Exposed bedrock is in such a case abraded, and thus the channel is deepened.

Mud, owing to the extremely slow rate of sinking of its fine particles and flakes, is always carried in true suspension. Sand grains and pebbles, which sink more rapidly, make their way downstream in a series of leaps. There is some turbulence in every flowing stream, and upward currents lift the grains and fragments. When they sink after every such lift, they are farther downstream. The greater the velocity of flow, in general, the greater the turbulence, and so the larger the pebbles that can be lifted and carried. The strip in which turbulence is greatest is closely associated with the thread of maximum velocity.

Enormous boulders, as large as houses in some mountain streams, which have obviously been moved by the streams in the direction of flow, can never have been surrounded by water so deep that current turbulence in it could lift the boulders. Occasionally, probably during a flood, the gravel on which such a large boulder rests is scoured away, leaving it badly supported. After a time, pressed onward by the current and unsupported in front, it rolls forward a short distance, and this process is repeated many times, though perhaps at long intervals.

[1] P. Marshall has demonstrated that sand grains cannot survive the crushing impact of grinding pebbles. *Trans. N.Z. Inst.* 58, pp. 507–32 (1927).

CHAPTER IV

The Cycle of Erosion; Youth of Rivers

IT is possible to picture an ideal series of landscapes such as may be developed successively during the wearing down of a part of the earth's surface by erosion; and examples of actual landscapes may be fitted in to match the deduced stages of such degradation, thus justifying the deduction. The whole series of changing reliefs produced by long-continued progressive erosion following a preliminary uplift of a land surface is a *cycle of erosion*, or *geomorphic cycle*,[1] whatever the pre-uplift form of the land may have been. It may have had any imaginable kind of relief, or absence of relief. The surface upon which eroding agents begin to work at the commencement of a cycle is the *initial* surface, its relief the *initial* relief; while the surface of very faint relief which the cycle theory requires shall eventually result from the prolonged action of normal erosion on a land surface without interruption by further uplift or other earth movements is a *peneplain*.[2] Another way of describing a cycle of erosion, now abandoned, however, as less useful, is in terms of time—the "cycle" being the period required for the development of a succession of changing landscapes from initial form to peneplain, though it is well recognised that the length of such a period in absolute units must vary within very wide limits.

A truly vast lapse of time[3] without relative movement of the levels of sea and land is necessary in order that a high land surface underlain by rocks that are resistant to erosion may be worn down to a peneplain, and if we were to form an opinion of the instability of the earth's crust based on the abundant evidence of recent

[1] Commonly termed also the "geographical cycle" by W. M. Davis, the originator of the cycle idea (Geographic Classification..., *Proc. Am. Ass. Adv. Sci.* 33 (1885)); the substitution of "geomorphic" for "geographical" in the designation of the cycle is advocated by Douglas Johnson.

[2] W. M. Davis, *Am. Jour. Sci.* 37 (1889). (Douglas Johnson prefers "peneplane".)

[3] Undoubtedly many millions of years (see Chapter XVII).

movement in disturbed regions like California, Japan, and New Zealand, the conclusion would be inevitable that a cycle of erosion can never reach an advanced stage. The evidence afforded by stratigraphical geology, as well as the reasoned interpretation of present-day landscape forms, is, however, sufficiently strong to convince us that cycles of erosion have proceeded far enough in bygone times to produce very extensive peneplains.

A cycle is introduced by uplift, or by its equivalent the with-drawal of the sea to a lower level. It simplifies the elementary study of landscape forms to assume that such uplift or emergence takes place rapidly. It is not to be regarded as ever sudden (cata-strophic); but it is possible for it to take place so rapidly that the amount of erosion that goes on during a movement is negligible as compared with that which follows its completion.

Geological evidence indicates that there are very slow as well as relatively rapid earth movements. It seems safe to assert that the results produced by erosion will ultimately be very much the same whether the erosion accompanies and follows a slow or a rapid uplift, provided that sufficient time is available after the movement to allow a cycle to run its course; but such an assertion must be qualified by a free admission that the type of landscape forms developed during certain early stages of the cycle may be controlled very largely by the rate of uplift. Consideration, for example, of the effects associated with very slow uplift introduces the possibility of the land wasting away as rapidly, or nearly as rapidly, as it rises. Similar results are, indeed, to be looked for with even relatively rapid uplift where the materials of the land are very weakly resistant to erosion. Special study of such cases leads some workers to undervalue the cycle scheme of Davis as a basis of description of landscapes and of a descriptive terminology for their features. One may, however, follow Davis in regarding special cases of this kind as more or less exceptional. All such require explanation, but it is possible to fit their explanations into the framework of the cycle scheme.

For the present the postulate of rapid uplift may be adhered to, or this may be assumed to be the general case to be first investigated, exceptions being reserved for discussion later—that is to say, the effects of such erosion as accompanies uplift may be minimised, and even, in an elementary statement, disregarded. There is thus provided a simplified condition, or case, for elementary or pre-liminary study, a case which, however, is not hypothetical only, but is rather common in nature, as is indicated by the frequent occurrence of landscape features that agree with its deduced forms.

The initial surface thus uplifted may have previously been a land surface, or it may have emerged from the sea. It may have been formerly flat or may have had any known kind of relief. Further, the relief after rapid uplift may be the former relief un-modified except by incipient erosion, or the pre-existing relief may have been altered by inequality of uplift, former flatness being perhaps replaced by newly developed corrugations.

The uplifted mass may consist of rocks of any kind, and the arrangement of these may be according to any kind of geological structure. It may be, for example, composed entirely of practically homogeneous massive rock—a granite batholith or extensive out-cropping of schist of uniform character; or, on the other hand, stratified rocks may prevail, with alternating strata weak and resistant to erosion; and the stratified formations may be hori-zontally bedded, homoclinally tilted, folded, overthrust, or faulted.

The amount of uplift (relative to sea-level) may be uniform throughout the area, as would be the case if a cycle were initiated by sinking of ocean-level; or, on the other hand, uplift may be uneven.

The possible initial forms on which erosion may begin its work of developing *sequential* forms are thus almost infinitely variable, and it is, therefore, not surprising that the sequential forms in nature also present great variety. Allowance being made, however, for initial differences of form, material, and structure, features of certain kinds are characteristic of landscapes in various stages of the cycle of erosion, so that stages thus recognisable become of great systematic value in the classification and description of land forms.

As a theoretically simple case with which to introduce the study of the cycle of erosion, a previously flat or almost flat surface may be assumed to be upraised to become the initial form, and cases in which moderate or strong relief is inherited from a former cycle may be reserved for later study (Chapter XIX). The nearly flat surface selected for the initial form may be a *plain of deposition* built of material deposited in flat layers either of marine sediments or of gravel or finer alluvium spread by rivers over lowlands; or, alternatively, it may be a peneplain that has been developed by protracted erosion of the land surface in an earlier cycle. The abundance of sedimentary rocks of marine origin now forming land shows that the erosional history of most land areas began with emergence of a sea floor. In nearly all cases uplift has been renewed from time to time in such regions, and so present-day land forms on them are rarely referable to the cycle initiated by the first

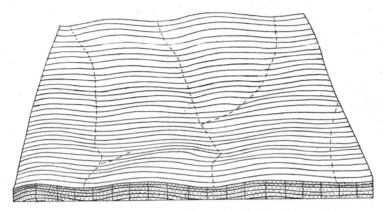

Fig. 6. Diagram of an initial surface and consequent drainage lines in an ideal first cycle, showing conformity of the surface with beds underlying it.

emergence. Clearly, however, there must have been such a "first" cycle, and deductions concerning the probable forms of the landscape of the first cycle are helpful in the explanation of many features of the landscape of the present-day or nth cycle.

In order to simplify the case still further, uplift of the formerly flat surface may be assumed to be slightly irregular. This is, of course, a gratuitous assumption, but is merely a selection of a common enough variety of case. The uplifted surface is now diversified by broad inequalities of quite small relief and very gentle slopes. The arrangement of these may be quite haphazard (Fig. 6). If the new land has emerged from the sea, however, as an island of broadly domed form, its marginal parts at least will have definite radial slopes, and if a strip of newly emergent sea floor

borders a former land as a "coastal plain", it may be expected to
have a fairly uniform slope in the seaward direction. In general,
slopes will be sufficiently steep to give streams formed by the
run-off from the new surface a definite direction of flow.

The strata immediately underlying the surface, if it has originated
as a plain built of sedimentary layers, will be warped during
upheaval to the same extent as the surface, so that the initial
surface and beds below it maintain their conformable relationship.
The topmost layer of material will generally be uniformly weak[1]
and unconsolidated, but some of the buried strata may be quite
hard and capable of proving resistant to the erosion of the future.
Among these are, more especially, layers of calcareous organic
debris that are very soon cemented into limestones, but layers of
sand may become indurated also, forming sandstones. There will
be present also at some depth, great or small, a basement of more
ancient rocks beneath the recent deposits, which rest on their
worn surface as a floor. These basement rocks, which are relatively
very hard and resistant in most cases, and which may have a complex, perhaps intensely deformed, structure, will sooner or later be
exposed over parts at least of the surface if erosion proceeds to
sufficient depth.

When rain falls and water runs off as streams from an initial
surface, the streams are guided by any initial hollows or wrinkles
that may be present (Fig. 6), and follow the initial slopes. Such
streams are *consequent* (Powell), since they are guided by, or consequent upon, ready-made slopes and corrugations. The valleys
which these streams soon cut with the help of the waste they pick
up are *consequent valleys*, while the divides, or water partings,
between these are *consequent divides*, for their positions are to an
equal extent consequent on the initial form of the surface. Complete river systems and valley systems all of consequent origin,
each consisting of a main with perhaps many tributaries, may thus
come into existence.

In a "first" cycle strata below the surface will be inclined in the
same direction as the surface, and consequent streams will flow in
the direction of the dip. The practice of calling every stream that
follows the direction of dip consequent has nothing to recommend

[1] "Weak" and "resistant" are to be understood in the sense of "easily eroded"
and "resistant to erosion".

it, however.[1] Streams that flow in the direction of the dip of the strata they cross may, if it is necessary to indicate this fact, be referred to as "dip" streams[2] or "cataclinal",[3] while those flowing in the reverse direction are "anti-dip"[2] or "anaclinal"[3] streams. It is in most cases inadvisable to term cataclinal streams "resequent",[4] as is sometimes done, for this implies that there has been a re-establishment of drainage along the lines of former consequents.

The stage of the cycle entered on when the *infantile* streams that originate on the initial surface begin to incise valleys below it is *youth*. (Later stages in the life-histories of rivers and their valleys are *maturity* and *old age*.) The characteristic features of youth (and also of maturity) in rivers and their valleys on the one hand and in the landscape, or land surface as a whole, on the other are usually treated separately.

Young valleys may be considered first. Their characteristic sequential features result, in the main, from a general steepness of initial gradients and, where uneven uplift may be assumed, variation of initial gradients from point to point. Steepness of gradients leads to concentration of the erosive activity of young streams on downward cutting (*vertical corrasion*), while changes of gradient cause variation in the intensity and rapidity of vertical corrasion along the course of the stream, causing the cut channel, or true (sequential) valley, to be of irregular depth in the stage of early youth. This is in accordance with Gilbert's principle, "erosion is most rapid where the slope is steepest".[5]

Initial gradients along consequent stream courses may be in some parts uphill, or reversed as regards the direction of flow, in places where the streams flow into and through hollows originating as dimples during uplift or inherited from a former relief (perhaps a legacy of former glacial erosion). All such hollows must become consequent lakes in the new cycle.

Vertical corrasion, leading to deepening of consequent valleys, goes on in such parts of the stream courses as now have steep gradients and contain streams having, therefore, such rapidity of

---

[1] H. Baulig has criticised the misuse of "consequent" as applied to river directions. *Jour. Geomorph.* 1, pp. 224–9 (1938).
[2] Wooldridge and Morgan, *The Physical Basis of Geography*, pp. 199–200 (1937).
[3] J. W. Powell, *Exploration of the Colorado River of the West*, p. 163 (1875).
[4] "Resequent" forms are described in Chapters IX and XXIII.
[5] G. K. Gilbert, *Geology of the Henry Mountains*, p. 102 (1877).

flow that they are capable of transporting a greater quantity of waste than is supplied to them and they have picked up for themselves. In the channels of such streams detritus does not accumulate; on the contrary, the bedrock floor of the channel is exposed and rapidly worn down by the train of rock fragments dragged over it by the current.

Where the supply of waste is limited but includes a proportion of boulders or large cobbles, much of the deepening that goes on where hard bedrock is exposed in the stream bed is due to the excavation of *potholes*—round vertical shafts, 2 or 3 ft. across and with a depth sometimes greater than their diameter—which result where boulders or cobbles are whirled around for a long time by eddies. As the first boulders are worn away in the boring process, others take their place, and so some very well rounded stones, generally worn to small dimensions, are found in each pothole. The process of valley deepening by excavation of confluent potholes may be compared with the first roughing out of the interior of his dugout canoe by a modern savage equipped with an auger.

As a result of the concentration of erosive activity on downward cutting, the young valleys that the streams are now excavating in this early stage of the river are steep-walled—mere trenches in the uplifted surface—and narrow-floored, being filled from wall to wall by the streams in them except at times of very low water. Where stream corrasion alone is responsible for the formation of a young valley, it is cut as a parallel-walled trench of the same width from top to bottom (Pl. VII, 2). The trench can be vertical only where the stream that is cutting it is quite straight. Where there is any accidental curvature in the consequent course, the momentum of the stream carries the thread of fastest current against the outer, concave bank, so as to corrade and undercut it, and the stream is thus able to move over in that direction as it cuts laterally. This is *lateral corrasion.* Combined with vertical corrasion, which is going on at the same time, it causes the parallel-walled trench due to stream corrasion unassisted by any other processes of valley formation to be cut down diagonally, so as to have one overhanging wall, which leans one way or the other according to the direction of stream curvature controlling lateral corrasion.

The development of such narrow, trench-like valleys is possible in actual landscapes only where streams are cutting down very rapidly through exceptionally tough, unweathered rock, which is free from joint crevices. Examples are found, however, in the Gorner and Aar gorges in Switzerland—well known to tourists—and in trenches cut by various streams through the Amuri limestone formation of New Zealand.[1] Such gorges are, indeed, commonest in limestone, for, though this rock may be shattered during deformation by earth movements, its fractures are commonly healed again by calcite deposits in veins that fill all the joint crevices.

Parallel-walled canyons are really rare landscape features, because few rocks will stand for long as vertical or overhanging cliffs. So

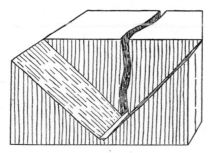

Fig. 7. Diagram comparing the volume of material actually excavated by a down-cutting stream (rear block) with that of the material removed when down-cutting is accompanied by widening of the valley to a **V** shape (front block).

young valleys are generally opened out to a more or less broad **V** shape as a result of the occurrence of rock falls and general downslope transference of badly supported material from the sides (Pl. VIII, 1). Rock debris slips down progressively as the gorge is deepened, and is carried away by the stream. The quantity thus removed is very much greater than that actually excavated by vertical corrasion in the strict sense (Fig. 7); but it is the deepening of the channel by vertical corrasion that makes possible the development of the **V**-shaped young valley.

Only in straight reaches is the **V** form of a young-valley profile symmetrical. More commonly some accidental initial curvature has been increased by lateral corrasion during excavation until the

[1] When selecting examples of young valleys it is impossible to confine attention to "first-cycle" features. Most of the known illustrative examples of geomorphic forms that simulate those of a "first" cycle are of necessity taken from districts that have been uplifted more than once.

valley has become somewhat winding, so that the river takes its course along a narrow valley floor (of river width only) between interlocking spurs of the upland on either hand. Its **V**-shaped cross-profile is now asymmetrical (Fig. 8, strips 5 and 5′), having steeper side slopes (T, T') in the coves, or amphitheatres, against which the stream has cut (*undercut slopes*)[1] than on the tapering spurs running down to the convex banks, which are said to have *slip-off slopes* (S, S') because of their mode of development.

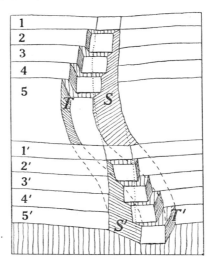

Fig. 8. Increasing curvature of a valley due to lateral corrasion accompanying downward valley cutting. Strips 1, 1′ show portions of the initial, slightly curved course; while strips 2–5 and 2′–5′ show progressive increase of curvature as the valley is deepened.

Small rivers may even wind in **S**-shaped curves developed by lateral corrasion during valley-cutting, and undercut slopes may approach each other to the point of intersection (Pl. VIII, 2).[1]

In a first cycle the only tributaries as yet in existence in early youth are, like the main rivers, consequent, occupying subsidiary wrinkles of the surface or flowing down the side slopes of the major hollows or furrows. Where initial slopes are rather steep, these *secondary consequents* may be numerous and closely spaced, but where initial slopes are gentle, few streams may be formed, at

[1] These curves resemble true "incised meanders" (p. 223), and may be confused with them (J. Blache, *Jour. Geomorph.* 2, p. 201 (1939)).

any rate where the surface material is open-textured, for precipitation sinks into the nearly level ground, to become ground water and be drained off by the main streams, which are cutting trenches.

While consequent tributaries are young, they commonly fail to obey Playfair's law of accordant junctions, as they do not succeed in deepening their valleys as rapidly as main streams, with which they make junctions that remain *discordant*, or "hanging". Discordant tributary junctions are frequently met with in young stream-cut valley systems in later as well as first cycles. They are common, for example, in the Wanganui River system, in New Zealand. In the more widely opened valleys of the Rangitikei and

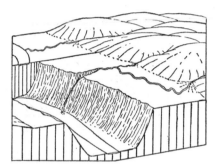

Fig. 9. Development of a discordant junction after initiation of a new cycle. The rear block shows a former condition, in which junctions were accordant, obeying Playfair's law.

Awatere Rivers also, all small tributaries make discordant junctions, but in these cases the initial forms at the beginning of the present cycle were flat-floored open valleys of an earlier land surface, and the main streams have cut for themselves in the new cycle deep, steep-sided trenches (Fig. 9). In their rate of downward cutting they have far outstripped their small tributaries, and so these now cascade from mere notches high on the walls of the main trenches.

When valleys are of **V** shape, their top widths (in homogeneous materials, in which uniform side slopes may be expected) must depend on their depths. Thus a young trench cut to varying depths in different parts because of a variable initial gradient will exhibit also variety of width (Fig. 10).

Another effect of initial accidental changes in gradient from point to point must be the occurrence of rapids, and perhaps falls, along the courses of many infant consequent streams. On a first-cycle surface, however, and on any other that is in a similar way underlain by easily eroded materials, such infantile inequalities of gradient will be smoothed out as young valleys are rapidly deepened. They are transient features, indeed, that will be obliterated by the infantile erosion that accompanies even rapid uplift. Where, on the other hand, an uplifted mass consists of resistant rocks and the initial surface is accidented by fault scarps, falls and rapids due to initial surface inequalities last longer and are to be found in some young landscapes (Chapter XXI). Where, also, the initial surface

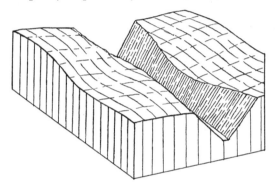

Fig. 10. Variation of width with depth in a young valley.

on which water streams begin to flow is one that inherits relief developed by ice erosion in the recently terminated Glacial Period, strongly discordant tributary junctions (glacial hanging valleys) are usually present, and, so recent has been the climatic change, the streams descending from these are still infantile in resistant rocks, and plunge as falls from the lips of the hanging valleys (Pl. IX, 1).

Other falls and rapids, of a kind that may make their appearance in a "first" cycle, are developed when down-cutting young streams discover rocks of unequal hardness;[1] and these are generally much longer-lived than any consequent upon initial inequalities of the surface are likely to be. Some rocks, such as shales, mudstones,

---

[1] Strictly such features, being developed by erosion controlled by rock structure, are "subsequent" (Chapter VII), though occurring in the course of a river that may be itself consequent.

volcanic "ashes", unindurated sediments generally, and much-jointed or crushed and shattered rocks in fault zones, yield very rapidly to corrasion; others, such as fresh igneous rocks, most metamorphic rocks, limestones, quartzites, and little-jointed indurated sediments, are worn down at a very slow rate. If, therefore, a young stream crosses a geological boundary from a resistant to a weak rock, the weak rock downstream has the channel cut more deeply into it than has the resistant rock upstream, and at the boundary an abrupt steepening of the channel gradient is developed. At such a point there will be a fall or rapid, according to the nature of the junction between the two kinds of rock.

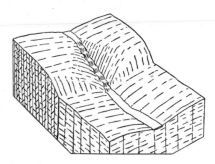

Fig. 11. Development of a rapid at the junction between resistant and weak rocks.

Rapids usually develop, rather than falls, where a junction between resistant and weak rock slopes back, is vertical, or over-hangs but slightly (Fig. 11). At the steep slope by way of which the stream descends from the resistant rock, after a deep trench has been rapidly incised in the weaker rock downstream, the velocity increases, and so, before the stream has actually left the surface of the resistant rock, it has its capacity for corrasion enormously increased. As a result, the edge of the resistant rock is cut away much more rapidly than deepening of the channel in the same rock takes place farther upstream, affording another example of Gilbert's principle "erosion is most rapid where the slope is steepest"; and the stream descends by a steep slope with rapids in a notch in the edge of the resistant rock instead of plunging over its edge.

It sometimes happens, however, that such a slope steepens into a fall as it works farther upstream by a continuation of the same process (*headward erosion*); or a fall may develop in the course of a river cutting a young valley in massive homogeneous rocks. The initiation of the process is in most cases obscure, but, once it is started, "plunge-pool back-scour" at the foot of the fall may deepen the valley below more rapidly than the ordinary processes of vertical corrasion above, and the fall works its way upstream, gaining increasing height as it goes. Such falls are *autogenetic*. A great fall in the lower course of the Orange River, in South Africa, is probably of this kind.[1] Similar headward extension and valley-head steepening by plunge-pool erosion in numerous small intermittent streams go on in deep amphitheatre-headed valleys in basaltic volcanic domes (Pl. IX, 2), notably in the Hawaiian Islands (Stearns),[2] and certain cataracts in Norway "appear to have gained steepness by this process" (Davis).

Falls, as distinguished from rapids, are developed by vertical corrasion where rivers cross the edges of outcropping strata of resistant rock, and especially where these are horizontal or only gently inclined, and where they overlie weak materials. The resistant beds, or fall makers, may be lava flows or indurated sedimentary strata. This class of fall, the classic illustration of which is Niagara Falls, may be referred to as the Niagara type. Once the fall is established by exposure of the edge of the fall maker in the channel of the river, the underlying weak material is easily and rapidly excavated by the splash and swirl of the water dropping into the plunge pool, which it hollows out beneath the fall (Fig. 12). The edge of the fall maker is thus left overhanging and without adequate support. Blocks of it fall away from time to time, forming a fresh, unworn lip. A fall of this kind retreats rapidly upstream, leaving a steep-sided trench, or canyon, the transverse profile of which contrasts conspicuously with that of the valley above the fall. Examples are figured in Plate X. In the case of the Wairua Fall, in the North Auckland district of New Zealand (Pl. X, 1), which affords a very good example of a sharp-edged fall retreating up-valley by plunge-pool erosion and thus developing a steep-sided trench, the river, instead of crossing the outcrops of sedimentary strata exposed by erosion as is the case in the majority of similar falls, is engaged in cutting a new young valley across a

[1] W. M. Davis, *Bull. Geol. Soc. Am.* 43, p. 438 (1932).
[2] See Chapter XIV.

lava flow that has invaded the floor of its former valley. The lava rock itself, though free from joint cracks and resistant to erosion in its surface layer, is weakened below by the presence of tension joints due to shrinkage during cooling, the result being effective undermining of the edge of the superficial strong layer by plunge-pool erosion.

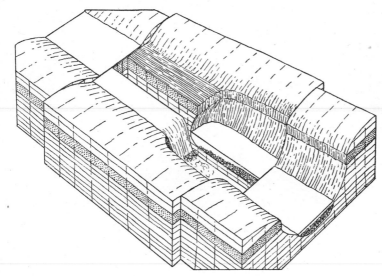

Fig. 12. Dissected block diagram of upstream retreat of a fall in horizontal strata. The middle block is cut in two longitudinally, with the halves separated so that the profile of the edge of the fall may be shown. A canyon is developed below the fall.

Resistant inclined strata dipping at moderate angles upstream make falls in the same way as do horizontal beds; but in this case the falls can retreat only a short distance, for, as the general surface is worn down, falls give place to short rapids and later disappear. Resistant strata dipping downstream form rapids rather than falls, unless their dip is very steep, in which case cascades are formed. These, like all such features, are short-lived, being worn down to rapids, and later disappearing.

In the discussion of the development of valleys of young rivers in this chapter it has been assumed that all the streams are consequent in origin, new-born in the current cycle. Where, however, the initial surface is derived from a land that has been reduced to a peneplain in an antecedent period of erosion, such a surface has already, prior to uplift, its pattern of streams, its river systems; and a proportion of these will survive into, or be inherited by, the landscape of the newly opened cycle. If the preliminary earth movements are rapid and rather strongly differential, so that upheaval is uneven or undulatory, newly born consequents may predominate on the newly uplifted land and play almost as important a part in valley development in the new cycle as they do where the initial form is an upheaved sea floor, but if uplift is more uniform, a greater proportion of the previously flowing streams will be inherited into the new cycle. In particular, such rivers, or parts of rivers, will survive as succeed in deepening their channels appreciably while uplift is in progress, and so entrenching themselves in the landscape, so that they are able, as it were, to defy the efforts of warping and tilting of the surface to deflect them from their courses.

Such survivors will be either the larger and more vigorous rivers or such parts of rivers as flow in the direction in which slopes are steepened. All rivers inherited from an anterior cycle might be placed in the category of "antecedent" rivers by somewhat extending the definition of that class (Chapter XI). "If, however, the technical term 'antecedent' were thus extended, it would embrace nearly all drainage systems" (Wooldridge and Morgan).[1] When it is necessary to insist on the fact that rivers have persisted from a former cycle after nearly uniform uplift has introduced another, they are best described as "inherited". Although a different meaning for this term has been suggested—as a synonym for "superposed"—it has not come into use (and is not required) in that sense.

[1] *The Physical Basis of Geography*, p. 209 (1937).

CHAPTER V

Lakes as Young Consequent Features

LAKES will be present as consequent features in the infantile stage on any surface dimpled by rapid irregular uplift, and the larger and deeper of these may have a long life. Among such are inland seas, like the Aral and Caspian Seas, which occupy the larger dimples of an extensively uplifted ocean floor. Lakes in general, however, are short-lived, and those formed at the initiation of "first" cycles have in most cases long since disappeared. This is true especially of lakes that originate high above sea-level.

In the steeper parts of the courses of the consequent rivers formed by the overflow from dimple lakes on an infantile uplifted surface, deep trenches will soon be cut (*egf*, Fig. 13), and the heads

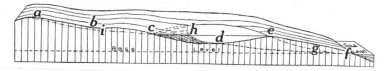

Fig. 13. Draining and filling of a lake on an infantile surface. Initial profile along a consequent stream, *abcdef*; lake, *ce*; later profile, *aichdgf*.

of these will develop farther back (as from *e* to *d*) if the gradients are steep enough. Thus the outlets of lakes are cut down as notches, and the lakes are gradually lowered and drained off. At the same time corrasion will be in progress in all the headwater streams (such as *abc*) that supply a lake with water. These streams, therefore, carry abundant waste, and all the coarser and the bulk also of the finer waste is dropped in the lake. (In Fig. 13 the profile *chd* represents the lake as partly filled with waste before the outlet is cut down.) Much waste being thus deposited in lakes, and even built up above lake-level by inflowing streams, they are rapidly reduced in size. That lakes act as traps for sediment is made obvious by comparison of inflowing and outflowing river waters. The crystal-clear waters of the Rhone as it leaves the Lake of Geneva and of the Waikato as it leaves Lake Taupo afford examples.

35

Lakes, whatever their origin and whatever their size, must eventually share the same fate. Low-lying lakes are doomed to disappear from the landscape by filling alone, but in the case of many lakes only partial filling takes place and lowering of the outlet finally disposes of the lake.

Consequent lakes due to warping of previously eroded land-surfaces are obviously possible, but not many such are recognisable

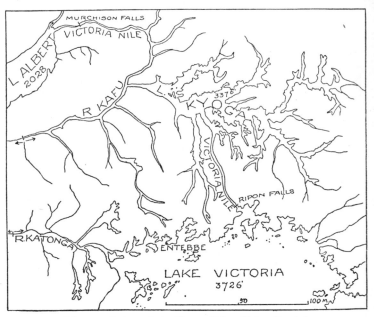

Fig. 14. Lakes of the Upper Nile. (After Davis.)

in existing landscapes, many supposed examples finding a more credible explanation as due to differential vertical corrasion by glaciers. In equatorial Africa, however, lakes have been formed by recent warping of a land surface at the headwaters of the Nile[1] (Fig. 14). Such lakes have intricate embayed outlines, as a result of the relief of the surface that is flooded, thus contrasting with the theoretical simple outline (Fig. 13) of a lake on a dimpled uplifted plain.

[1] W. M. Davis, The Lakes of California, *Rep. State Mineralogist Cal.* 29, pp. 179–80 (1933).

The headwater area of a region drained by the Kafu and Katonga rivers has been slightly down-warped, so that their valleys now slope eastward instead of westward as formerly. The branching Kafu head-waters have thus been transformed into the branching Lake Kyoga, 150 miles in length. The Katonga headwaters are more submerged in the broad Lake Victoria, of similar measure in diameter. Parts of both rivers now flow backwards into their lakes. Lake Victoria is the chief source of the Nile, which flows northward from it into Kyoga Lake by one of its branches and out by another. The little eroded Ripon Falls, next north of Lake Victoria, and the extremely narrow gorge below Murchison Falls, north-west of Lake Kyoga, testify to the recency of the time when the lakes were formed and the present course of the Nile was assumed. (DAVIS.)

Instead of being warped at the introduction of a new cycle of erosion, a surface may be broken by great faults, so as to consist

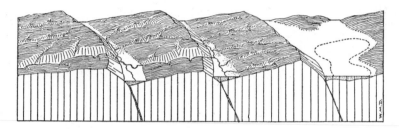

Fig. 15. Great fault blocks of the northern Sierra Nevada, California, with the plain of Honey Lake on the east. (After Davis.)

thereafter of irregularly heaved blocks, and where such deformation proceeds sufficiently rapidly lakes will occupy undrained re-entrants of the surface (Fig. 15). Classic examples of young lakes on the lowest parts of tilted fault blocks occur in southern Oregon and the adjoining part of California, and large-scale examples of lakes of fault-block origin are Tanganyika and Baikal. Deformation by faulting has probably taken place sufficiently slowly in many block-faulted regions, however, where climatic conditions have been humid, to allow rivers to maintain courses in gorges through the block mountains as they arose, and across the intermont troughs or basins also by filling these with deposited waste instead of allowing them to become lakes at any stage of the uplifting and deforming series of earth movements. "In all cases any lakes that were thus formed occupy merely such parts of the basins as are not otherwise

filled" (Davis). Lakes, some large, some small, may occur, therefore, on the floors of intermont basins, marking incidents where
earth movements have locally gained in the race against erosion
and deposition (Fig. 16). The lake Issik-kul, in Turkestan (100
miles long and 30 to 40 miles wide), is situated in a trough of this
kind between parallel scarps bounding fault-block mountains that
overlook it on the north and south sides. This lake, which is in a
dry region, is augmented by inflow through a distributary from the
River Chu, but has no outlet and has become somewhat salt.[1]

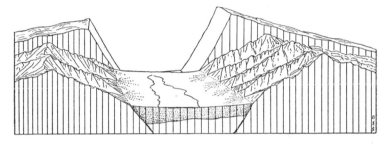

Fig. 16. An intermont trough between block mountains. In the foreground
block the trough is partly filled with alluvial detritus with a shallow lake on
its surface. (After Davis.)

In arid regions, where tectonic intermont basins are not drained
by outflowing streams, the lowest parts of the surfaces of their
alluvial filling (Fig. 16)—washed in by local and ephemeral
streams from the surrounding mountains—are partly covered by
shallow lakes that shrink to small dimensions or dry up altogether
between the infrequent rains, owing to excess of evaporation over
precipitation in the region. Ephemeral lakes of this kind are *playa*
lakes, and the plains of saline silt left bare when they dry up are
playas, or, if kept wet by seepage of ground water, *salinas*. Examples
of larger and permanent salt lakes in the deepest parts (remaining
unfilled with detritus) of intermont basins in arid regions are the
Dead Sea and the Great Salt Lake of Utah. Salt lakes, of course,
do not overflow, and their levels, and more especially their areas,
are maintained more or less constant by the balance between
evaporation and precipitation in the regions in which they occur.
Many of them, including the two cited as examples, have been in
the recent past, in an epoch of less intense evaporation, very much

[1] W. M. Davis, A Summer in Turkestan, *Bull. Am. Geog. Soc.* 12 pp. (1904).

larger than they now are, and "Lake Bonneville", which existed in the Glacial Period as an inland sea nearly 20,000 square miles in extent, covering the site of the Great Salt Lake and a great part of the surrounding region, had for a short time an overflow outlet.

Initial hollows in which water collects to form lakes, instead of being due to accidents of uplift or deformation, may be inherited from an earlier land relief, or may even be pre-existing shallow dimples on an emerging sea floor, such as are present on the recently emerged and lowlying coastal plain of Florida. Countless hollows that have become lakes, both large and small, are present as an inheritance from the Glacial Period in those regions which, like Canada and Finland, were overspread by continental glaciers and scoured unevenly by them down to fresh, unweathered bedrock over large areas of surface just before the present, or post-Glacial, cycle of normal erosion was ushered in in such regions by the melting of the ice.

The great North American lakes, from those of the St Lawrence system north-westward 2000 miles toward the Arctic Ocean, are all associated with the scouring action of the vast ice-sheets which covered north-eastern North America in the Glacial Period, although it should not be asserted that they are wholly due to the excavation of their basins by ice action. Lake-basin production there may have been aided by warping of the earth's crust and by morainic obstruction of pre-Glacial river courses. (DAVIS.)

Among glaciated mountains also the current cycle of normal erosion, still in its infancy, has had as its initial forms the features left over from the foregoing cycle of glacial erosion. Many small rock-rimmed lakes are present in glacial cirques in all such regions, and there are generally also lakes (Pl. XI, 1) in ice-scoured hollows on upland benches, as well as strung out in line along the floors of glaciated valleys, and others are ponded by dams of glacial rock debris. These small lakes are countless. Larger lakes occupy more deeply gouged-out rock-rimmed basins, especially in the piedmonts or fringes of groups of glaciated mountains. Without making any attempt here to discuss and evaluate alternative theories of tectonic origin that have been proposed in explanation of such piedmont lakes, one may follow Wallace[1] in his rejection of them and com-

[1] A. R. Wallace, The Ice Age and its Work, *Fortnightly Rev.* 54, pp. 616–33, 750–74 (1893).

plete acceptance of an explanation of the lakes as the result of differential deepening by glacial corrasion under the thickest parts of the deep ice of great valley glaciers.

The importance of glaciation in the production of lakes may be judged by the number and size of such lakes in various parts of the world. For example, Okanagon, Arrow, Slocan, and Kootenay, in British Columbia, 60, 95, 23, and 68 miles in length, and the 65-mile Lake Chelan in Washington, all in valleys of the Columbia River system, occupy basins of glacial excavation. The same is true of the piedmont lakes of the Alps, including Annecy, Geneva, Thun-Brienz, Lucerne, Zurich, Constance, Ammer, Würm, and Chiem on the north, and Maggiore, Lugano, Como, Iseo, and Garda on the south. Some of these lakes are over 1000 feet deep. (DAVIS.)

To the foregoing might be added a list of lakes in every glaciated mountain region, the English lakes (Pl. XI, 2), for example; while the New Zealand list includes Manapouri, Wakatipu, Wanaka, Hawea, Ohau, Pukaki, and Tekapo.

Piedmont lakes are fringed at their lower ends by terminal moraines, in some cases very extensive, and morainic dams in some cases impound water in large areas outside the mountain fronts, so that the lakes are thereby much enlarged, as well as having their levels held up considerably above the lips or rims of the actual rock basins within the valleys. Notable examples are Lakes Constance and Garda, and some of the New Zealand lakes.

The deeper and larger of the lakes of glacial origin will survive for aeons, as man counts time, but rivers are busily at work pouring waste into them, and, geologically speaking, their days are numbered. Many quite large lakes have already disappeared from the landscape in the few thousand years that have elapsed since the melting of the glaciers, and the great deltas already built by inflowing rivers in many lakes—for example, those of the Rhone and Rhine in Lakes Geneva and Constance—testify to the rapidity with which even large lakes like these are being filled.

Lakes that are not due in simple fashion to the existence of undrained hollows in the initial surface may also be classed as young consequent features of the landscape, for they originate as a result of local modifications of pre-existing features—most often the blocking of river valleys. Their causes are accidents interfering with the normal course of events of the cycle in progress, and these locally introduce new young forms, among which are the lakes. A glance at a simple classification of lakes used by Davis[1] will help to make this clear.

Among the classes of lakes recognised *warped-valley lakes, fault-basin lakes,* and *glacial lakes* have already been discussed. In addition to these the list comprises *landslide lakes, volcanic lakes, river-made lakes, artificial reservoirs,* and *lake-like bays and lagoons.*

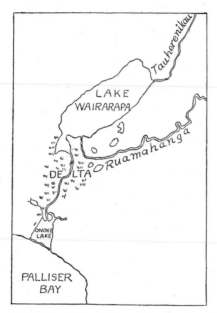

Fig. 17. Wairarapa Lake, New Zealand, formed by ponding of the Tauherenikau due to growth of the Ruamahanga delta.

An additional class, "lakes formed by local subsidence", might be added, to include *sag ponds*, mentioned by Davis, which are formed along the lines of active faults, *earthquake lakes* (Hobbs), formed by settlement or readjustment on alluvial plains during earthquakes, *pit lakes* (Hobbs), due to melting of ice blocks buried under fluvio-glacial deposits, forming kettles, and lakes in sinkholes and subsided areas underlain by limestone that is undergoing solution.

Bays enclosed by bay-bars of sand or gravel and so converted

[1] W. M. Davis, *loc. cit.* pp. 179–87; another useful and more elaborate classification is given by W. H. Hobbs, *Earth Features and their Meaning*, p. 424 (1912).

41

into lagoons, being really shore-line features need be no more than mentioned in this chapter. Onoke Lake (Fig. 17) serves as an example; its companion lake, Wairarapa, is of "river-made" origin.

River-made lakes include a rather varied assortment developed during progressive changes in river meanders and features of deposition on the floors of valleys that are being filled with alluvial deposits. Other river-made lakes are those ponded either in tributaries by rapid deposit of waste on the floors of main valleys (Fig. 17), or in main valleys by the upbuilding across them of fans of waste brought in by tributaries. (A better understanding of these can be attained after the principles governing deposition of waste in river valleys have been discussed in Chapter xv.) The cutting off and conversion into a lake of what might be regarded as an arm of the sea at the head of the Gulf of California by the fan-like delta of the Colorado River comes under this head. Actually tectonic sinking of an earth block appears, however, to be the main cause of the origin of the Salton Basin, the great hollow, more than 2000 square miles in extent, which lies north of the Colorado delta, with much of its floor below sea-level.[1] When the Colorado River has flowed into it, the basin has contained a large lake, but owing to aridity the lake dries up when, as at present, the Colorado takes a more direct course to the Gulf of California.

Landslide lakes (Fig. 3) and those volcanic lakes that are dammed by lava flows (Fig. 18) have much in common apart from the origin of the dam, which in each case blocks a valley. Of similar form are the large lakes held up by some of the dams of man's making as artificial reservoirs, or, in the case of the widely spreading Gatun Lake, in Panama, as a route for ships between oceans; and another class of small, but in some regions numerous, impounded lakes must be added—namely, those formed in valley systems of coastal lowlands blocked by dunes of blown sand of beach origin. All such lakes impounded in valley systems have usually intricate outlines, with embayments extending up tributary valleys, but their details of outline are related in all cases to the nature and stage of relief of the landscape that they partly submerge.

An example of a large landslide lake is Waikaremoana (Pl. XII) in New Zealand. Lake Nicaragua, in Central America, is held

[1] J. P. Buwalda, The Salton Basin, Southern California, *Science*, 71, pp. 104–6 (1930).

up by a volcanic dam. New Zealand examples, chosen for purposes of illustration, are Lake Rotoaira (Pl. XIII, 1) and Lake Omapere

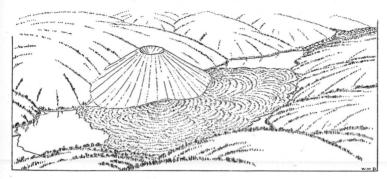

Fig. 18. Lakes impounded in river valleys by lava. (After Davis.)

(Fig. 19). The diversion of drainage in the case of the latter has taken place across a former main divide, affording a small-scale parallel with Lake Nicaragua, the formation of which has caused

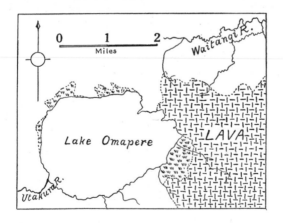

Fig. 19. Lake Omapere, New Zealand. Its water spills westward through a newly cut gorge instead of draining eastward as formerly.

former Pacific drainage to spill over eastward into the Caribbean Sea. A small lake ponded by blown sand near Auckland, New Zealand, is figured in Pl. XIII, 2.

Davis's division "volcanic lakes" includes also those in craters

43

and in some of the much enlarged craters termed "calderas" (Fig. 20). Lake Taupo, the largest lake in New Zealand, has been

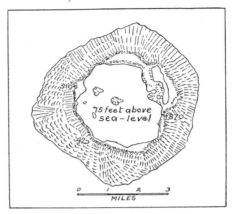

Fig. 20. Caldera lake on the volcanic island of Niuafou, in the South Pacific. (After Jaggar.)

explained as formed in part by volcanic explosions,[1] though in part also by subsidence along faults, high scarps of which bound it most conspicuously on the western side (Fig. 21).

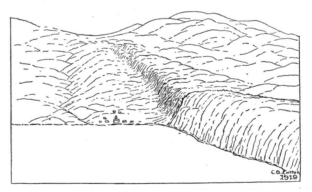

Fig. 21. Fault-scarp of the western shore of Lake Taupo, New Zealand, running inland in a southerly direction.

Lake floors, together with all the marginal features resulting from delta building and development of shore-line forms both by erosion and by deposition of waste, become initial surfaces of a

[1] Marwick and Fyfe, *N.Z. Geol. Surv. Bull.* 37, p. 27 (1937).

special kind when lakes are drained, and on these a cycle of erosion must locally develop through infancy and youth. The silt-covered floors especially demand a brief reference at these stages of erosion. Fine silt, deposited widely and evenly from the lake waters, if present in sufficient quantity, fills in hollows and levels off the lake floor. Some lake-floor plains are very uniformly level over large areas. Such, for example, is the plain forming the valley of the Red River of the North, in Minnesota, North Dakota, and Manitoba. It is a part of the floor of the vast extinct "Lake Agassiz", which at its largest covered 110,000 square miles, and which was ponded towards the end of the Glacial Period between the northern ice sheet and the gentle northward slope of the surface of North America. The consequent rivers on it are still infantile. This is the case also in the Imperial Valley, the lake-floor bottom of the Salton Basin, in arid Southern California, which, being below sea-level, is not in danger of deep erosion.

Lake floors at higher levels, however, have young valleys incised in them in the same manner as level sea floors uplifted without warping or emergent owing to eustatic sinking of sea-level. A broad "lacustrine coastal plain" fringing the southern shore of Lake Erie, for example, is undergoing dissection as a result of its very recent emergence from beneath the lake waters, and the larger of the consequent streams that cross it have already cut young valleys to a depth of 150 ft. below its surface.

CHAPTER VI

Maturity of Rivers; Superposed Rivers

In the account of the activity of young streams given in Chapter IV, it was assumed that the streams flowed in their infancy at considerable heights above the sea, under which condition their average slopes and velocities would be high and they would cut downward energetically. There is, however, in all cases a sharp downward limit to such active vertical corrasion. As a stream cuts down so as to approach *base-level*—as defined by Davis,[1] following Powell, the originator of the base-level idea, this is an imaginary extension of sea-level under the land—the rate of deepening rapidly decreases, for the level of the stream, though it approaches base-level, can never quite reach it except where it enters the sea. In order that the water of a river may be able to flow, its surface must have a certain slope down to the mouth, which in the case of rivers flowing into the sea is at base-level (sea-level). Every part of the channel of the stream must, therefore, remain at such a height that there will be a gradient steep enough to carry off the water. The necessary slope is steeper for waste-laden water than it is for clear water.

Fig. 22. Longitudinal profile of a graded river, showing the relation of grade to base-level.

The minimum necessary slope varies not only in different streams and at different times, but also in the same stream and at the same time with varying conditions, chief among which is distance from the mouth. The necessary slope becomes steeper with increasing distance from the mouth, mainly because towards the source the volume of the stream is less.[2]

A stream that has attained the minimum slope under existing conditions is said to have reached *grade* (Davis), or to be *graded* (Fig. 22). The profile of a graded stream approximates to a hyperbolic curve, the so-called *profile of equilibrium*. There are in all cases, however, small departures from the ideal curve, which are due largely to irregularity in the rate of increase of stream volume downstream, an increase that results in part from the junction of tributaries of various sizes at irregular intervals.

A factor that influences the steepness of the graded slope at any

[1] See *Geographical Essays*, pp. 381–412.
[2] "*Ceteris paribus*, declivity bears an inverse ratio to quantity of water." G. K. Gilbert, *Henry Mountains*, p. 114 (1877).

particular place and time is the amount of waste being supplied farther upstream. This material has to be transported, and the fact that the profile is graded at any place implies that the supply of waste to the stream by tributaries and in various ways from the valley sides is exactly equal to the amount the stream can carry past that place. If the supply were greater, the surplus would be deposited farther upstream in the river channel, which would thus be steepened, giving the flowing water progressively higher velocity and transporting power until it was able to carry the whole of the waste supplied to it. If, on the other hand, the supply were less than the stream could dispose of, its bed would be swept clear of waste and it would further deepen its channel, reducing the slope and so decreasing its own velocity and transporting capacity. The graded condition, therefore, represents equilibrium between the amount of waste supplied and the transporting capacity of the stream, and also between the processes of vertical corrasion and deposition in the channel of the stream.

When, owing to excess of transporting power over waste supply, a stream cuts downward to establish or maintain grade, it is said to *degrade*; and the process is termed *degradation*. When, on the other hand, owing to excess of waste supply over transporting power, a stream deposits in and so builds up its channel to establish or maintain grade it is said to *aggrade*; and the process is *aggradation*. In streams that are not yet nearly graded degradation goes on rapidly, as is shown by the prevalence of narrow, steep-sided valleys among those of young rivers. Once grade is established vertical corrasion goes on infinitely more slowly, though it does not necessarily cease altogether. Afterwards the slope of the graded profile will be further reduced in steepness, but only with extreme slowness, and possibly with some intermittent reversals of the process, for it can take place (except under changed conditions, for example, of climate) only as the supply of waste falls off owing to gradual reduction of relief in the whole valley system.

Falls, rapids, and lakes (Fig. 13) introduce irregularities into the longitudinal profiles of rivers that traverse them, and so must be smoothed out and disappear before a river is graded. The complete elimination of such features marks the end of the stage of youth in a river, and the establishment of grade marks the passage of the river from youth to *maturity*, the next main stage of the cycle, though rivers in a transitional condition from youth to maturity, may sometimes be conveniently referred to as *adolescent*.

Fig. 23. Graded reaches. The longitudinal valley profile of a transverse stream crossing the outcrops of resistant (*H*) and weak strata (*S*) is shown on the front edge of the block diagram. The river is graded on the weak but not on the resistant rocks.

Fig. 24. Looking through the Boulder gorge of the Colorado (site of the Boulder dam) at a graded reach of the river farther upstream. (Drawn from a photograph.)

Most rivers become mature earliest in their lower courses, where their volumes are largest; and generally the mature, graded valleys extend from the lower courses gradually headward. The last statement is true only in a general way, however, for it takes no account of the hardness of, or resistance offered to erosion by, the rocks over which a river flows. A river crossing the outcrops of alternating weak and resistant rocks will very early develop *graded reaches* across the outcrops of weak rocks, while the profile remains for a long time irregular and steep across resistant rocks, where falls and rapids still survive (Figs. 23, 24).

Graded reaches may be high above the *general*, or *permanent*, base-level, which is sea-level, but each is governed by a *local*, or *temporary*, base-level, which is the level of the first outcropping ledge of the next resistant rock downstream.[1] The wearing away of

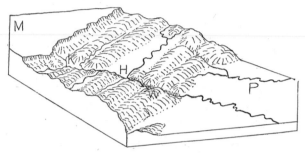

Fig. 25. Graded reaches of the Hunho system above a local base-level in the gorge of the Hunho. "Adjustment to structure" is shown by parallel ridges. M, Mongolian plateau; P, Peking; K, Kalgan; H, Hunho valley system; W, gorge through Western Hills. (After Barbour, redrawn.)

this resistant rock takes place so slowly as to be practically neg-ligible as compared with the rate at which the adjacent weak rock can be degraded. Thus, though a temporary base-level of this kind is always being lowered, grade is maintained meanwhile across the weak rock next upstream. In course of time grade is established across the resistant rocks also, the graded reaches become joined each to the next, and the stream becomes graded and mature for a great part of its length.

The North China region presents large-scale examples of rivers and river systems graded with respect to temporary base-levels. The rivers descend from the north-west towards the plain of North China and cross the outcrops of resistant strata that form parallel

---

[1] The conception of local, or temporary, base-levels, like that of the general base-level, was introduced by Powell (*Exploration of the Colorado River of the West*, p. 203, 1875).

ridges with a north-easterly trend in a belt of folded strata between the margin of the Mongolian plateau and the plain. The temporary base-level in the Western Hills of the Nankou Range thus holds up the Hunho and its tributaries to form a system of graded valleys 1200 ft. above the plain (Fig. 25).[1]

In the ideally simple case of streams eroding flat-lying or only very gently warped strata underlying a newly emerged sea floor, such as that pictured in Fig. 6, an alternation of weak and resistant rock outcrops likely to develop local base-levels controlling graded reaches would be unlikely to occur; but where the initial form at

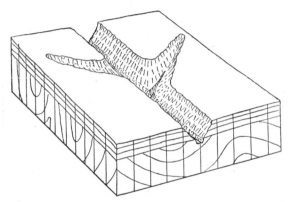

Fig. 26. Young landscape underlain by compound structure. Streams are being superposed on an undermass of folded rocks from a flat-lying cover.

the beginning of the current cycle is an ancient land surface, this structural arrangement is not uncommon. It may be present also beneath newly spread sediments on a land that has just emerged from the sea. In such a case, if the superficial layer of sediment is somewhat thin, the edges of weak and resistant strata beneath it may be soon discovered and exposed by streams as they deepen their early consequent valleys. They are afterwards confronted with the more difficult task of deepening their still ungraded valleys in rocks of diverse structures and generally more resistant to erosion than is the material immediately underlying the initial land surface (Fig. 26). This structure is *compound* in that it comprises beds with two contrasting arrangements, simple above in the *cover*, and com-

[1] G. B. Barbour, Geology of the Kalgan Area, *Mem. Geol. Surv. China*, A6, pp. 8–9 (1929).

plex below in the *undermass*, upon which the cover rests unconformably.

When streams that are consequent on the surface forms and the
associated simple structures of a cover, which may have suffered no
deformation other than slight tilting or very gentle warping, cut
through it and discover an undermass of older rocks with different
structure, they become *superposed consequents*. Streams that are other
than consequent, if they develop on a thick cover during early stages
of a cycle of erosion, may also become superposed[1] (Chapter XI), and
their stream patterns may be stencilled on the quite discordant

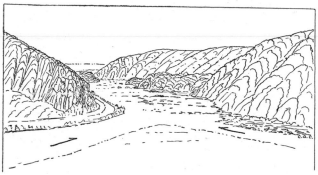

Fig. 27. The Shenandoah (right) unites with the Potomac (left) to pass through
the Blue Ridge of Virginia in a superposed consequent water gap. (Drawn
from a photograph.)

rock structures of an undermass. A series of stages of superposition
is possible, beginning with that in which rivers are still flowing
mainly on the cover and have exposed only occasional ledges of an
undermass in their channels, and ending with that where they have
cut down far into an undermass from which prolonged erosion has
entirely removed the cover. An interesting intermediate stage is
that at which only occasional remnants of the basal beds of the
cover remain here and there in the landscape on the highest parts
of ridges. From such remnants the former widespread extension
of the cover may be inferred, and the superposed origin of the
valleys demonstrated.

[1] This term as adopted from Maw and used by Powell (*loc. cit.* 1875) was
originally "superimposed". It was shortened to "superposed" by McGee.
Richthofen termed the valleys of such rivers "epigenetic" (*Führer für For-
schungsreisende*, p. 174 (1886)).

4-2

Systems of valleys with definite patterns resulting from superposition and entirely unrelated to the rocks and structures across which they are stencilled are recognised in various regions. Notably such an explanation has been adopted for the rivers of the south of France,[1] and river courses transverse to hard-rock ridges in the eastern United States have recently been shown to be superposed from a former widespread cover of marine strata on which they had taken consequent courses[2] (Fig. 27). One of the most striking of known examples is the system of radially arranged valleys of the English Lake District, which are believed to be superposed from a dome-shaped uplift of a former cover, with its centre over Helvellyn.

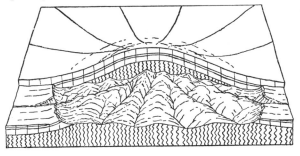

Fig. 28. Development of radially arranged superposed consequent valleys.

Though they are entirely removed from the central area, a ring of the covering strata still surrounds the district[3] (Fig. 28).

As suggested on an earlier page in this chapter, the graded profile of a river that has entered on the stage of maturity, and will become more and more fully mature and eventually old, may not be continuously lowered and reduced in steepness throughout these stages, though in the long run such degradation is inevitable. A phase, or phases, of aggradation may temporarily steepen a graded river profile as a whole or the profile of a graded reach. More or less contemporaneously with the grading of river valleys, dissection of the whole upland region is in progress (Chapter VII); a vast number of small new valleys and ravines come into existence in the stage of youth, and thereafter and until the cycle is far advanced

[1] H. Baulig, *Plateau central de la France*, pp. 456–7 (Paris, 1928).
[2] Douglas Johnson, *Stream Sculpture on the Atlantic Slope* (New York, 1931).
[3] J. E. Marr, *The Scientific Study of Scenery*, pp. 145–6 (London, 1900).

the valleys are becoming wider. Throughout all this time the proportion of the whole area that is occupied by valley-side slopes steep enough to yield abundant waste is increasing. The waste has to be carried away down the main valleys, and river loads must, therefore, increase during this phase. Later, however, as relief is lowered by the wasting away of ridges and spurs during the progress of the cycle, the weakening slopes will yield less and less waste. If the discharge of waste from the general surface, and, consequently, the loads of waste carried by the rivers, reach their maxima before the rivers are graded, the gradually diminishing loads during river maturity can and will be disposed of by rivers that flow down courses of gradually diminishing declivity, which is equivalent to saying that slow degradation will go on uninterruptedly after the graded profile has been first developed.

If, on the other hand, as it seems probable will sometimes be the case, the maximum of waste discharge and river load is not reached until after the rivers have become graded, then a phase of steepening by aggradation may intrude after streams are graded, though this must be followed in later maturity by renewed degradation. Deposits spread on the floors of valleys during the aggradational phase will then be gradually removed again, and weakening of gradients will continue throughout all the latter part of the cycle.[1] An aggradational phase may fail to occur even in this case, however, for run-off of surface water will be facilitated by the development of an elaborate system of tributaries, "and it is possible that the increase of river volume thus brought about from youth to maturity may more or less fully counteract the tendency of increase in river load to cause aggradation" (Davis).

Other causes of possible temporary aggradational phases can be suggested, and any two or more causes may be in operation simultaneously.[2] As a river after it is graded flows generally in a wider channel than it has hitherto had in youth, when it has been confined to the narrowest limits by downward corrasion, loss of depth in the stream may involve such loss of velocity and transporting power that a steeper gradient will be required to carry the load.

[1] W. M. Davis, The Geographical Cycle, *Geog. Jour.* 14, pp. 481–504 (1899); reprinted in *Geographical Essays*, see p. 260.
[2] W. M. Davis, Rock Floors in Arid and in Humid Climates, *Jour. Geol.* 38, pp. 139–40 (1930).

Again, as a river develops increasingly large curves by lateral corrasion, its length increases, with the result that it loses some fall, velocity, and carrying power, the automatic remedy for which loss is aggradation.

Yet another cause of aggradation is loss of river volume by underflow through porous alluvial deposits which the river has laid down. Even a thin alluvial veneer on a flat valley floor may draw off some water in this way from a river, but if some aggradation has already taken place, there may be more underflow in the thicker layer of alluvium that has been formed. Such underflow is part of a general seaward movement of ground water, which may in places leak from instead of seeping into a river. As alluvium contains more open spaces, is more permeable, and thus offers less resistance to a down-valley flow of the upper layer of ground water than does bedrock, the presence of alluvial filling in the valley may, by facilitating underflow, cause an appreciable reduction of the volume and carrying power of water flowing on the surface. The effect in this case is likely to be cumulative, further aggradation leading to further loss of river volume, and this in turn to further aggradation.[1]

In all cases decreasing load in late stages of the cycle—i.e. after uplands have been worn down to small relief—must eventually terminate these aggradational phases, and a river will not only carry away piecemeal the alluvium it has itself deposited in its valley, but will also "return to the long-postponed task of slowly wearing down the rock basement of its first graded course" (Davis).

CHAPTER VII

The Landscape in Youth and Maturity

SIMULTANEOUSLY with the river cycle, which has been outlined in the foregoing chapters, the landscape, or general land surface, also runs through its stages of youth, maturity, and old age. Although parallel, however, the stages of the landscape cycle are never quite co-extensive with those of the river cycle. As different

Termed "Lehmann's principle" by W. M. Davis, Meandering Valleys and Underfit Rivers, *Ann. Assoc. Am. Geog.* 3 (1914).

criteria for stages, and especially for the important transition from youth to maturity, must be applied, it is quite possible for a young landscape to be traversed by mature rivers, while, on the other hand, a landscape may reach maturity while its rivers are still young.

Essentially the early stages of the landscape cycle involve first the gradual modification and, later, the destruction, or elimination from the landscape, of the initial surface and its replacement by forms of relief developed wholly in the current cycle. When this goal is attained by the erosional processes, the landscape is mature, but as long as parts of the initial, or infantile, form are preserved, it is still young.[1] Usually only a beginning has been made when the parallel-walled, or more commonly open V-shaped, valleys of young rivers, such as have already been described, are developed. Though these valleys are entirely the result of erosion in the new cycle, they are narrow, and if widely spaced occupy only a part, perhaps a small proportion, of the total area. Throughout the stage of youth the general outlines of the relief are determined by the form of the initial surface, which is still retained by the *doabs*,[2] or strips on the interfluvial areas. Generally these are broad at first, but later they are nibbled away until they become narrow or discontinuous, and

---

[1] While this criterion of maturity is strictly applicable in landscapes of homogeneous rocks, considerable latitude must be allowed in its application in regions of heterogeneous rocks. Small residuals of an initial form may survive in places where rocks are exceptionally resistant long after the initial surface has been destroyed and the land surface reduced to a level far below it over other and much larger parts of a landscape. In such a case a strict application of the rule would require the landscape as a whole to be classed as young, whereas a great part of it (excluding only the residuals) may be far advanced in, or even have progressed beyond, the stage of maturity. "Parts of the intricately dissected Allegheny Plateau, with no upland remaining, are for sound reasons commonly accepted as the type of a mature plateau"; but another plateau in large part reduced to a peneplain may "yet have scattered monadnocks with summits preserving appreciable expanses of the original upland" (Johnson). Rigid application of the rule announced in the text would require the latter to be classed as young; but Johnson rules that it is old. An alternative method of classifying landscapes as young, mature, and old, advocated by Johnson (Available Relief and Texture of Dissection: a Discussion, *Jour. Geol.* 41, pp. 293–305 (1933)) is based not on survival of any, or of any specified proportion, of the initial form, but on the proportion of the actual mass of material available for removal—i.e. standing above the average level of what will be local base-levels when streams become graded—that has actually been removed, the landscape being mature when from one-third to two-thirds of such mass has been eroded away.

[2] W. M. Davis, The Drainage of Cuestas, *Proc. Geol. Ass.* 16, pp. 75–93 (1899).

eventually they disappear, marking the passage of the landscape from youth to maturity.

On a newly emerged surface (i.e. in the case of a first cycle), and especially on one without steep gradients due to inequalities of uplift, consequent streams, including tributaries, are generally spaced rather widely and, in early stages of erosion, streams of other kinds have not yet been developed. From the air, therefore, the newly cut young valleys may be scarcely noticeable, and large tracts may appear to retain the initial forms without modification. Plateau regions in which the initial form of the present cycle is an uplifted peneplain of a former cycle may also retain strips little modified by erosion (infantile) on the broad or narrow interfluves between deeply incised valleys. This is the case on the Blue Mountains upland and Southern Tableland of New South Wales (Pl. XIV, 1).

The destruction of an upland by the development of valleys cut below its surface is *dissection*. One may also think of the "dissecting" agencies as developing land forms by a process of *sculpture*. As the cycle progresses towards maturity the initial form, or infantile surface, will be dissected and eventually destroyed, in part by deep development of valleys already present in early youth (consequents, together with those persisting in some cases from an antecedent cycle), and in part by the birth and development of new valleys of various kinds that come into existence in the course of the cycle.

Consequent valleys alone, without assistance from those of other origin, rapidly dissect some surfaces that have somewhat steep initial declivities, especially when these are underlain by soft materials. On a surface of minutely diversified initial relief, streams, mainly secondary consequents, are numerous and closely spaced, and such of them as run at first down the steeper slopes at once begin the work of dissection. When the closely spaced valleys of these are incised to some depth, the sloping sides of adjacent valleys intersect. The surface is then maturely dissected, for no remnants of the initial form survive on the interfluves. Where the superficial material is unconsolidated fine sediment, such dissection takes place so rapidly that, as compared with the rate at which most erosion proceeds, it may be considered instantaneous. It will, at any rate, be far advanced before the most rapid of initial upheavals is complete, and so one need not expect to find any strongly warped and uplifted sea floors, for example, in a stage of youth or immature dissection.

On even moderately inclined surfaces, if the ground is not too absorbent, so that there is considerable run-off, large numbers of closely spaced consequent streams are formed. These deepen their valleys side by side, so that the initial surfaces on those parts of the doabs that separate the deepest parts of the young ravines are soon destroyed, and the sides of adjacent ravines thereafter intersect, the doabs being replaced by sharp ridges (Fig. 29 A).

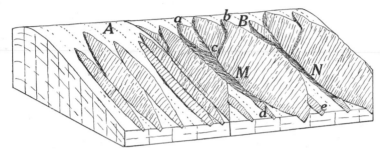

Fig. 29. Dissection of a slope by consequent streams (A); and development of master streams (B).

If consequent streams on a sloping surface cut deeply, some of them, favoured perhaps by the accident of draining initially larger areas, incise more deeply than do their neighbours on either hand. These become *master streams* (Fig. 29 B: *M, N*). As their ravines become deeper (without change of angle of their V slopes) the sides are worn back so as to cut through the ridges separating them from the smaller streams beside them, which have been left behind at higher levels, and these are compelled to run down into the valleys of the master streams as their tributaries. (Thus *a* and *b* join the master *M* at *c*.) A few master streams may soon receive practically the whole drainage of the surface (Fig. 30), though near the foot of the slope, where the master valleys are shallow and narrow ("bottle-necked"), diminutive beheaded streams (Fig. 29, *d, e*) will still remain, which are remnants of at least some of those that have failed in this "struggle for existence" among streams. The process of diversion of the headwaters of streams to be added as tributaries to their neighbours as a result of widening of the valleys of the latter is *abstraction* (Gilbert). It is well illustrated among the very numerous "bad-land" ravines that have been cut by ephemeral streamlets on pumiceous debris (volcanic "mud") spread over hillslopes near Lake Rotomahana, New Zealand, by volcanic explosions (Pl. XIV, 2).

Other things being equal, plains uplifted bodily without deformation require a vastly longer time for their complete dissection than do surfaces with diversified initial relief. On such a plain, if it is underlain by unconsolidated material, most of the precipitation sinks immediately into the ground to join the ground water. Also

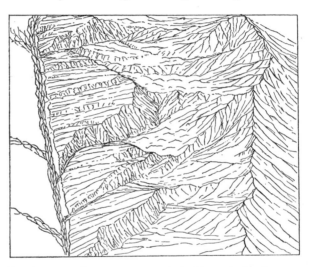

Fig. 30. Development of master streams in bottle-necked valleys on a sloping surface. Dry Canyon, Death Valley, California. (From a photograph.)

temporary streams and sheet floods formed on the horizontal surface are so sluggish that they do not corrade. Thus considerable areas of such surfaces may survive for a long time, even though built of soft materials. That is to say, they are stable forms, such as one may expect to find undestroyed by dissection among existing landscape features. Little-dissected extensive plains of river-laid gravel and finer materials that are trenched by main rivers but not by their tributaries are in this category—for example, high parts of the Canterbury Plain (Chapter XVI) fringing the New Zealand Alps.

Uplifted sea floors also, if not strongly warped or tilted, are stable forms in youth. Most known examples in this stage are *coastal plains* (Fig. 31) emergent as strips narrow or broad bordering pre-existing lands that have been upheaved along with them. It is usual to refer to the pre-existing land as an "old land" when it is to be contrasted with the newer land of the coastal plain, but one may avoid confusion with the use of "old" as a cycle stage by substituting "ancient land", or perhaps "hinterland".

Whether or not slight seaward tilting accompanies its uplift, as is probably sometimes the case, the surface of a coastal plain has a

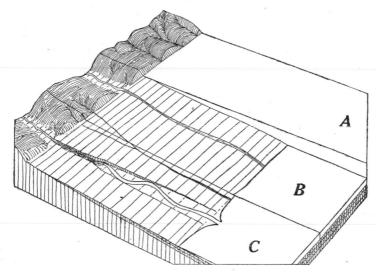

Fig. 31. A coastal plain. *A*, pre-existing land with the sea at the level of the ancient shore line; *B*, coastal plain emergent, as though the sea had suddenly withdrawn from it; *C*, coastal plain with extended river graded across it in the soft marine sediment.

more or less uniform slope seaward, and is drained by more or less parallel consequent streams that take seaward courses upon it. Minor irregularities of the surface may obviously guide such streams into somewhat roundabout courses, however, and two or more may unite before reaching the sea. All the larger rivers will have their headwaters in the ancient land behind the coastal plain. They are, in fact, the rivers of that land *extended* across the newly emerged surface; and, as they cross it in courses consequent on its slope, they are *extended consequents*. The larger, at least, of them carry so much water that they are competent to cut down and grade their courses very quickly wherever this may be done without cutting through the weak unconsolidated coastal plain deposits; and this is one of those almost instantaneous occurrences that may be expected to be completed during the time occupied by rapid uplift. Broad areas of the interfluves (doabs) between these larger rivers may, however, long remain undissected, and so young coastal plains are well-known landscape features.

The question of the stability, or longevity in the cycle, of uplifted plains, including coastal plains, involves consideration of the concept of *available relief* due to Glock[1] and redefined by Johnson.[2] Without accepting, or attempting to frame, such a definition as will make possible a precise quantitative statement of

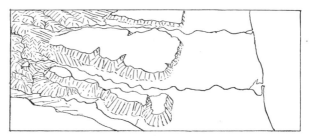

Fig. 32. Right: a very young coastal plain. Centre: a somewhat dissected coastal plain. Left: the ancient land. Osaka Bay, Japan. (After Cushing.)

the available relief of any district, one may take it to be at any particular place and time the height of the surface undergoing dissection above the local base-level controlling dissecting streams. Obviously in the cases referred to in the two preceding paragraphs, small available relief is a factor favouring slow dissection, while with large available relief relatively rapid dissection of an uplifted plain may be expected unless rivers are very widely spaced.

A coastal plain forms the south-eastern seaboard of North America. It increases in breadth south-westward, and is especially broad around the Gulf of Mexico. Some parts of this coastal plain are still young, but others are maturely dissected. Instructive "pocket" examples of coastal plains fringe the coast of Japan as a

[1] W. S. Glock, Available Relief as a Factor of Control in the Profile of a Land Form, *Jour. Geol.* 40, pp. 74–83 (1932).
Douglas Johnson, Available Relief and Texture of Topography: a Discussion, *Jour. Geol.* 41, pp. 293–305 (1933).

result of a very recent uplift.[1] In the great bays along the south coast of Honshu, successive uplifts have caused two parallel strips of sea floor to emerge, the higher of which is somewhat dissected and the lower undissected (Fig. 32). As the hinterland is mountainous, towns and villages have been built on the coastal plains.

As extended consequents cut down through coastal plains in the vicinity of the former shore lines, where the marine deposits underlying them usually have a thin edge, the rivers in such a case become

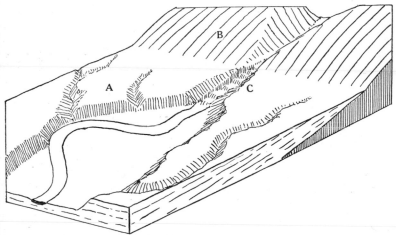

Fig. 33. Fall-line rapids in an extended river. A, coastal plain; B, ancient land; C, fall line. (After a diagram by Davis, redrawn.)

superposed on more ancient rocks beneath this cover. Generally the rocks of the undermass are relatively resistant to erosion, and so corrasion, which has rapidly graded the rivers and opened out the valleys in their lower courses, is here checked, and the extended rivers have ungraded steep descents, with falls and rapids, in this part of their courses (Fig. 33). Where there is a row of extended rivers crossing a long coastal plain, there are generally such ungraded superposed parts in all of them, and the line passing through these (roughly parallel to the ancient shore line) is the *fall line* (or *fall zone*).

While young coastal plains are under consideration, it may be as well to warn the reader of a pitfall dug by the adoption in

[1] S. W. Cushing, Coastal Plains and Block Mountains in Japan, *Ann. Ass. Am. Geog.* 3, pp. 43–61 (1914).

systematic geomorphology of the term "coastal plain" for a feature, or rather group of features, definitely originating as the result of uplift of the sea floor. There are coastal lowlands and plains bordering the sea that have come into existence in other ways, but these are not "coastal plains" in the technical sense, though frequently wrongly described as such by geographers. Moreover, paradoxically, a coastal plain when it becomes maturely dissected is no longer a plain, but, according to the usage of geomorphic terminology, it is still a "maturely dissected" or even "mature coastal plain".

Besides systems of consequent valleys and any others that may have been present since infancy on a young uplifted surface, more are developed on it and share in its dissection. They are cut by new streams that come into existence in the course of dissection and can be classed mainly in two categories, "insequent" and "subsequent".[1] A third class, "obsequent", perhaps better termed "anaclinal", is recognised, but is of minor importance. Streams of these classes have this in common, that they extend or grow in length headward, or by *headward erosion*, deepening valleys for themselves as they extend.

Insequent streams develop in great numbers in the course of the dissection of level upland surfaces (including coastal plains) underlain by fairly homogeneous material or horizontally bedded formations, and in soft materials may extend headward very rapidly. They may start as steep ravines cut by concentrated rain wash collecting in any slight hollows that have been accidentally formed in haphazard positions on the sides of main valleys, perhaps where rock slides have occurred. They are thus generally tributaries, but independent insequents may develop in cliffs bordering the sea. As the gullies grow longer and deeper they receive an increasing amount of water both from the run-off and from ground water sinking into the level upland and now seeping out along the banks and around the steep heads of the young insequent ravines. Thus headward erosion is accelerated. Insequents are without guidance as to the directions in which their heads extend, unless a greater volume of ground water seeping in from one side may cause a

---

[1] "Insequent" and "obsequent" are terms invented by W. M. Davis, who also adopted "subsequent", as previously used by Jukes.

stream to bend in that direction. This may perhaps explain the tendency of many insequent streams to head up any slope the initial surface may have.

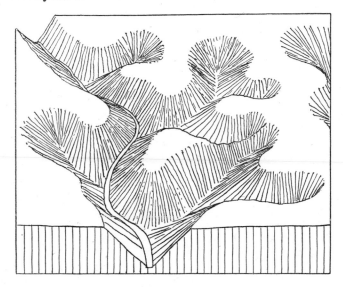

Fig. 34. Insequent dissection. (After a diagram by Davis, redrawn.)

Fig. 35. Maturely dissected coastal plain of eastern Italy. (After Davis.)

The first-formed insequents in their turn develop insequent tributaries, and as these also work their way headward into the doabs (interfluves) the area of undissected surface is reduced with increasing rapidity (Fig. 34). On the coastal plain of eastern Italy (Fig. 35) doabs have been destroyed and replaced by round-crested ridges and spurs, and dissection is *mature*. The streams dissecting such a "mature coastal plain" are extended consequents, new consequents, and insequents.

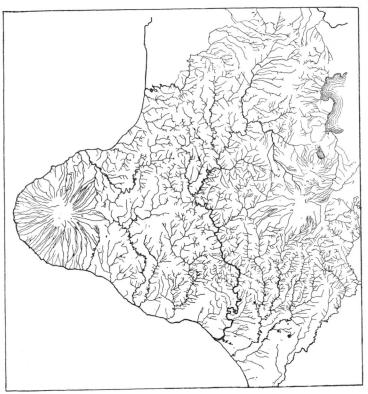

Fig. 36. Insequent drainage pattern exhibited by the tributaries of the Wanganui and neighbouring rivers (New Zealand). Compare this (central area of map) with the patterns of radial consequents on the volcanic mountains Egmont (west) and Ruapehu (east). (From Marshall's *Geology of New Zealand*.)

The river pattern, as seen on a map, that results from development of insequent drainage, has been likened to the branching of an apple tree, and called *dendritic*. A broad strip of the North Island of New Zealand, drained by the Wanganui and several other consequent rivers with many insequent branching tributaries, exemplifies well the dendritic pattern (Fig. 36). This district is underlain by soft marine formations of great thickness, and is nearly all maturely dissected to sharp ridges and spurs by streams, most of which are not yet graded throughout their lengths.

Where homogeneous rocks are maturely dissected by consequent and insequent streams, as in the examples cited above, the side slopes of the valleys—that is to say, all the hillside slopes—tend to develop at the same angle, so that ridges, spurs, and valleys assume symmetrical transverse profiles except where such symmetry is interfered with by the effects of lateral stream corrasion developing contrasting under-cut and slip-off slopes around valley curves. This is Gilbert's *law of equal declivities*. It was stated by him as though slopes were developed entirely by streams of water running down their declivities, but is true, nevertheless, as applied to the sum of the effects of the processes of rain-wash, soil creep, etc., that are reducing land slopes to gentler declivities, as is proved by the constant recurrence of symmetry in land forms on homogeneous and horizontally bedded rocks.

In homogeneous material, and with equal quantities of water, the rate of erosion of two slopes depends on their declivities. The steeper is degraded the faster. It is evident that when two slopes are on opposite sides of a divide the more rapid wearing of the steeper carries the divide toward the side of the gentler. The action ceases and the divide becomes stationary only when the profile of the divide has been rendered symmetric.[1]

Subsequent rivers also come into existence during the process of dissection, and these also owe their extension to headward erosion, guided in this case, however, by the outcrops of weak rocks occurring as strips or broader belts. Obviously the nature of the rock, whether weak or resistant, determines the rate at which gullies can develop and be extended headward by erosion. Where the rocks are all equally resistant (or uniformly weak), insequent streams come into existence and branch in all directions impartially; but where a main stream crosses zones of alternately weak and resistant rocks, tributary streams that begin to nibble back on the outcrops of weak rocks are enormously favoured thereby, and the development of new streams on the resistant rocks may take place

[1] G. K. Gilbert, *Geology of the Henry Mountains*, p. 140 (1877).

so slowly in comparison as to be negligible. It is the tributaries that start on the weaker outcrops and are afterwards confined to and guided in the direction of their headward erosion by weaker zones of rock that are chiefly effective in dissecting the land surface.[1] These are *subsequents*, and the divides between them are *subsequent divides* (Fig. 37).

Where weak formations outcrop as continuous belts, subsequents develop along them rapidly and become graded almost at once with respect to the levels of the main streams at their junctions, which are local base-levels for the tributaries. (In fact, the level of every point on a river may be regarded as a local base-level for the

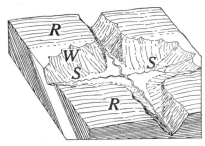

Fig. 37. A hypothetical early stage in the development of valleys by newly formed subsequent streams, *S*; on a weak belt of rocks, *W*; between resistant belts, *R*.

river above that point with all its tributaries.) With the exception of some that are located on the crush zones, sometimes termed "shatter-belts", of faults, which may have any accidental orientation, weak formations are usually members of inclined series of strata, in which weaker and more resistant layers occur alternately, with parallel outcrops. Subsequent divides become more or less prominent ridges of the resistant members of the series, and both these and the subsequent valleys are elongated in the direction of the geological *strike*. So they may be referred to as "strike" features, or longitudinal.

Where, as is usually the case, longitudinal subsequent rivers develop as tributaries, the mains must be transverse. Such main

[1] So rapidly do subsequent valleys develop that the intermediate "cuesta-bridge" stage, represented at the right in Fig. 37, appears not to be represented by an example in any landscape (W. M. Davis, *Ann. Ass. Am. Geog.* 5, pp. 67–8 (1915)).

rivers may be antecedent, superposed, or even in some cases deeply cut consequents of a first cycle. These transverse rivers may still have ungraded gorges, where they cross resistant rocks, but the subsequent tributaries that join them in graded reaches farther upstream may be thoroughly graded, having no hard-rock difficulties to contend with. Such, for example, are the tributaries of the Hunho system of North China (Fig. 25). The main river is literally "held up" for a relatively long period by the resistant-rock barrier through which it must laboriously deepen its gorge. As it does so an upstream subsequent tributary easily lowers the floor of its already graded and open valley to an accordant depth.

Fig. 38. A subsequent lowland on a belt of weak rocks.

The valley of a subsequent river on a belt of weak rocks soon becomes widely opened, and simultaneously the general surface-lowering processes acting over the whole breadth of the belt reduce it to low relief as compared with steep and less fully mature forms of high relief that still survive on adjacent hard-rock belts. Thus elongated *subsequent lowlands* are developed (Fig. 38), through which subsequent rivers take leisurely courses, and locally on weak-rock belts a far "older" stage of landscape development will be found than on alternating hard-rock belts.

CHAPTER VIII

Shifting Divides and River Piracy

ON a mature surface divides are well defined and so contrast strongly with the very poorly defined divides generally present on the same surface while it is still young. The well-defined divides of maturity are, however, by no means fixed in position for all time, but shift laterally, and in some special cases migrate rapidly and far. Being defined by the intersections of slopes of adjacent valley sides, they are liable to displacement as the result of any changes in these slopes, and especially as the result of more rapid valley deepening on one side than on the other. Such slow migration (Fig. 39) is *creeping*; but, should diversion by abstraction of one

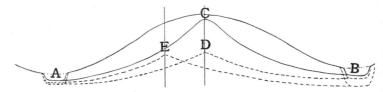

Fig. 39. Profile of a shifting divide. *C*, original position of the divide; *D*, possible later position after some lowering of relief; *E*, another possible position, where lateral shift has taken place because valley *B* has been deepened more rapidly than *A*.

stream into the system of its neighbour take place, the result is *leaping*, for the whole head-water drainage system of the abstracted stream is transferred in a moment and added to that of the other. There is no longer a divide between them. (In Fig. 39 this takes place if the creeping of *E* towards *A* goes on until the stream *A* is abstracted and flows down the slope *EB* into *B*.)

Even a main divide along the crest of a mountain range may slowly migrate an appreciable distance, and some have obviously done so as a result of more rapid erosion on one side of the range than on the other. The reasons for this may be quite unconnected with rock structures, or with differences of rock hardness, which are capable of causing migration and will be considered later. One cause of migration is found where rivers on one side of a range

68

have much shorter courses to the sea than have those on the other side. A classical example of this is the retreat that has taken place of the scarp known as the Blue "Ridge", in North Carolina.[1] As far as they affect erosion, the rocks are practically homogeneous in the Blue Ridge region, and it is therefore quite clear that this is not a

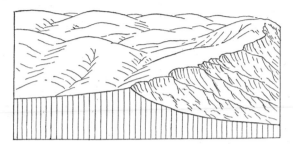

Fig. 40. Davis's diagram of the scarp of the Blue "Ridge", North Carolina.

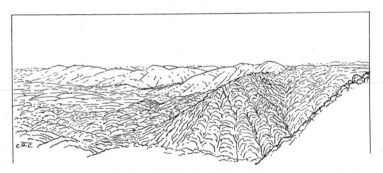

Fig. 41. The scarp of the Blue "Ridge". Highland plateau at right; Piedmont at left. (Drawn from a photograph.)

case of structurally controlled retreat of an escarpment (Chapter x). North-west of the divide (Figs. 40, 41) relief is weak, though the land surface is high above the sea, for the streams on it are head-waters of members of the Mississippi system, and their waters follow a long and somewhat roundabout route to the sea. The descent, on the other hand, south-eastward from the divide is so steep as to be almost wall-like, with a drop of 1500 ft. to the heads

[1] W. M. Davis, The Stream Contest along the Blue Ridge, *Bull. Geog. Soc. Philadelphia*, 3, pp. 213–44 (1903).

of the streams on the Piedmont, at the rear of the Atlantic coastal plain, whose courses to the sea are comparatively short.

Similar migration of the crest-line divides of mountainous islands in the trade-wind belts may take place, for here there is heavy precipitation on the windward side, while the lee side is relatively rainless. An example of this kind is found on the island of Oahu, Hawaiian Islands (Figs. 42, 43), where the north-eastern

Fig. 42. Shifting divide between the head of Nuuanu valley (in the distance, through the gap) and the Pali (meaning "cliff"), near Honolulu, Oahu, Hawaiian Islands. View south-westward. (Drawn from a photograph.)

half of the Koolau Range has been entirely destroyed by deep erosion and the crest line has been forced back south-westward towards the leeward side of the range, the slope of which is only dissected.[1]

Shifting takes place also of the divides between the opposed heads of rivers, and may be pushed rapidly and very far where these are subsequents developed or developing on the same weak belt of material. Proofs of such rapid migration of the divide between

[1] C. E. Dutton, Hawaiian Volcanoes, *U.S. Geol. Surv. Ann. Rep.* pp. 214–17 (1884); H. T. Stearns, *Geology and Ground-water Resources of the Island of Oahu, Hawaii*, pp. 26–9 (Honolulu, 1935).

opposed streams may sometimes be seen if remnants of valley-floor gravels of the weaker stream, or of the valley floor itself, are left

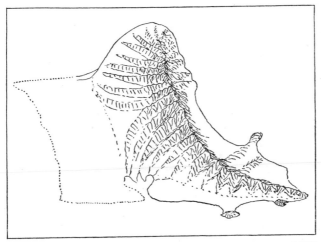

Fig. 43. Koolau Range, Oahu, Hawaiian Islands; the steep Pali (cliff) is conspicuous along the north-eastern slope. (After W. M. Davis, redrawn.)

as terraces bordering the narrower and more newly cut valley of its more vigorous competitor, which flows in the direction opposite to the slope of the terraces (Fig. 44).

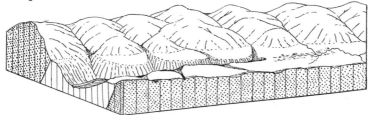

Fig. 44. Creeping divide between the heads of subsequent rivers on a belt of weak rock. Remnants of the valley floor of the now shrunken river on the right now border the more vigorous river flowing to the left, which is extending its valley by headward erosion.

The weaker stream, having been robbed of its headwaters and any headwater tributaries it may have had, is now of diminished volume. So the valley bottom near the divide will probably be swampy.

A well-known example of a creeping divide of this kind is that

71

in northern France between the head of the Bar, which is being pushed back, and a tributary of the Aire, which is more vigorous as a result of recent deepening of the valley of the Aire itself (Fig. 52, *A*). On the ill-defined divide between the heads of the Bar and the Aire tributary, the last diversion of an incoming side stream from the shrinking Bar system was hastened artificially in the eighteenth century. A very similar creeping divide separates

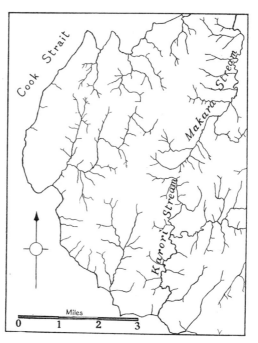

Fig. 45. The Karori and Makara valley systems, separated by a low and creeping divide.

the heads of the Karori and Makara, near Wellington, New Zealand (Fig. 45). The divide is low and ill-defined and is creeping northward, a side stream of the Makara that enters it from the west being now in danger of transference to the Karori system.

Diversion of streams by abstraction as a part of the process of development of master consequents, as already described, is only one of several ways in which such changes in river courses are brought about. Diversion of headwater streams to become tributaries of other rivers is generally termed *capture*, and the diminished lower courses of the former rivers, where they survive at all, are *beheaded*. "River capture" may be understood as including abstraction, but is sometimes limited in its application to a process of

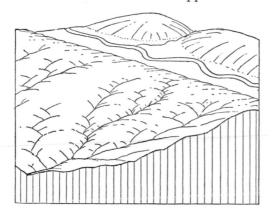

Fig. 46. A high-level river threatened with capture by a developing insequent. (After a diagram by Davis.)

Fig. 47. A tributary of Clark Fork (left) threatens to capture Rock Creek (right), towards which a divide (across centre) is creeping. Big Horn Basin, Wyoming, described by Mackin. (Drawn from a photograph.)

diversion by streams developing headward at a rapid rate under certain favourable conditions so as to tap and lead off the waters of others. This process has been called also "river piracy".

The most favourable condition for capture to take place is that a stream with an outlet at a relatively low local base-level shall be

73

developing by headward erosion and pushing the divide at its head towards a river that flows at a higher level, being perhaps held up by a hard-rock barrier it has to cut through in its lower course, or following a roundabout route to the sea[1] (Figs. 46, 47, 48). The stream that effects a capture may be insequent or subsequent.

It is most often subsequent streams that succeed in making captures and transverse streams that are beheaded, for the former

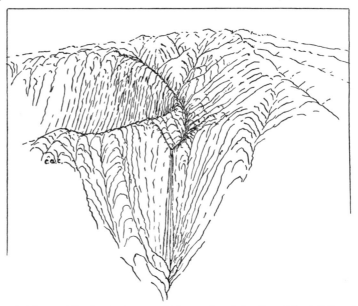

Fig. 48. The rapidly developing amphitheatre-headed valley at the left threatens to capture the headwater stream in the V-shaped valley (centre) above the waterfall. Maui, Hawaiian Islands. (Drawn from a photograph.)

extend headward rapidly, and develop uniformly graded gentle declivities, while the deepening of the latter is delayed until they can grade their hard-rock gorges farther downstream. In Fig. 49, *a*, a transverse river is threatened with capture by a subsequent that may be regarded as a tributary of another transverse river, the latter being larger and having, therefore, a more deeply cut valley than the threatened stream. In Fig. 49, *b*, the former upper course of the transverse river has been captured and added to the valley system of its nearby competitor, as a result of continued headward

See Postscript at the end of this Chapter.

erosion of the *diverter*, as it has now become. What remains of the transverse river is a beheaded stream. Before capture took place the divide between the would-be diverter and any former tributary of the river threatened with capture that existed on the same weak belt may have crept a long distance (after the manner of the creeping illustrated in Fig. 44) before capture became imminent. Towards the end of the process such creeping is accelerated as the volume

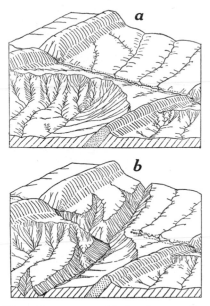

Fig. 49. Diagrams illustrating capture of the headwaters of one transverse stream by a subsequent tributary of another. In stage *a* capture is imminent; while in stage *b* it has taken place. (After a diagram by W. M. Davis, redrawn.)

of the diverter is augmented by seepage of ground water fed by leakage through the bed of the threatened river.

The right-angle turn that a captured transverse river makes at the point of diversion (Fig. 49) is termed the *elbow of capture*. It would be a mistake, however, to assume that all right-angle turns in river courses, as shown on maps, indicate that captures have occurred, for many such turns, especially in block-faulted regions, are of consequent origin. Still, when other indications of recent capture have been smoothed out of the landscape by long-continued erosion, a suspected elbow of capture appropriately located as regards underlying structures may be the only remaining evidence of a capture that has occurred in the distant past. Nor should the absence of a conspicuous elbow lead to the rejection of a theory of capture founded on other good grounds, for, obviously, an elbow is a feature of the capture of transverse streams only.

Recent captures are very easily identified by an association of special features that develop rapidly and conspicuously in consequence of the event. Changes occur in stream profiles, because the valley of the diverter, though graded or nearly so for the volume of water it was formerly carrying, is much too steep after diversion takes place for the enlarged stream that now flows in it. This is the case especially at its former head—that is, in the vicinity of the elbow or point of capture. So degradation begins, and a youthful trench is cut by the diverter; and this extends headward up the captured river, which has for a time (until regraded) to flow down a steep slope into the diverter. Tributary streams joining the newly entrenched part of the river must also deepen their valleys anew as their local base-level (the level of the main stream) is progressively lowered (Fig. 49, b).

In course of time, when the deepened trench at the point of capture is widened also, the new divide between the captured and

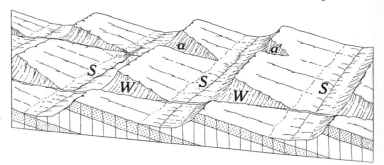

Fig. 50. Air gaps indicating former captures. W, water gaps; a, a', air gaps; S, subsequent valleys.

beheaded portions of the former river is pushed back so as to shorten the beheaded stream still further, and in the case of a beheaded transverse river, its head is gradually transferred to the outcrop of the next resistant stratum downstream. The former gorge through this outcrop, still a "water gap" in Fig. 49, b, when no longer traversed by a stream, becomes an "air gap" (Fig. 50, *a*, and Fig. 51). When the floors of adjacent valleys are further lowered by subsequent erosion, such an air gap may remain as a mere notch in the skyline of a subsequent ridge (Fig. 50, *a'*).

Fig. 51. Air gap in Sallings Mountain ridge, Virginia, 400 ft. above the adjacent lowland; described by F. J. Wright. (Drawn from a photograph.)

While a capture is still of recent occurrence (Fig. 49, *b*) the new head of the beheaded stream is usually poorly defined, however, for it now rises in a swampy flat that was part of its valley floor before its headwaters were diverted.

Here, and downstream also, the river will show characteristic effects of substantial reduction of volume, which makes it too small for its valley, or "underfit". Special features of the valleys of underfit rivers (not all of which have been beheaded by capture) will be discussed in Chapter XII.

Perhaps the best-known examples of rivers that have been beheaded by capture are the tributaries of the Meuse, of which it has been robbed by members of the Moselle system on the one side and the Seine on the other[1] (Fig. 52). The Aire, whose waters go now by way of the Aisne to the Seine, was formerly the head of the now shrunken Bar, a tributary of the Meuse, while what is now the head of the Moselle formerly, and rather recently, passed through a now abandoned valley from Toul to Pagny, where it joined the Meuse. In the latter example the elbow of capture, near Toul, is very sharp.

[1] W. M. Davis, The Seine, the Meuse, and the Moselle, *Nat. Geog. Mag.* (1896); reprinted in *Geographical Essays*, pp. 587–616 (1909).

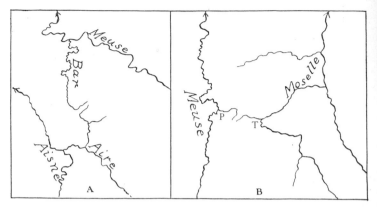

Fig. 52. Captures. *A*, the Bar is beheaded, and its headwaters (as the Aire) are added to the Aisne; *B*, a former tributary of the Meuse becomes the head of the Moselle; *T*, elbow of capture, at Toul; *P*, Pagny.

Fig. 53. The Kaiwarra capture, Wellington, N.Z. Diverter (right) and captured stream (left) are deeply entrenched. The former level of the latter is indicated by the terrace (left); and accordant with this is the abandoned course through an air gap (centre; middle distance).

78

A small example of capture at Wellington, New Zealand, presents all the features of recent capture (with the one exception of the non-essential elbow of capture) very closely grouped, so that they are seen in a single view (Fig. 53). The diverter and captured stream in this case are strictly in line (Fig. 54), because both have developed, the captured stream first and the diverter later, by

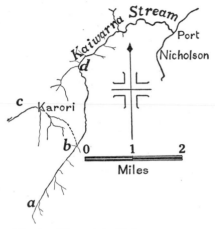

Fig. 54. Map of the Kaiwarra capture.

headward erosion along the same shatter belt in a fault zone. This weak zone was encountered at *b* by the insequent head *cb* of the Karori Stream, which developed thence to *a* as a subsequent. Later the insequent head of the Kaiwarra, working back from *d*, discovered the shatter belt half a mile north-east of *b*, and, working back along it as a subsequent to *b*, captured at that point the subsequent head of the Karori. The Kaiwarra was favoured by having a much shorter course to the sea than the Karori.

Postscript. Another condition favouring capture (in addition to those mentioned on pp. 73–4) is found where one stream has a heavier load of waste than its neighbour, perhaps because it emerges from a mountain valley and carries coarse gravel. The more heavily loaded stream will have a steeper gradient, and at an equal distance from its mouth will flow at a higher level, than the adjacent stream which carries less (and finer) waste, and is liable to be captured by the latter. Captures due to this cause have been noted by Rich at the Book Cliffs escarpment, Utah, and by Mackin in Wyoming. J. L. Rich, Origin and Evolution of Rock Fans and Pediments, *Bull. Geol. Soc. Am.* 46, pp. 999–1024 (1935); J. H. Mackin, The Capture of the Greybull River, *Am. Jour. Sci.* 31, pp. 373–85 (1936).

CHAPTER IX

Subsequent Erosion on Folded Rocks

WHEN it has been necessary in the preceding chapters to refer to steeply inclined strata in their relation to subsequent features and transverse valleys, the assumption has been made that rock formations in homoclinal[1] attitudes and with folded structures would underlie an initial surface only if inherited from some former relief.

Development of subsequent rivers and divides takes place in a first cycle on simple structures such as have been postulated in Chapter IV only in the special case of coastal plains that emerge with some initial dip of their underlying strata. In this case consequent streams flow in the same direction as the strata dip and are transverse to their strike, and when dissection is mature there may be considerable development of subsequent valleys and divides parallel to the margin of the ancient land, between it and the new shore-line. A "belted coastal plain" (Davis) results.

The case has now to be examined, however, in which initial upheaval is accompanied by close folding, with development of steep dips (Fig. 55). The primary consequents might be expected to follow courses corresponding to the axes of synclines, for in these positions are the theoretical furrows of the initial surface, and such streams would, therefore, be longitudinal, or parallel to the general direction of the strike of the strata. The Jura Mountains are still drained in part by longitudinal streams that have been regarded as originating in this way as consequents of the first cycle, though the range has been eroded in more than one cycle.

In most regions of folded rocks, however, longitudinal or primary consequents, and indeed all consequents, have long since been eliminated from the landscape. They may perhaps be better relegated to a category of forms to be ascribed to certain hypo-

[1] The term "homocline" was introduced by R. A. Daly (Homocline and Monocline, *Bull. Geol. Soc. Am.* 27, pp. 89–92 (1916)) to replace the ambiguous "monocline" where it is used to signify a succession of strata dipping continuously in one direction. The synonym "unicline", being a hybrid, is less acceptable.

thetical stages of infancy and youth of the landscape cycle never realised in nature among mountains of closely folded rocks. Rapid destruction of initial forms must indeed go on during the early stages of upheaval in folds, and must be complete long before upheaval ceases, however rapid the earth movements may be. In the study of erosion on some simpler structures it is often convenient to make a harmless, though unrealistic, assumption that upheaval completes its work of preparation of initial forms of mountains or plateaux so rapidly that the processes of erosion do not appreciably

Fig. 55. An initial surface on folded rocks.

alter them during their growth, or that the commencement of erosion is magically delayed until the process of upheaval is complete. In the present case, however, this simple assumption must be discarded and the fact faced that vast erosion accompanies mountain growth.

The forms of youth on the huge amorphous pile of heterogeneous form and substance over closely folded structures are unimaginable, and one cannot think of this pile as a mountain range until it begins to present features of early maturity. Any hypothetical initial or infantile forms one may conjure up for such a pile of folds have never had real existence as mountains. Even where structures are less disordered, and folds more symmetrical, the processes of upheaval were building features that would have been, if they could have escaped contemporaneous erosion, totally different from those of any actual mountains. Such features, if they could have been preserved for our inspection, though higher and in some cases more symmetrical in form, would not present the diversity and grandeur of real mountain scenery.

The restored and theoretically unworn initial form of a range must be an immense pile of crowded, squeezed, and broken arches of rock. At a later time, after deep erosion has taken place, the limits of the range, though not its height, may be expected to correspond with the limits of this composite arch, but no agreement may be looked for between hypothetical surface forms of individual arches and the details of mountain peaks. The mountains, even in the early stage of maturity into which such initial forms would be sculptured as they rose, must have been very different in their general aspect, in drainage pattern, and in all details from mountains that exist in the same regions to-day. Present-day mountains on folded and overthrust rock structures may be likened to the ruined foundations of ancient lofty buildings, all the super-structures of which have crumbled to decay.

The foregoing remarks apply in particular to "fold" mountains rather than to "block" mountains, if one may revert temporarily to an outworn classification of mountain types, for block mountains (Chapter XXI) may preserve fairly well, or at least vividly suggest, the broad outlines of their initial forms. Most block mountains are, however, mere incidental features of the *re-uplift* of a folded mass.

Not many years ago all the great mountain ranges of the world that are carved out of folded rocks were believed to have originated as "fold" mountains, which implied that they were now in process of reduction by erosion for the first time, or were *one-cycle* mountains. The immensity of the time interval that has elapsed since the period of folding of even the younger (as regards date of folding) of mountain ranges is now better realised, however, and the time required for the destruction of strong relief even on the most resistant rocks can be but a fraction of this, even when allowance is made for the succession of regional uplifts (or long-continuing regional uplift), which, according to the doctrine of isostasy, must accompany the degradation of the initially upheaved folded mass.

In every mountain range of folded rocks that has been critically examined, moreover, evidence has come to light to prove that the mountains as they exist to-day are in reality dissected plateaux. They are *two-cycle*, or perhaps *multi-cycle*, mountains, the region having been since the folding worn down by erosion to fairly low relief at least once, and probably more than once, prior to the upheaval, generally a broad upwarping, that has introduced the current cycle of deep and mature dissection. In the Atlas Mountains, for example, evidence, long overlooked, that the modern mountains owe their relief to very recent upheaval of a peneplain truncating the folded strata and also the relief that was developed on the "Alpine" orogenic structure in the first cycle has quite recently been pointed out.[1] Such later, broadly domed uplift, affecting the folded mass and also the surrounding region, has been suggestively correlated with the original folding paroxysm as a necessary after-effect.[2]

Mountains that have passed through a stage of peneplanation in the course of their development may be recognisable as such owing to the preservation as plateaux or plateau remnants of parts of the peneplain that was the initial form of the cycle of erosion now current. Such a surface is dissected infinitely more slowly than are the tumbled crests of an upheaved pile of folds. Those parts of it that are evenly uplifted are encroached upon by erosion only little by little as dissection proceeds, surviving longest where underlain by the most resistant rocks or where situated farthest from the main rivers. It is justifiable to suspect that mountain ranges on which no peneplain remnants are found have also had a multi-cycle origin, and the suspicion often receives a considerable amount of confirmation from an accordance of summit levels, which suggests restoration of a peneplain destroyed by erosion but formerly existing a little above the summits of many surviving peaks (Chapter XVII).

It is quite conceivable that the mountains formed by the original folding—the "Alpine" orogeny in the case of most "modern" mountains—were not nearly as high as a reconstruction of their piled-up folded structures might suggest. The piling together of

[1] A. C. Lawson, The Atlas Mountains of Morocco, *Scientific Monthly*, 32, pp. 97–115 (1931).
[2] A. C. Lawson, Isostasy, *Univ. Cal. Chronicle*, p. 390 (Oct. 1924); The Geological Implications of Isostasy, *Bull. Nat. Res. Council*, 46, pp. 11–13 (1924).

6-2

rock folds does not probably form initially a very great protuberance on the earth's surface, for the folded rocks are probably thrust downward as well as upward, room being made for them by lateral flow of the material of the "substratum". As the initial protuberance is reduced in height by erosion, however, the whole folded mass must rise to maintain isostatic equilibrium,[1] and so will be eroded to a depth considerably greater than the height of the original protuberance.

In the Alps

the folding of the strata is not the direct cause of the present mountain range, but...the latter came into existence later by elevation....We have distinct proof in the structure of these mountain ranges that folding is not the necessary corollary of mountain-making even in the Alps and that the more elevated parts of the Alps owe their height to a vertical movement of the earth's crust....Recent investigations have shown that the vertical movement which caused the elevation was very considerable even in the...Pleistocene. These proofs are given by the surface features of the mountains....The mountain region which had just been elevated had some other surface features than the Alps of to-day. The mountains were not so high; their forms were more rounded; their valleys were broader and not so deep as to-day.[2]

The present problem is to deduce a reasonable concept of the erosion of a folded mass in its first cycle, and this may be done in terms of the deduced process of destruction of a simplified initial surface with strong corrugation above folds of similar form, such as is shown in Fig. 55. It may be assumed that the hypothetical longitudinal or primary consequents in the synclines of the surface will be fed by tributaries—secondary consequents—running down the flanks of the initial arches, and thus in the directions of dip of the anticlinal strata. As they flow down steep slopes, such streams will degrade rapidly and soon cut deep trenches; and where, in their down-cutting, they expose outcrops of weak strata they will send out along them other tributaries developing headward as subsequents on the weak-rock outcrops. In the diagram (Fig. 56) *A* represents the initial form, while surfaces *B* and *C* are developed in successive stages of erosion. Subsequent valleys and ridges will develop apace, and innumerable captures will divert the waters of

[1] A. C. Lawson, *loc. cit.*
[2] A. Penck, The Origin of the Alps, *Bull. Am. Geog. Soc.* 41, pp. 65–71 (1909).

secondary consequents into new courses, so that both secondary and primary consequents dwindle.

Consequent features must be so ephemeral in the development of drainage forms on folded rocks, that one need not expect to find the stages of their replacement by subsequents illustrated by examples in actual landscapes, though some features on the valleys of the Jura Mountains have been, perhaps mistakenly, so interpreted.

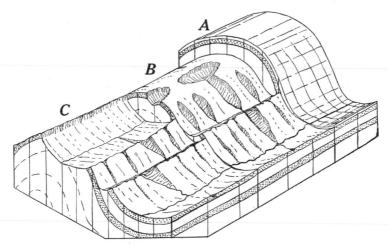

Fig. 56. Development of subsequent drainage on folded rocks.

Though the foregoing deduction of early stages of the development of drainage may be pure hypothesis, there can be no doubt that at some early stage of the erosional history of a mass of folded stratified rocks subsequents extend headward along all suitably exposed belts of weak material, at the expense of streams of all other types that may be present, causing these to shrink in length and volume as they are robbed of their headwaters and tributaries. The general process that results in the transfer of the bulk of the drainage to streams in subsequent valleys on weak zones is *adjustment to structure* (Davis). Beginning in the stage of youth of a first cycle, if not yet perfectly developed it continues in maturity of the landscape, and in later cycles. An example of adjusted drainage is the Hunho valley system of North China, described by Barbour (Fig. 25).

85

The drainage pattern that results from adjustment appears on a map as a system of subparallel rivers aligned on the strike of the rock formations in a general way, but making occasional right-angle turns to cross strike ridges (generally in gorges) (Fig. 57). This is

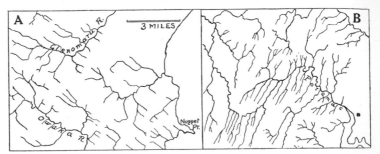

Fig. 57. *A*, trellised stream pattern in southern New Zealand. Subsequent streams are developed in adjustment to structure on north-westerly striking outcrops of steeply dipping strata. *B*, trellised drainage systems aligned on the strike of folded strata of the Appalachian system in eastern North America.

trellised drainage, and contrasts strongly with the dendritic pattern found where streams are mainly insequent. The origin of the transverse, generally short, portions of the river courses in a

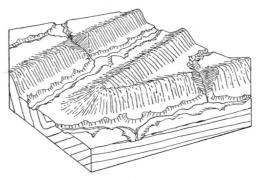

Fig. 58. Strike ridges, with two meeting in the form of a V, as developed in the Allegheny Mountains. (After a diagram by W. M. Davis, redrawn.)

trellised pattern, in which the rivers break through the outcropping edges of resistant formations, is usually obscure, and especially so if the surface has been subject to erosion in more than one cycle. Some of these may possibly be relics of secondary consequents of a

first cycle, as suggested in Fig. 56, and others of primary consequents that might cross low sags in the crests of initial anticlines,
as suggested in Fig. 55; but parts of antecedent and superposed
river courses are just as likely to be present in the transverse reaches
of many trellised patterns. The longitudinal members will be quite
parallel only on the simplest folded structures, but on pitching
folds they will converge; while the dividing ridges, situated on the
outcrops of the harder strata, will assume V-forms in plan (Fig. 58)
or curve around in canoe-end shapes (Fig. 59).

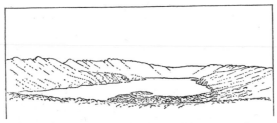

Fig. 59. Dip slope of an outcrop ridge (Mt Difficult Range), curving around
with the strike in a pitching syncline; Wartook Reservoir, Victoria, Australia.
(After a sketch by E. S. Hills, redrawn.)

In mountainous regions of folded rocks erosion has proceeded to
such a great depth below the hypothetical initial surface that no
survivals of tectonic forms such as anticlinal ridges may be expected
to occur; and even in a first cycle such forms must have been very
unstable and prone to destruction. Being initially high above local

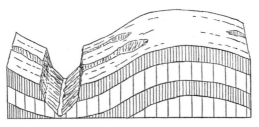

Fig. 60. Conditions of structure and incipient erosion favouring destruction of
an anticlinal ridge by rock sliding in a first cycle.

base-levels and flanked by steep surface slopes in the direction of
the inclination of the strata, they would tend to collapse by rock
sliding as soon as the primary consequent valleys in adjacent
synclines began to be deepened by erosion (Fig. 60). It seems

unnecessary[1] to postulate, as has sometimes been done, a very doubtful weakening of anticlines owing to a supposed development of tension in them during folding, but if anticlinal belts of the initial form were in reality thus weakened, they would come to be occupied by subsequent valleys.

Where, however, subsequent valleys have developed along anticlinal axes, leaving between them "synclinal" divides, these synclinal subsequent ridges and summits of "synclinal" mountains are, without exception, capped and protected by residual portions of resistant rock strata overlying weak formations, while other

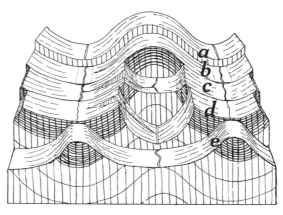

Fig. 61. Development of synclinal subsequent ridges.

parts of the same resistant strata, which have formerly been present at a greater height than the present mountains, have been removed by erosion.[2] A simplified version of this process (termed "inversion of relief" by de Martonne)[3] is presented in Fig. 61. In the succession *a–e* it is almost necessary to interpolate another stage between *c* and *d* to account for the great deepening of the subsequent valley that takes place in *d*—a stage of destruction of relief by erosion, to be followed by general uplift; but it is conceivable that this deepening might be due to some other cause. In any actual case the erosional history is likely to be much longer and more complicated.

[1] "Unnecessary, to say the least." W. M. Davis, *Nat. Geog. Mag.* (1890).
[2] W. M. Davis, *Science* (1888).
[3] E. de Martonne, *Traité de géographie physique*, 5th ed., p. 706 (1935).

Synclinal divides have been a subject of remark and often a source of wonder to observers who have failed to realise the depth to which erosion has proceeded, with the removal from some landscapes of layers of material miles in thickness. Such features are, however, not of such general occurrence throughout mountain landscapes as the attention they have attracted might seem to indicate. In any "inversion of relief" that has occurred, anticlinal divides of any anterior facies of the landscape that have been replaced in this process by anticlinal valleys are not necessarily—and probably are very rarely—consequent features; and the whole

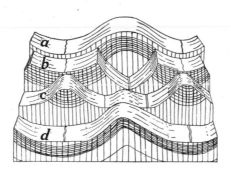

Fig. 62. Evolution of resequent ridge and valleys, stage *d* of diagram, developed from surface *a* through intermediate stages *b* and *c*.

process is best regarded as merely a part of the more general one of subsequent stream development and adjustment to structure previously outlined. The phrase "inversion of topography" was applied by Davis only to cases of actual demonstrable inversion caused by the filling of valleys by lava flows, which have later become ridges, as in the case of those on the slopes of the Alban volcano, near Rome, the Meissner ridge, in Hessen, or the Montagne de la Serre, in Auvergne (Fig. 201).

After a vast thickness of material has been removed by erosion during and following a succession of uplifts, the folding of rock strata formerly deeply buried, but now exposed at the surface, may be still parallel in a general way to that of the initial surface. This is, of course, unlikely to be the case except where folds are broad, open, and symmetrical, but in structures of this kind it may happen that a folded resistant stratum has such a relation to base-level that, as overlying weaker formations are eroded away, streams migrate down the dips of the resistant surface into synclinal positions, and stripped, unbroken anticlines form ridges between them. Such

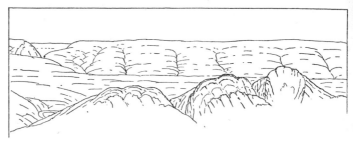

Fig. 63. Resequent anticlinal ridge (forming distant skyline) of resistant Table Mountain sandstone—the Klein Zwartberg, Cape Colony. (After W. M. Davis, redrawn.)

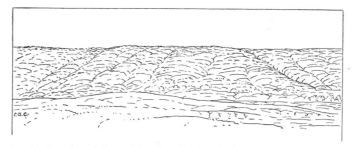

Fig. 64. Stripped anticline of hard rocks forming a ridge, believed to be resequent; Walkers Mountain, Virginia: described by F. J. Wright. (Drawn from a photograph.)

synclinal valleys and anticlinal ridges are unlikely to be actual survivals—throughout long-continued and deep erosion—of consequent forms, but generally must be the results of successive new adjustments to structure at successively deeper levels. They are then *resequent* (Davis) (Fig. 62). In the mountains of Cape Colony, which are formed of very ancient folded rocks, and have been exposed to erosion for a vast period, there are anticlinal ridges and synclinal valleys that are explained as resequent[1] (Fig. 63); and others are known in the Appalachian region (Fig. 64).

W. M. Davis, The Mountains of Southernmost Africa, *Bull. Am. Geog. Soc.* 38, pp. 593–623 (1906).

Notwithstanding the prominence given in landscape descriptions to both anticlinal and synclinal ridges, the majority of subsequent ridges in mountains of folded rocks are localised on the outcrops of exposed edges of inclined resistant strata. Sometimes the resistant character of a ridge-forming stratum is quite obviously in contrast with the weakness of its neighbours; but the contrast is not always so conspicuous, and stream action is able, in the course of untold ages, to search out differences in the texture, solubility, degree of induration, closeness of jointing, and probably other properties of rocks that are not otherwise apparent.

CHAPTER X

Homoclinal Features and Structural Benches

BY the time that a district of stratified rocks is maturely dissected by subsequent streams, the ridges and uplands forming the divides between these have generally assumed profiles determined by the inclinations of the strata (Fig. 65). In general they are not symmetrical, for the law of equal declivities does not apply to this case, where the rocks are not homogeneous but are contrastingly weak and resistant to erosion on opposite sides of each crest-line. Moderately inclined strata now outcrop as *homoclinal*[1] *ridges* (Pl. XV, 1, 2), bounded by *escarpments*[2] (Pl. XVI, 2) and *dip slopes*.

The dip slope is the back or gentler slope of the ridge, and is determined by the inclined upper surface of the resistant ridge maker stripped of softer overlying material and itself only very slightly eroded, though generally reduced a little in steepness, and

---

[1] Homoclinal: see footnote, p. 80.
[2] In common language "escarpment" and "scarp" have the same meaning, any line of cliffs, or abrupt slope breaking the continuity of a surface. Economy of words and the necessity for precision in nomenclature have led to the almost invariable use of "scarp" in this sense in geomorphology, while "escarpment" is limited to the meaning defined in the text. It may be considered to be a contracted form of "structural escarpment".

somewhat roughened and seamed by shallow valleys cut by streams flowing on it in the direction of the dip and sometimes described as "resequent" (p. 25).

The survival of dip-slope surfaces contrasts strongly with the depth of erosion on parallel belts of weaker rocks. Where dip slopes are very steep the contrast between these and escarpment slopes is

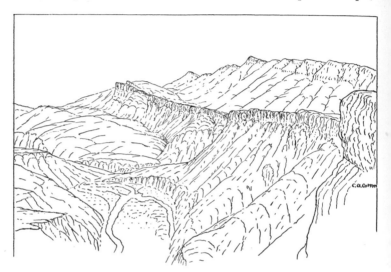

Fig. 65. Escarpments of homoclinal ridges developed on the outcrops of limestone strata, Waipara valley, Canterbury, New Zealand.

lost, and so homoclinal ridges on steeply dipping strata grade into *hogbacks*, which are found also on outcrops of vertical ridge makers (Fig. 68 and Pl. XVI, 1).

Structural escarpments, such as are found forming the steep fronts of homoclinal ridges, are developed by erosion wherever outcrops of resistant strata and also those of weaker formations underlying them are exposed as belts on the surface, as they commonly are along the sides of subsequent valleys. The escarpments of homoclinal ridges, as they slope in the direction opposite to the dip of the strata, are said to have "anti-dip", "anaclinal", or "obsequent"[1] slopes.

[1] W. M. Davis, The Geographical Cycle (1899), *Geographical Essays*, p. 264 (1909). Strictly "obsequent" means reversed in direction of slope or flow, but

Escarpments are formed on the exposed edges of horizontal strata also. The ridge maker, or escarpment maker, outcrops in the crest-line and upper part of the face of the escarpment in some cases as a steep, and even vertical, cliff, the latter being well exemplified in the steep "krantzes" of the escarpments of horizontal strata in South Africa (Fig. 66). Below is the contrasting gentler slope on the weaker underlying rock, though this is always somewhat steepened by talus from the escarpment maker. With varying rock hardness, climatic conditions, and rate of attack by erosion con-

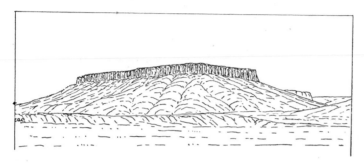

Fig. 66. "Krantz", or escarpment cliff, of Table Mountain sandstone, Bokkeveld Mountains, South Africa. (Drawn from a photograph.)

ditioned by relief, however, the sharpness of an escarpment edge may vary from a cliff to a smoothly rounded form (Fig. 67).

The process of development of an escarpment involves retreat of the escarpment, or a shifting towards the direction of the dip of the crest-line divide at the escarpment edge—a phase of the more general process of "homoclinal shifting". The resistant rock of the escarpment is affected but little by corrasion of the obsequent streams that arise on it until these become very steep; but on the softer material below, these streams burrow back so as to leave the edge of the escarpment maker badly supported, and even, it may be, overhanging (Pl. XVI, 2), so that blocks are constantly breaking away and falling from a retreating sharp edge, which is analogous to that of a waterfall in rocks of similar structure, but extends along the length of a linear outcrop. More or less rapid retreat is thus

it has become rather well established in the sense of "anaclinal" without other implication, and may be safely used in this sense, though the practice has been criticised by H. Baulig, *Jour. Geomorph.* 1, pp. 224–9 (1938).

characteristic of escarpments, and is generally made manifest by the presence of a sheet or thin talus slope of coarse waste, which is derived from the edge of the resistant escarpment-making stratum and streams down across the outcrops of the underlying rocks. This mode of retreat requires the development (and persistence) in the escarpment profile of slopes that are steep above and relatively gentle below, and this is the explanation of the characteristic concavity of such profiles.

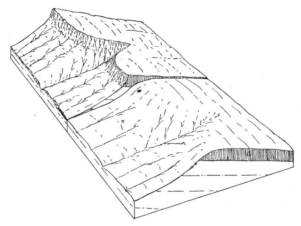

Fig. 67. Sharp-edged and rounded escarpments.

Hogbacks on vertical and nearly vertical strata have profiles not only symmetrical but also persistently concave on each side; and, of course, they differ from homoclinal features in being fixed in position—rooted, as it were, on their ridge makers.

Homoclinal ridges grade into *cuestas*,[1] which are developed on escarpment-forming strata of very gentle inclination (Fig. 68). Cuestas are necessarily broad, and present also greater contrast between escarpment and dip slopes than is found in typical homoclinal ridges. The dip slopes, indeed, are sometimes so extensive and so nearly level that they have the appearance of plains, while near escarpment crests they are regarded as plateaux—the Marne Plateau, for example, in Northern France[2] (Fig. 69).

[1] W. M. Davis, The Drainage of Cuestas, *Proc. Geol. Ass.* 16, pp. 75–93 (1899). Pronounced *questas*.
[2] D. W. Johnson, *Battlefields of the World War*, p. 217 (New York, 1921).

In the direction of the dip, however, the gentle slope merges into the lowland plain, or flat subsequent-valley floor, developed by erosion on the overlying weak stratum. Such a lowland between

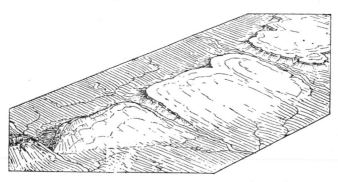

Fig. 68. Transition from a hogback (left) through a homoclinal ridge to a cuesta, and thence to a mesa (right). (After Davis.)

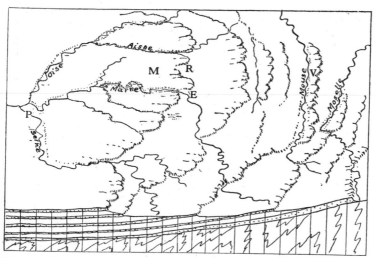

Fig. 69. Cuestas of Northern France. *E*, Épernay; *M*, Marne "plateau"; *P*, Paris; *R*, Rheims; *V*, Verdun. (From a diagram by Johnson, redrawn.)

two cuestas is commonly a broad and important landscape feature; together with the dip slope bounding it on one side and the escarpment on the other it is sometimes termed a *vale* (Fig. 70). Where subsequent features are developed during the mature dissection of a coastal plain of simple structure, they are alternating vales and cuestas parallel with the coast, making it a "belted coastal plain", exemplified by parts of the Atlantic coastal plain of North America.

Various groupings of cuestas have been recognised, such as *wide-spaced*, *close-set*, and *overlapping*,[1] which depend on variations in relative thickness of the resistant and weak formations, and on the measure of the relief.

Cuestas, as well as hogbacks and homoclinal ridges, are crossed here and there by transverse streams. As these pass through hard-rock outcrops, they remain relatively young when subsequent valleys are already widely opened, and on the steep sides of their

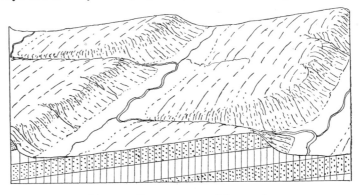

Fig. 70. Cuestas separated by a *vale*.

gorges bare-rock outcrops are exposed, which reveal the succession and dips of strata, making clear the relations between the surface forms of subsequent landscape features and the structure of the underlying rocks. Even obsequent streams that join the subsequents as tributaries may cut somewhat deeply into the escarpments, especially where cuestas are widely spaced. Their headward erosion embays a cuesta, so that its crest-line becomes sinuous and its escarpment no longer a straight line of cliffs but "scalloped" (Pl. XVII, 1); and the sinuosity may increase as long as these small streams are still deepening their valleys. Later, however, when obsequent, as well as through transverse, valleys are so deeply cut that development of embayments along their lines has ceased,

---

[1] W. M. Davis, The Principles of Geographic Description, *Ann. Ass. Am. Geog.* 5, pp. 78–83 (1915).

salients between them continue to be worn back as escarpments of diminishing height, so that a fading escarpment in a late-mature landscape becomes more and more nearly straight.[1]

Bevelled cuestas (Fig. 71) are developed in a youthful stage of dissection of a peneplain beneath the surface of which are gently inclined strata. Cuestas of a former cycle (*A*) have long ago been worn down by prolonged erosion (*B*), and a remnant of the peneplain

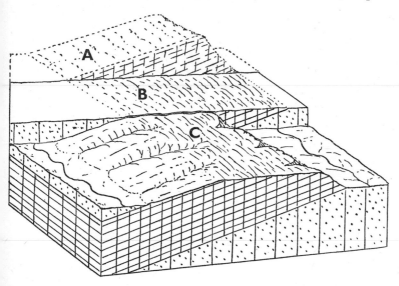

Fig. 71. Development of a bevelled cuesta.

that was the initial form of the current cycle bevels the present-day cuesta (*C*). In the case of a cycle introduced by uplift of very moderate measure (as in Fig. 71), the bevelled cuesta is a stable form, and, though strictly it is a youthful element of the landscape, its destruction is delayed until late in the cycle, when forms of full or late maturity will replace it. The best-known two-cycle or bevelled cuestas are those of eastern and south-eastern England, recognised by Davis.[2] The chief cuesta makers are here the lime-

Wooldridge and Morgan, *loc. cit.* pp. 202–3, and Fig. 119.
See especially W. M. Davis, *Die erklärende Beschreibung der Landformen*, Fig. 96 (1912); see also Wooldridge and Linton, Influence of Pliocene Transgression on the Geomorphology of South-east England, *Jour. Geomorph.* 1, pp. 40–54 (1938).

stones of the Mesozoic sequence, and vales are developed on the broad outcrops of the weaker strata.

The process of *homoclinal shifting*[1] affects not only all retreating escarpments, in the case of which migration of crest-line divides is obviously taking place, but also—in the case of progressive deep dissection resulting from progressive or continuous uplift—all parallel lines and belts of subsequent origin in the landscape. Under these conditions vales and cuestas—or subsequent valleys and homoclinal ridges—must migrate, or creep, laterally in the direction of the dip of the strata (Fig. 72). Obviously the extent of such

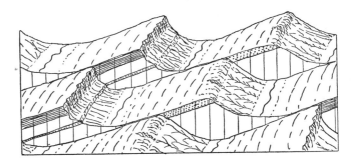

Fig. 72. Homoclinal shifting. Three successive profiles developed during progressive erosion.

migration is greatest (other things being equal) in the case of very gently dipping structures.

Zigzag courses of streams, the general trend of which is diagonally across the strike, may in some cases be ascribed to homoclinal shifting.[2] The river may be straight at first (being possibly superposed), but by the time the surface is dissected into homoclinal ridges the course has become zigzag (Fig. 73, *B*), as those parts that cross weak-rock outcrops have migrated down dip slopes until they have become longitudinal; and these are connected by transverse reaches crossing the outcrops of the resistant beds by the shortest paths. Such courses, with many right-angle bends, are common but all have not necessarily been developed in the same way. The

---

[1] "Monoclinal" shifting of Gilbert, *Geology of the Henry Mountains*, p. 14 (1877).
[2] G. K. Gilbert, *ibid.* p. 136 (1877).

joining-up of successively captured transverse streams by reaches of subsequent origin produces a similar result (Figs. 50, 70).

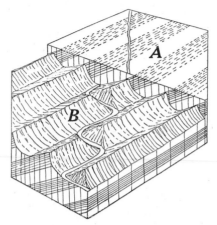

Fig. 73. Development of a zigzag from a straight river course by homoclinal shifting.

Mesas and *buttes*[1] are features closely related structurally to cuestas and homoclinal ridges, though subsequent streams are not

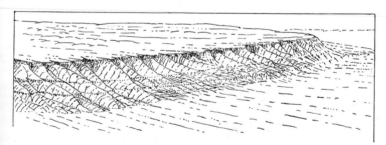

Fig. 74. Escarpment of a mesa, Rock Springs, Wyoming. (Drawn from a photograph.)

responsible for their isolation. They are salient features capped by large or small remnants of resistant horizontal strata overlying weaker material, and are bounded on all sides by escarpments. Large table-like forms are mesas (Figs. 68, 74) and small residuals are buttes (Fig. 75, Pl. XVII, 2). The length and breadth of a butte

[1] Pronounced *may-sa* and *bewt*.

are, at most, not much greater than the height; but a mesa may be many square miles in extent, its surface being a structural plateau. Mesas are cut up by dissection and further reduced in size by

Fig. 75. A South African "kopje", or butte; a remnant of a horizontal breccia stratum overlying sandstone. (Drawn from a photograph.)

retreat of the escarpments that bound them, for erosion on these is rapid owing to weakness of the materials underlying the lower slopes, though steepness is maintained owing to the resistance offered by the capping formation. Thus mesas are reduced in the course of time to buttes, and later disappear.

Fig. 76. Dissection of the margin of a mesa, Arizona. (Drawn from a photograph.)

Mesas are particularly well developed where horizontal sheets of lava lie over weaker materials and their margins retreat as escarpments dissected by streams (Fig. 76). Some mesas are remnants of blocks of country (consisting of horizontal strata) that have been uplifted between faults; the escarpments around these have retreated from the original fault boundaries of the blocks (Fig. 77). Even differential depression of a block of resistant stratum bounded by faults may preserve it from destruction for so long that the general lowering of the land surface at some future time may leave it standing as a mesa, just as resistant rocks downfolded as synclines may later become mountain crests. Table Mountain (Fig. 196),

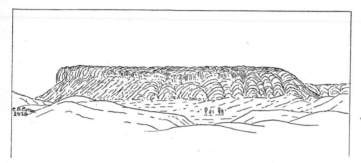

Fig. 77. Horohoro mesa, near Rotorua, New Zealand.

South Africa, seems to be the result of such survival after a long erosional history.[1] Higher-standing surrounding parts of the same resistant stratum were destroyed by erosion in an age long past.

Related in form and structure to mesas are *stripped structural plateaux*, or simply *structural plateaux*, in some cases of vast extent, which develop at the stage of maturity in regions of horizontal strata if relatively very weak materials are stripped away by erosion so as to expose the structural surface of a resistant stratum. Such features occur widely in Africa and are of broad extent in the down-stepping series of the Colorado Plateau in the south-western United States (Pl. XVIII, 1). In these regions semi-aridity may delay the destruction of a structural plateau by escarpment retreat and marginal dissection. In the limestone structural plateau of the south of France, and elsewhere in southern Europe, development of

[1] W. M. Davis, The Mountains of Southernmost Africa, *Bull. Am. Geog. Soc.* 38, pp. 593–623 (1906).

swallow-holes and underground drainage channels due to the solubility of the rock prevents the formation of surface streams and so delays normal dissection of the surface. Even without special retardation of erosion, however, the dissection of structural plateaux on *thick* resistant strata is a slow process, and so they are stable, or long-lived.

The development of a featureless plateau by complete, or nearly complete, removal of overlying weak material is controlled by the level of the surface of the resistant plateau-making layer in very much the same way as the lowering of the general land surface to a peneplain is controlled by the general base-level. The edge of the hard stratum is wasting away as an escarpment, and where streams

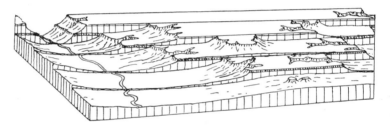

Fig. 78. Dissection and destruction of a structural plateau, with accompanying development and progressive destruction of benches and mesas. (After a diagram by Davis, redrawn.)

cross the edge its level is for them a local base-level. Thus a stripped structural plateau is closely analogous with a peneplain, but less permanent (unless developed close to general base-level).

A structural plateau developed close to the general base-level is indistinguishable from a peneplain until it is uplifted to be the initial form of a new cycle, as has occurred in the Blue Mountains of eastern New South Wales, when the features that make their appearance during its dissection will resemble those (to be described) characterising the stages of destruction of any structural plateau (Fig. 78).

As dissection proceeds, streams, some of them consequent, some perhaps antecedent, but many also insequent, cut valleys that may be deep and very steep-sided, being bounded by escarpments (Fig. 79). These valleys separate jutting points and peninsulas of the structural plateau (Pl. XVIII, 2; and Fig. 79), and later isolate portions of it as mesas and buttes. Finally all these are consumed, having wasted away at their margins by the process of escarpment retreat.

In the course of a single cycle on horizontally bedded formations, similar structural features may reappear more than once if there are successive resistant strata to be exposed by erosion. Lower plateaux begin to emerge as fringing step-like *structural benches* (Fig. 78) long before the highest plateau is destroyed or even more than marginally dissected. Structural benches bordering a valley are broad or narrow mainly in response to variation in the pattern

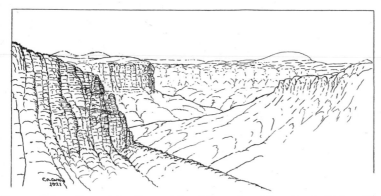

Fig. 79. The valley of the Grose, Blue Mountains, New South Wales. The Blue Mountains plateau is the upper surface of the resistant Hawkesbury sandstone, and is in course of destruction by the opening out of valleys, the sides and heads of which are escarpment cliffs that are in most places unscaleable.

of weak and resistant, thick and thin strata; for, other things being equal, the escarpment at the outcrop of a thick resistant layer will retreat slowly, and that of a thin layer more rapidly; and each bench is constantly being narrowed by retreat of its own marginal escarpment while, at the same time, being extended in width as that above it recedes. Depth, or juvenility, of a valley below also speeds up escarpment retreat, and this retreat sharpens their edges. The high escarpments of the Colorado plateaux where they are most freshened and steepened thus by rapid erosion at the base crumble back at such a rate that they are fringed by vast landslides,[1] though elsewhere their retreat is slower and more orderly (Pl. XVIII, 1).

[1] W. M. Davis, An Excursion to the Grand Canyon of the Colorado, *Bull. Mus. Comp. Zool. Harvard*, 38, pp. 121–6 (1901); An Excursion to the Plateau Province of Utah and Arizona, *ibid.* 42, pp. 36–8 (1903).

The longitudinal profiles of the streams dissecting plateau benches long remain ungraded, being broken by falls and rapids where they descend over the outcrops of resistant layers. In these steep descents the streams are confined in narrow gorges, or canyons, but such valleys open out widely where streams flow over weak-rock outcrops as they cross broad plateau benches. The side slopes of young canyons deeply cut in a succession of weak and resistant horizontal beds are characteristically broken by narrow structural benches, or *structural terraces*, and their escarpments (Pl. XVIII, 2). Amphitheatre-headed embayments in such escarpments develop as the back wall retreats at places where little concentrated drainage enters the heads of small side-branch streams.[1] Elsewhere these streams work back in narrow-headed ravines into the bench or plateau above.

CHAPTER XI

Transverse Valleys; Superposed and Antecedent Gorges

THE origin of the valleys, or parts of valleys, by way of which transverse reaches of the rivers in a trellised pattern break through strike ridges and anticlinal divides, has given rise to much discussion, the outcome of which is that it has become obvious that no single explanation of such transverse courses can be given. Some may be ancient consequents inherited from a first cycle, in which their positions were determined by the transverse synclinal folds of an irregularly folded or warped initial surface. Some others, though these are no doubt exceptional, are to be regarded as being as truly subsequent as the parallel streams aligned with the strike of the stratified rocks, having been developed by headward erosion along transverse or diagonal belts of crushed rock. Others, again, may be consequents of a later cycle that has been introduced by upheaval of a well-developed peneplain accompanied by warping or tilting strong enough to establish streams in entirely new courses, and cause the abandonment or partial abandonment of former courses

[1] W. M. Davis, *loc. cit.* p. 33 (1903).

adjusted to the structure. Some transverse courses may possibly result from inheritance of courses diverted by abstraction in a former cycle which reached an advanced stage of senility; in that condition departures from former adjustment may have been brought about by the development of wide valley floors cut by lateral stream corrasion across the reduced relief features on the resistant formations when these have been weakened by deep weathering. A great many transverse courses are certainly, however, remnants of formerly more continuous transverse and diagonal courses superposed on the landscape from unconformable covering strata that have long since been entirely removed from the surface by erosion either in the present or in a former cycle, though such valleys may have been broken into short lengths and largely replaced in the drainage systems by subsequents developed on the underlying structures.

Most of the foregoing explanations of short transverse reaches may be applied also to some or other of the great gorges by way of which many large rivers make their way through mountain ranges. If such gorges were blocked, so that the rivers were compelled to abandon them, other spillways would generally be available, perhaps somewhat longer and more roundabout, but broadly open and unobstructed, through which the rivers could take easy courses as consequents around the mountain barriers. It is obvious, therefore, that when the rivers took the courses in which they have entrenched themselves in their present deep gorges through the mountains, the apparently easier ways around the ranges were not open to them; they are of more modern development than the *initiation* of the transverse courses.

Superposed and *antecedent* origins of transverse gorges are possible, but in many cases there is doubt as to which is the correct explanation; while a third hypothesis has also to be considered, namely, that of headward erosion, put forward as a competitor of the hypothesis of antecedent origin to explain great transverse gorges.[1] Though headward development of subsequents on crushed zones is quite probably the correct explanation of some minor transverse gorges, there is no evidence or probability of such guidance in the development of great gorges through mountain

[1] F. Löwl, Die Entstehung der Durchbruchstäler, *Petermanns Mitteilungen*, p. 405 (1882).

ranges, and without it there is little to be said in favour of the hypothesis of headward erosion.

The origin of superposed consequent courses has been touched upon in an earlier chapter, and the theory of antecedent rivers may now be outlined. Where uniform or nearly uniform uplift at the initiation of a cycle results in inheritance of a complete pattern of streams ("antecedent" in the broadest use of the term—p. 34) from an ancient land surface into the infancy of the new cycle, such streams must take their chance of survival in competition with vigorous competitors, and in most cases they are likely soon to lose their distinctive character. There is a possibility, however, of some short transverse portions of river courses having had this origin.

Large rivers of strong slope, well inclosed in steep-sided valleys, or, in other words, vigorous adolescent rivers, have the best opportunity to persist across a belt of rising or writhing country, because a great deformation would be required to throw them from their courses. Small streams or large ones of faint slope in an open low country are more easily deflected. (DAVIS.)

In the true antecedent type "the essence of the antecedent relationship is a successful contest waged by rivers against *localised* uplift" (Wooldridge and Morgan). It was in this sense that antecedent rivers were recognised by Powell,[1] who had in mind the probability that some "rivers have held their courses through mountain ridges that slowly rose across their path; the rivers concentrating the drainage of a large headwater region upon a narrow line, cut down their channels as the land was raised" (Davis). Though the course of the Green River through the Uinta Mountains (Pl. XIX, 2), for the explanation of which Powell conjured up the antecedent type, is now regarded as a case mainly of superposition, the idea of antecedence seems to be valid in its application to many other gorges. Davis has suggested as better examples, "the Rhine below Bingen, the Meuse in the Ardennes, or several of the Himalayan rivers in the gorges that they have cut through the youngest marginal ridges of the range". One might add the Danube at the Iron Gate,[2] and the lower gorge of the Isker. The course of the Meuse through the Ardennes is alternatively explained as

[1] J. W. Powell, *Exploration of the Colorado River*, pp. 163–6 (1875).
[2] J. Cvijić, *Pet. Mitt. Ergänz.* 160 (1908).

superposed,[1] and such is now held to be the correct explanation of various supposed examples of antecedent gorges in the Rocky Mountain region, but the place of these is taken by innumerable other examples in warped and faulted regions, notably those in which a surface far advanced towards senility, either bare or with shallow cover only, has been deformed and upheaved. Andrews[2] insists that the world is dotted over with such antecedent gorges. Notable examples he cites in Australia are those of the Snowy, Hawkesbury, Clarence, and Brisbane rivers. Davis has claimed also as a positive case of a river antecedent to a block-mountain uplift one that ' holds its course" through the Canyon Range of south-western Utah.[3]

Lawson's interpretation of the history of the Nile brings it also into the category of antecedent rivers. Upwarping took place transverse to the course of the ancient Nile, ponding it for a time as a great lake of which the Sudd is a shrunken remnant. The lake was so large that evaporation from its surface prevented outflow, but when it was reduced in area by partial filling, it overflowed again northward, and the young valley of the middle Nile, broken by cataracts, has been cut through the uplift.[4]

Air gaps in the crest-lines of recently uplifted ranges, especially in the case of smaller examples, may remain as evidence that rivers have for a time persisted in their courses across the uplift, but later have been *defeated* and turned aside into new courses. A deserted valley across one of the fault-block ridges of southern Oregon, now an air gap, has been described (Fig. 80). Where large rivers have persisted in antecedent gorges it must generally be assumed that many smaller and less vigorous rivers that are unable to cut down their channels as fast as the land rises have been ponded and turned aside into new consequent courses. Many streams so defeated must become tributary to their more vigorous neighbours, which, thus reinforced, are the better able to maintain their antecedent courses in spite of further uplift.

[1] J. Cornet, Études sur l'évolution des rivières belges, *Ann. Soc. Géol. Belg.* 31, pp. 260–500 (1904).
[2] E. C. Andrews, The Origin of Modern Mountain Ranges, *Journ. and Proc. Roy. Soc. N.S.W.* 67, pp. 251–350 (1934).
[3] W. M. Davis, The Explanatory Description of Land Forms, *Cvijić recueil de travaux*, p. 321 (Belgrade, 1924).
[4] A. C. Lawson, The Valley of the Nile, *Univ. Cal. Chronicle*, 29, pp. 235–59 (1927).

There are in New Zealand a number of rivers which have the appearance of antecedents in that they make their way in gorges through ranges that have recently been uplifted, mainly as fault-bounded tilted blocks, around the ends of which there were, apparently, during and immediately after the earth movements, comparatively low tectonic gaps, and through these gaps consequent drainage would have spilled if the uplifts had taken place very rapidly, or if there had been no rivers in existence in the region prior to the deformation. It thus seems that the rivers are antecedent to at least the greater part of the uplift of the ranges that they cross, but it is not definitely known whether they took their present courses in a phase of emergence without notable deforma-

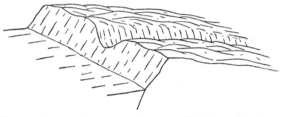

Fig. 80. Deserted antecedent gorge in an uplifted lava block south of Fort Klamath, Oregon. (After Douglas Johnson.)

tion possibly preceding the great deformation (the "Kaikoura" earth movements, at the end of the Tertiary, correlated by Andrews with the Kosciusko uplifts in Australia) to which the present-day major relief features owe their origin, or whether they were guided by the first wrinkles of the surface as it emerged from the sea, and have maintained the consequent courses then assumed during a continuation of the movements, although in the later and more intense paroxysm the shape of the surface and the pattern of mountain blocks changed considerably, so that what are now relatively low gaps in the tectonic framework do not necessarily coincide in position with the earliest-formed wrinkles on the writhing surface.

An explanation of the through-going gorges may be found by making either of the foregoing assumptions, but it may be said in favour of accepting the latter one that some at least of the great water gaps seem to have consequent relationship to high-set gaps or crest-line sags in the framework. This is a type of river course recognised by Davis in the mountains east of the Adriatic Sea as "consequent on some early stage of the warping and antecedent to the rest".[1] It has been suggested that such courses should be placed in a special *anteconsequent* class.[2] The importance of making a distinction, where possible, between true, or typical, antecedent rivers and the anteconsequent variety is related to the fact that the former are two-cycle and the latter one-cycle features; but unless it is thought necessary to emphasise this distinction, which is of more geological than geographical importance, antecedents

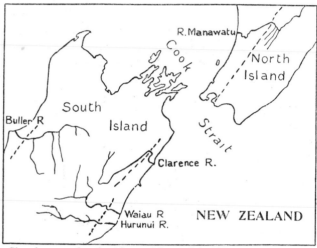

Fig. 81. Sketch-map, showing the positions of the Manawatu, Buller, Clarence, Waiau, and Hurunui gorges.

may be classed with antecedents, of which they may be considered to be a variety.

Among the New Zealand rivers of anteconsequent, or doubtfully true antecedent, origin the most conspicuous examples on a large scale are the Manawatu River (Fig. 81), in the North Island, which leads the drainage from a large area on the eastern side of the island to the western coast by way of a gorge cut at a low sag in the main dividing range; the Buller, in western Nelson (Fig. 81); the Lower Clarence gorge, which provides an outlet through the Seaward

---

[1] W. M. Davis, An Excursion in Bosnia, Hercegovina, and Dalmatia, *Bull. Geog. Soc. Phil.* 3, p. 38 (1901).
[2] C. A. Cotton, Block Mountains in New Zealand, *Am. Jour. Sci.* 44, p. 253 (1917).

Kaikoura—Sawtooth range for the consequent drainage of the great tectonic depression of the Middle Clarence Valley (Figs. 81, 82); and the twin outlets from the Culverden Plain. In the last-mentioned example the Waiau and Hurunui Rivers (Figs. 81, 83) have cut gorges nearly 2000 ft. deep through an uplifted block of country, either of which would suffice to drain the area, while if neither were

Fig. 82. The Middle Clarence Valley, a great tectonic depression (modified by erosion) between the Kaikoura (right) and Seaward Kaikoura uplifts. The outlet gorge, which is 3000 ft. deep and impassable, is at the left. View looking south-west.

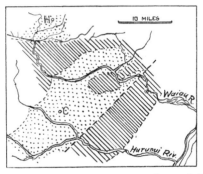

Fig. 83. Antecedent or anteconsequent gorges and gravel-filled tectonic basins in North Canterbury, New Zealand. Lined areas are uplifted blocks crossed by gorges; stippled areas are gravel-filled basins; H, Hanmer; C, Culverden.

present an easy outlet is now open to the south. Small-scale examples of courses that are possibly anteconsequent occur very commonly in New Zealand, especially in the South Island, but an alternative hypothesis of superposition has to be considered in most cases—and must not, indeed, be lightly dismissed when larger through-going gorges are under investigation.

The Nepean gorge, in New South Wales, is clearly anteconsequent, though of an unusual variety. Where the peneplain that is arched up over the Blue Mountains is bent in a strong monoclinal flexure along the eastern flank of the arch, a trough developing parallel to this flank has guided the Nepean River in a consequent course; but it appears that the river, taking a westward swing on the floor of its open valley before the monoclinal uplift ceased, became incised on the slope (Fig. 84). Perhaps the Blue Mountains arch expanded eastward during the last stage of the uplift.

In the case of gorges through mountain ranges that are of *superposed* origin, in contrast with antecedent gorges, the range through which the gorge has been cut instead of rising during the

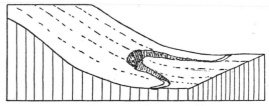

Fig. 84. Diagram of the Nepean gorge.

gorge cutting was in existence with full relief prior to the commencement of the incision of the river valley across it, being, however, temporarily buried beneath a cover of essentially weak material when the river took its present course at a higher level over the surface of this cover. Many gorges that have been supposed to be antecedent have afterwards been shown to be superposed, and the same fate may await others. In a number of cases that have been carefully examined, the decision between the two possible explanations remains in doubt, failing the discovery of decisive evidence in favour of either.

Land surfaces of strong relief developed in long-past ages have been extensively buried beneath thick deposits of relatively weak covering strata of river-laid or other terrestrial origin, and in the course of modern erosion such surfaces may be stripped of their cover and emerge again in more or less altered forms but retaining most of the relief they had before burial. Many courses, however, taken by rivers on the covering material, generally as consequents, have been superposed on the undermass in such a way as to cross ridges, hills, or mountains of its surface in water gaps that have been incised as gorges simultaneously with the resurrection of the salient forms they traverse. The Clifton Gorge of the Avon, near Bristol, is explained in this way; and burial of spurs during a Pleistocene phase of aggradation, followed by development of a widely meandering course and superposition of this on the buried spurs, explains the gorges of the lower Severn valley.[1]

In some cases the buried hills or ridges have not yet re-emerged, but rivers cutting deep valleys through their own alluvial deposits

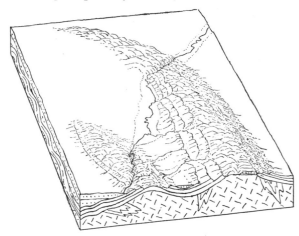

Fig. 85. Gorges of the Big Horn River, superposed from a former cover of weak superficial deposits, surviving parts of which are stippled in the front section. (After a diagram by Atwood and Atwood, redrawn.)

are superposed in gorges through ridges or valley-side spurs of hard rock that they have formerly buried. Such is the explanation of the gorges of the Rakaia and Waimakariri, which are constrictions of otherwise broad incised courses across the great alluvial plain of Canterbury, New Zealand (Pl. XIX, 1).

Superposition on a grand scale is now invoked to explain most of the great gorges by way of which rivers break through various ranges of the Rocky Mountains, though antecedence is not entirely rejected as a partial explanation of some of them.[2] Rivers, such as the North Platte, Wind River, Big Horn, and various tributaries

---

[1] L. J. Wills, Pleistocene Development of the Severn, *Quart. Jour. Geol. Soc.* 94, p. 168 (1938).
[2] See especially Atwood and Atwood, Physiographic History of the Rocky Mountain Region, *Bull. Geol. Soc. Am.* 49, pp. 957–80 (1938).

of the Colorado, including the Green River (Pl. XIX, 2), had taken courses over deep alluvial deposits of Tertiary age that had filled tectonic basins and partially buried the mountain ranges between them, and later deepening of such courses has led to superposition on the old rocks of the ranges, which have emerged with something very like their former relief, though now crossed by deeply cut young gorges (Figs. 85–7).

An explanation by superposition may solve the apparent mystery of a river that crosses in a gorge the low end of a range formed by an anticline or uplifted block of resistant rocks instead of taking a near-by "easy" way around it (Fig. 86), or of one that for no

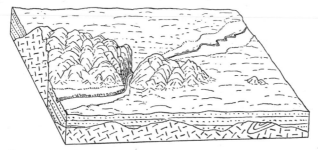

Fig. 86. Devil's Gate, Sweetwater River, Rocky Mountains. (After a diagram by Atwood and Atwood, redrawn.)

apparent reason makes a detour in a winding gorge among mountains instead of following a straighter course along an open lowland in weak rocks[1] (Fig. 87). Attention must be focused on the fact that, if superposition is the correct explanation, the "easy" ways were not available when the streams took their courses, but have been subsequently opened up owing to a gradual removal by weathering, creep, surface wash, and erosion by minor streams of the weak materials in the intermont areas down nearly to local base-level, which, however, is still controlled by the major river in spite of its having become confined in a narrow gorge through the hard-rock mountains and being still engaged in laboriously enlarging its valley therein.

In another type of structure that may lead to the development of transverse gorges by superposition, there are cores of hard rocks in

Excellent examples have been described from the middle course of the Zambezi.

anticlines or upheaved blocks beneath weaker cover. The deep-seated resistant cores may escape exposure at the surface during a first cycle in which a peneplain is developed, or, with deeper erosion, their higher parts may be exposed and planed off very thoroughly. In a new cycle the courses of consequent streams may cross these cores in any direction and be superposed on them as dissection proceeds. Even partial or local planation resulting from lateral stream corrasion developing wide valleys in an incomplete cycle (Chapter XII) may result in superposition of parts of rivers

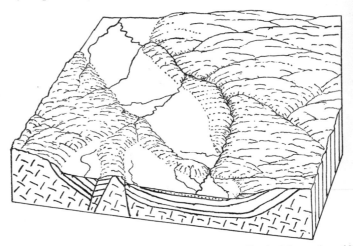

Fig. 87. Superposed course of the North Platte River, Rocky Mountains. (After a diagram by Atwood and Atwood, redrawn.)

on such structures, especially on low ends of pitching anticlines and upheaved blocks. Some of the smaller transverse gorges in the South Island of New Zealand, referred to on an earlier page as doubtfully anteconsequent, may perhaps be correctly explained by superposition of this kind.

Even in a first cycle, or, at any rate, without intercalation of a cycle of complete planation, an anticlinal core of resistant rocks may have consequents superposed on it. A possible example of this in the Haldon Hills district, New Zealand, may be variously explained according as various assumptions are made regarding the order in which the anticline traversed by transverse gorges and another adjacent to it that has been the source of consequent streams have been uplifted.[1] However it may be explained, there is here a very remarkable example of transverse gorges, for a number of very small parallel streams have been successful in maintaining water gaps through a hard core of old rocks underlying weak cover now in process of removal (Figs. 88, 176).

Mere superposition of stream patterns may often be assumed to have taken place in order to account for apparent anomalies in drainage systems of modern landscapes; and this does not imply or require any resurrection of buried mountains, or, necessarily, the

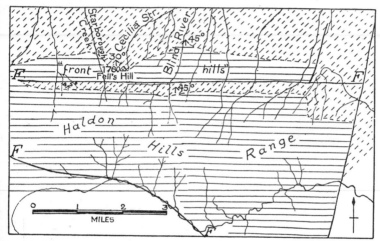

Fig. 88. Northward drainage of the Haldon Hills, New Zealand. A number of small streams have become superposed across the hard-rock core (indicated by ruled east-west lines) of the uplift forming the "front hills". (Compare Fig. 176.) (From a geological map by L. C. King.)

development of new mountains by differential erosion. Notable examples of superposed consequent rivers have been mentioned in Chapter VI. In the development of the rivers there cited there can be little doubt that superposition from an *unconformable* cover has occurred on a large scale. For the explanation of some water gaps through strike ridges it is possible, however, to formulate an hypothesis of superposition of consequents from *conformable* overlying formations taking place as erosion exposes deeper-lying folded

[1] C. A. Cotton, The Haldon Hills Problem, *Jour. Geomorph.* 1, pp. 187–98 (1938).

strata of a series whose upper members have escaped strong plication (Fig. 89). This is a possibly correct explanation of the water gaps, for example, in a prominent homoclinal ridge of limestone in the Clarence lowland, between the Kaikoura and Seaward

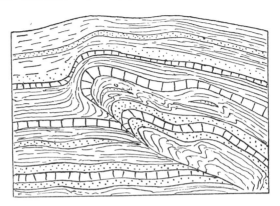

Fig. 89. A series of strata much more strongly folded at depth than at and near the surface. (After a diagram by de Martonne.)

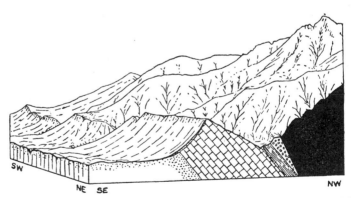

Fig. 90. Water gaps of superposed origin in a homoclinal ridge parallel with the front of the Kaikoura Mountains, New Zealand.

Kaikoura Ranges of New Zealand (Fig. 90), where very deep erosion has undoubtedly taken place. Superposition of some kind must here be assumed of streams that had their origin as consequents on the steep face of the Kaikoura Mountains, a range which came into existence as a result of upthrusting along a reverse fault (Fig. 90) contemporaneously with the tilting of the limestone

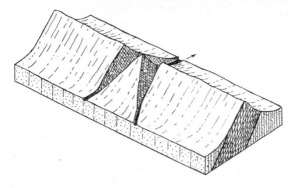

Fig. 91. The fork of a stream superposed on a homoclinal ridge.

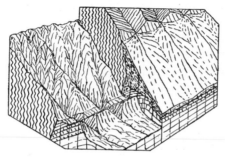

Fig. 92. Superposition from alluvial fans along a steep mountain front.

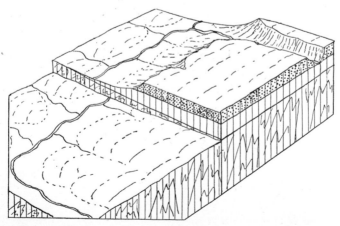

Fig. 93. Superposition of a subsequent river on an undermass.

homocline. A notable piece of evidence favouring some theory of superposition is the peculiar branching of some of the streams, which takes place upon the outcrop of the thick limestone stratum, so as to isolate island-like hills of it between the branches, a phenomenon that seems to result from a cause other than headward erosion (Fig. 91). In this instance an alternative explanation that has an equal, if not greater, chance of being the correct one is found in an hypothesis of simple superposition from an unconformable cover of alluvial fans that probably fringed the mountain front in an early stage of its dissection (Fig. 92).

Not only consequents but subsequent rivers also may be in certain cases superposed from an unconformable cover on to an undermass of alien structure (Fig. 93). Superposed subsequents may be looked for especially where coastal-plain formations on which "belted" features have been developed are stripped away from the floor of older rocks on which they were deposited. Broadly opened gaps, now abandoned by the large river that cut them, through the Watchung Ridges, of New Jersey, have been explained as parts of a former valley of the Hudson River occupied at a stage of its history when it had been superposed on these undermass ridge makers from a subsequent course it had followed in a vale[1] on a "belted" mature surface of a coastal-plain cover.[2]

Fig. 94. Probably superposed subsequent streams of the Spey system, New Zealand.

A superposed subsequent origin has been suggested for streams of the Spey system, tributary to the Conway River, New Zealand.[3] Their relations to the strike of covering strata that were formerly more widespread is shown in Fig. 94.

[1] Where such a subsequent vale lies between an undermass exposed by erosion on the one hand and an escarpment of a resistant stratum of the cover on the other it has been called by Davis an "interior lowland" and by de Martonne a "peripheral lowland".

[2] Douglas Johnson, *Stream Sculpture on the Atlantic Slope*, pp. 101-31 (1931).

[3] C. A. Cotton, *Geomorphology of New Zealand, Part I: Systematic*, p. 136 (1922).

CHAPTER XII

Lateral Corrasion and Meandering Rivers

As rivers become mature and graded progressively farther upstream the cessation of rapid down-cutting (which has come to an end with the passage from youth to maturity) is quickly followed by changes in the cross-profiles of their valleys. Valleys become more widely opened, for the sides slope back from the stream banks more and more gently as the interfluves are lowered, and at the same time flat valley floors develop and increase in width. During the stage of youth down-cutting has kept ahead of the agencies that tend to reduce the steepness of valley sides, so that the most these generally have succeeded in doing is to open the valley out to the typical V-shape. In the mature stage, when deepening no longer goes on rapidly, and may cease altogether for a time, erosion continues on the valley sides, which retreat with a tendency to develop more gentle slopes, but these are steepened from time to time at the base, as they are undercut by lateral stream corrasion.

Lateral corrasion, the work of the river in the valley bottom, meanwhile develops a flat valley floor. Though the river is now graded and has ceased to cut rapidly downward, it still has abundant energy. Wherever its current is directed against the valley side the bank is attacked by undercutting and is caused to recede, and thus the floor is widened.

Most rivers have already developed curvature in the stage of youth as an accompaniment of valley deepening. They wind between interlocking spurs in asymmetrical V-shaped valleys along the sides of which slip-off slopes alternate with undercut slopes. After such a river is graded enlargement of its curves still goes on, but, as lateral cutting is now no longer accompanied by vertical cutting, their further enlargement results in widening a flat valley floor. As the stream does not require the full width of the enlarged floor for its channel, it concentrates itself against the outer, or concave, banks of its winding course, towards which it is impelled by centrifugal force; and deposits the coarser material of its load of waste along the inner, or convex, banks, forming there flat areas of new land, which are covered by the river only at times of flood. These are the beginnings of a *flood plain* (Fig. 95). At first they are a series of short, crescent-shaped, but slightly sinuous strips that have been termed *flood-plain scrolls* (Davis) (Pl. XX, 1; Fig. 95, Stage 2).

The deposition of coarse alluvium (gravel or sand) along the convex banks of a stream that is enlarging its valley floor results in part from sluggishness of the current—and especially absence of turbulence in it[1] —along that side of the curved stream channel.

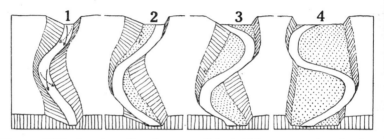

Fig. 95. Widening the valley floor. 1, slight initial curvature has developed during valley deepening into more symmetrical swinging in a valley with undercut and slip-off slopes; 2, 3, and 4, effects of lateral corrasion after valley deepening has ceased—trimming, sharpening, and blunting of spurs, and development of a flood plain.

There are, however, also cross-currents to be taken into account, an upper one of relatively clear water, not fully loaded with waste, that moves towards the outer bank, where it increases the corrasive power of the stream, and a return current along the bottom towards the inner bank (theory of "helicoidal flow").[2] This bottom water is laden with waste, much of which it drops in the sluggish water near the convex bank. The actual movement of water at any point is the resultant of the downstream and cross-stream currents. In the diagram (Fig. 95, 1) full arrows indicate the directions of currents in the upper layers of water, and the dotted arrows those of currents along the bottom.

Streams cut not only outward on curves, but also down-valley,

[1] J. B. Leighly, Turbulence and the Transportation of Rock Debris by Streams, *Geog. Rev.* 24, pp. 435–64 (1934).
[2] J. Thomson, On the Origin of Winding Rivers, *Proc. Roy. Soc.* 25, pp. 5–8 (1876).

being carried in that direction by an accelerating force due to the general slope. They thus cut into the interlocking valley-side spurs from the up-valley side, at first *trimming* them (Fig. 96), then

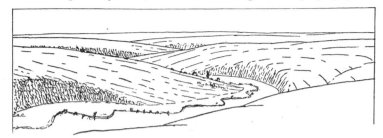

Fig. 96. Trimmed spurs in the valley of an English river, valley of the Windrush, looking west past Crawley. (After a sketch by Davis, redrawn.)

sharpening them, and eventually *blunting* them,[1] or paring them off altogether (Fig. 95, 2, 3, 4). By the time the spurs are pared off a valley floor is occupied by a flood plain that is continuous except where interrupted by the river, and this flat valley floor is bounded at each side by a line of bluffs—the undercut slopes of the valley sides.

The process of spur trimming and sharpening is sometimes varied by intersection of two concave undercut slopes (amphitheatres) taking place, so that the neck of a valley-side spur is cut through. The river abandons the former course around the spur end and takes a more direct one through the new cut. Thus island-like *cut-off spurs* may remain for a time isolated and surrounded by the flood plain (Fig. 98). *Narrowed spurs* are those that have been reduced to peninsula-like forms where cut-offs are, or have been, imminent, the spur neck being in some cases thinned to a sharp and serrate form.

Cutting-off and narrowing of valley-side spurs may occur even in river youth, where vertical corrasion is still going on as an accompaniment of lateral corrasion, especially in cases where relatively great lateral cutting accompanies valley deepening, as in the valleys of small streams in districts of deep dissection (Fig. 97).

Exceptionally, in tough, unjointed rocks, lateral corrasion undercuts valley-side slopes so that they overhang, and so the neck of

[1] W. M. Davis, Meandering Valleys and Underfit Rivers, *Ann. Ass. Am. Geog.* 3, p. 9 (1914).

a narrowed spur may be cut through below and yet remain intact above, forming a *natural bridge* (Pl. XX, 2). Natural bridges of this kind are less common than those developed by solution in limestone (Chapter xxiv).

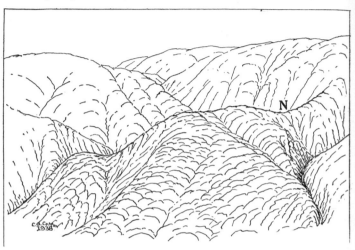

Fig. 97. Narrowed spur in the Ngahauranga valley, Wellington, New Zealand. A main highway has now been taken by way of a cutting through the narrow neck, *N*, of the spur.

Naturally, flat-floored valleys are opened out most rapidly in weak rocks. They are characteristic of dissected coastal plains (Figs. 33, 35),where erosion of uniformly unconsolidated materials is in progress, and of the weak belts of inclined and folded sedimentary formations which are occupied by the valleys of subsequent rivers. Another factor favouring rapid flood-plain development is small available relief, for in shallow valleys—that is, in those whose ultimate depths, limited by approach towards base-level, are small as compared with the ultimate breadth they may attain—a moderate amount only of waste has to be removed during the process of spur trimming. This condition is sometimes fulfilled where rivers in the current cycle are dissecting valley floors inherited from a former cycle (Fig. 98).

As a stage in the development of mature landscape in upland and highland regions of deep valley excavation, however, spur trimming and flood-plain extension must also be considered.

Fig. 99 shows a part of the valley of the Danube with interlocking spurs, but, as yet, without a flood plain. The idealised form of such a valley is shown in Fig. 100, *A*, and the stages *B*, *C*, and *D*

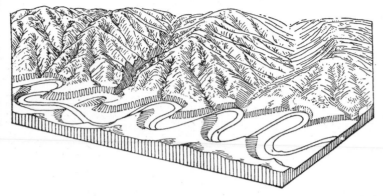

Fig. 98. Spur-trimming and flood-plain development in the valley of the Lamone (Italy), where a river is dissecting the floor of a valley of a former cycle. (After Davis.)

Fig. 99. Winding valley of the Danube, with interlocking spurs, Greine, Austria. (Drawn from a photograph.)

represent development from this V-shaped (but already graded) valley through an intermediate condition, with flood-plain scrolls and sharpened spurs, to an open valley with continuous flood plain bordered by bluffs. This stage in the valley of a small stream is illustrated in Fig. 101.

A continuous flood plain may also be termed a *valley plain*. During every flood the surface of such a plain has a layer of fine

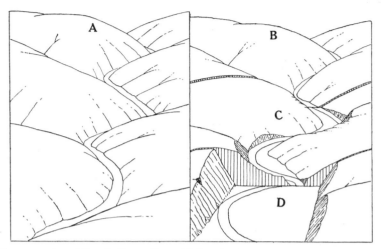

Fig. 100. *A* and *B*, winding valley with interlocking spurs; *C* and *D*, stages of the development of a flat-floored valley with flood plain bounded by bluffs.

Fig. 101. The Makara Stream, Wellington, New Zealand, meanders on a flood plain bordered by bluffs.

waste, or silt, deposited on it, owing to the checking of the current by friction when the flood water spreads over the plain as a thin sheet, the main flow of the stream taking place still (and with a velocity much greater than that at low-water times) along the regular channel. The deposit of silt may become very thick, and at low water a large river may flow between high banks of this material at a depth of 30 or 40 ft. below its flood plain, as, for example, in the case of large rivers of north-eastern Australia.

In the valley of a river that is cutting laterally, early formed twists and bends tend to develop into regular flowing curves even before the valley-side spurs have been trimmed off and the flood plain has become continuous. After that stage has been reached, and lateral corrasion is less impeded by the necessity of cutting through bedrock, free swinging of the river as it cuts away and reposits its own alluvium allows of the development of symmetrical curves, or *meanders* (Pl. XXI, 1), proportioned in size to the stream so that the radius of meander curves comes to be about eighteen times the width of the river channel.[1]

The concave curves of a river on a flood plain may intersect, with the result that meanders are cut off in a manner similar to the cutting off of spurs, but with less expenditure of energy on the part of the river, which has now only the weak alluvial deposits on the flood plain to undercut—so that cutting off of meanders is of frequent occurrence. It is a means of automatic regulation of the size of meanders, preventing their overgrowth. When meanders grow in radius by continual expansion due to undercutting of concave banks, so as to reach the maximum size appropriate to the stream, continuation of the same process makes them S-shaped ("dovetail" meanders of Davis), adjacent meanders approach each other, and their banks intersect, a shortened course is adopted by the stream, and an overgrown meander is abandoned. (Even without actual intersection taking place, a stream in flood may break across and scour out a new channel through a narrow neck.) The stream is relatively straight for a time, but soon develops new meanders. *Cut-off meanders*, recognisable as "ox-bow lakes", which later owing to partial filling become swamps, are characteristic features of flood plains.

It is sometimes found in a valley that has obviously been excavated and opened out by a river of considerable size that the stream now present has meanders of insignificant size, which may

[1] M. S. W. Jefferson, Limiting Width of Meander Belts, *Nat. Geog. Mag.* 13, pp. 373–84 (1902).

be taken to indicate that serious shrinkage of stream volume has taken place. If the shrinkage has been of recent occurrence, traces of former larger meanders may still be present on the flood plain with the smaller curves superimposed upon them. This is a characteristic of the valleys of *underfit* rivers.

Deep valleys and also those with widely opened floors may appear to an inexperienced eye far too large to be reasonably explained as the products of stream erosion, or, at any rate, the observer may find it difficult to credit that they have been excavated by the small streams now flowing in them, so that he is mistakenly inclined to postulate the former existence of a large river where now there is but a rivulet. In order to guard against such wrong conclusions it is important, therefore, to examine the effects actually produced in valleys by changes in the volumes of streams such as may be reasonably expected to occur in certain circumstances—the shrinkage of streams, for example, that are beheaded.

A river too large or too small to have eroded the valley through which it flows is a *misfit* river (Davis). If too large (*overfit*) for its valley, a river will rapidly alter the form of the valley to suit itself, expanding its curves and so cutting into the valley sides, and generally at the same time deepening the valley also to establish a new graded profile. The valley thus temporarily assumes features of youth such as may make it contrast strongly with the valleys of neighbouring rivers.

A river that has, on the other hand, shrunk until it is too small for its valley, is an *underfit* river,[1] and may be recognised as such, if it has a mature valley and well-developed flood plain, by the development of characteristic valley-floor features. Conspicuous among these is the shrinkage of meanders previously referred to. Many examples of such valleys have been observed and described, especially in cases of English, French, and German rivers that have been beheaded or have lost volume as a result of shifting of divides resulting from retreat of escarpments. A classical example is the valley of the Bar, a beheaded tributary of the Meuse.[2] The Windrush, shown in Fig. 96, is also underfit, and (Fig. 102)

---

[1] W. M. Davis, Meandering Valleys and Underfit Rivers, *Ann. Ass. Am. Geog.* 3, pp. 3–28 (1914).
[2] W. M. Davis, The Seine, the Meuse, and the Moselle (1896), reprinted in *Geographical Essays*. See especially topographic map, Fig. 95.

in the neighbourhood of Withington, the form of the Coln valley suggests a progressive diminution of the size of the river that has followed it. There are, first, large-scale meanders, indicated by the general form of the curving valley; second, much smaller meanders indicated by concave nips or re-entrants at various points on the side-slopes of the large meanders; and, third, the minute contortions of the existing stream.[1]

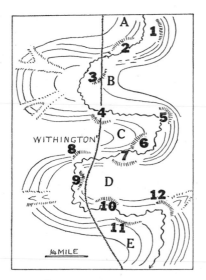

Fig. 102. Diagram of the valley of the Coln. "The spurs, lettered *A* to *E*, project into corresponding amphitheatre-like concavities, whose floor is above the present valley floor: thus the path of the original river at the time of its greatest volume is indicated. Successive concavities, numbered 1 to 12, are taken to represent indentations in the sides of the large meanders, caused by the river of medium volume.... The existing stream of small volume flows irregularly on the valley floors" (Davis.)

Undercut slopes resulting from lateral stream corrasion at a time when streams flowed in full-bodied curves and were busily engaged in trimming spurs may still be traceable on the valley sides, but are now fading out of the landscape, as they are no longer kept fresh by continued undercutting. In the valley of the Smiecha, a tributary of the Danube, for example, "nothing less than the centrifugal force of a large stream seems competent to originate a valley of so highly specialised a form" (Davis) (Fig. 103).

[1] W. M. Davis, The Drainage of Cuestas, *Proc. Geol. Ass.* 16, p. 91 and Fig. 16 (1899).

Tributary streams continue to bring their contributions of waste into the valleys of underfit rivers, but the main streams are incapable of transporting it all. Much detritus accumulates, therefore, as fans at the mouths of many small branch ravines, and these

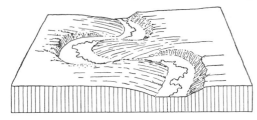

Fig. 103. Valley of the Schmiecha, at Kaiseringen, looking north. (After a diagram by Davis, redrawn.)

are confluent with talus slopes fringing valley-side bluffs and undercut amphitheatres, so that a former flood plain becomes more or less completely buried beneath these deposits, while portions that escape burial become swamps. Such valley-floor forms are conspicuous, for example, in the beheaded valley, now carrying a tiny underfit stream, shown in Plate XXI, 2.

Lateral corrasion continues, with development of a valley plain of gradually increasing width (*lateral planation*), long after the first paring-off of projecting spurs and establishment of the first continuous flood plain. Early formed valley-side bluffs that have resulted from vigorous undercutting are reduced in steepness by the complex of valley-side erosion processes that are always at work smoothing out slopes to gentler declivities; but renewed undercutting occurs at one point and another from time to time, and fresh undercut embayments, or valley-side amphitheatres, are formed. At first, while the width of the valley floor is no greater than the *meander belt*, or belt bounded by lines tangent to the outer curves of meanders of full development in proportion to the size of the stream, every full-sized meander may be expected to pare a slice from the base of the valley-side slope as it migrates downstream, impelled in that direction by the same down-valley momentum that earlier caused the stream to trim spurs, but now no longer delayed by the necessity of cutting away solid rock (Fig. 104). The downstream migration, which has now become rapid, as the stream can cut laterally with great rapidity where it encounters only the small resistance offered by its own deposited alluvium, has been termed *sweeping*. Speeded up, as though by a trick of animated photography, the downstream sweeping of a succession of meanders

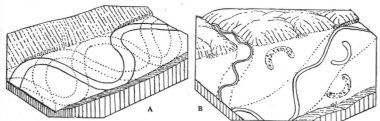

Fig. 104. *A*, lateral planation accompanying downstream sweeping of meanders; *B*, wide valley plain developed by lateral planation (meander belt bounded by dotted lines).

might be likened to the writhing of a snake or the transmission of a series of waves along a slack rope or curtain. Thus old and new maps of the same river valley may show meanders in quite different positions and of quite different shapes; and all maps of valley plains indicate the presence of many cut-offs and ox-bow lakes (Fig. 105).

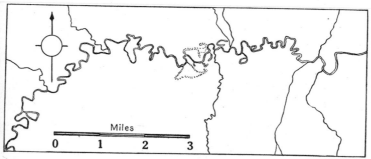

Fig. 105. Meanders and cut-off meanders of the upper Taieri River, New Zealand.

As the valley plain grows wider meanders impinge less frequently against the bedrock of the valley sides, but from time to time one pares a slice from it, as the meander belt, itself of writhing and changing form, swings to that side of the valley floor.

The development of open, wide-floored valleys naturally goes on most rapidly in weak rocks; and so in a region of alternately weak and resistant rock outcrops the valleys along weak-rock belts (together with such portions of transverse valleys as cross these belts) are widely opened out as subsequent lowlands (Fig. 38), which are in part wide valley plains, while transverse streams where they cross resistant formations are still in narrow water gaps.

Interfluves may be cut through by lateral planation, and diversion (by *abstraction*) of smaller streams to become tributaries of larger neighbouring streams may occur. Even adjustment to structure may be to some extent destroyed in this way.

The process of lateral planation at a stable gradient, or at constant level, cuts a bedrock floor (only thinly veneered with a flood-plain deposit of alluvium) which is nearly plane (if the slight concavity of the longitudinal profile of the river be disregarded), but which, in theory, must be slightly convex in transverse profile, as it is part of the surface of a very flat cone with its apex at the source of the river—and this is seen to be the true form when rising flood waters first invade strips close to the valley sides. Small streams of steep gradient have indeed occasionally succeeded in cutting laterally far enough to develop small "plains" that are quite strongly convex. They are termed *rock fans*.[1] Examples have been found by Johnson[2] in the desert ranges of the American South-West.

It is but a step farther to take up the debatable question of the probability of the development of extensive "plains of lateral planation", but the process of lateral corrasion by aggrading streams must first be touched upon. In the foregoing discussion of lateral corrasion the behaviour has been considered of streams with well-defined rather deep channels, which develop and continue to flow in meandering courses. Such are the channels of streams not over-supplied with waste, but yet fully loaded, for otherwise they would continue the process of valley deepening. Any coarse waste that is available for deposit is built into the basal part of the flood plain veneer on the convex and down-valley sides of swinging and sweeping meanders, and this is afterwards buried to a varying

[1] W. M. Davis describes a "rock fan" as "perfectly imitating an alluvial fan but of different origin". An Excursion in Bosnia, Hercegovina, and Dalmatia. *Bull. Geog. Soc. Philadelphia*, 3, p. 37 (1901).
[2] Douglas Johnson, Rock Fans in Arid Regions, *Am. Jour. Sci.* 23, pp. 389-41 (1932).

depth beneath the silt spread during floods. Coarse waste is not available for deposit in such quantities as to fill up the channels of the streams and so cause them to flood frequently, to spill over sporadically into new channels across the flood plains, and to spread layers of coarse waste over the valley floors.

In streams with these latter characteristics, typically flowing in anastomosing, or *braided*, courses (Pl. XXII, 1), as contrasted with the well-defined meandering courses previously described, the very fact that they flow in such unstable channels is sometimes taken as proof that coarse waste is being deposited in the actual stream channels, filling them so as to cause the streams to distribute themselves into new channels which are in turn built up and abandoned, so that the level of the whole flood plain is raised, and the river is *aggrading*. In the present state of knowledge, however, it is not asserted that all streams in braided courses are positively aggrading. It is known, on the other hand, that some aggrading rivers of low gradient flow in meandering courses, building up their flood plains with layers of silt spread during floods.[1]

Aggrading streams in ever-shifting, ill-defined, braided channels are capable of lateral corrasion. Their lateral-cutting ability, indeed, seems greater than that of meandering streams,[2] probably because the currents in some of the many channels more frequently strike against the valley sides. Beginning the process of lateral corrasion combined with aggradation in a V-shaped valley (Fig. 106, *A*), a stream may be expected to cut a more broadly open V floor (*C*), with smoothly cut, inclined side slopes that may be either nearly plane or of varying inclination, but these will be buried, progressively as they are cut, by the alluvial deposits of the aggraded flood plain (*B*). Very probably well-directed search will reveal examples of such V floors exposed by later stripping away of the alluvial cover, though they are likely to be modified by development of terraces during such stripping. Obviously, the slower the rate of aggradation accompanying lateral corrasion, the more nearly level will be the floor cut on the bedrock of the valley, and the thinner the alluvial veneer upon it.

R. J. Russell, Lower Mississippi River Delta, *Louisiana Geol. Surv. Geol. Bull.* 8, p. 123 (1936).
W. M. Davis, Rock Floors in Arid and in Humid Climates, *Jour. Geol.* 38, p. 139 (1930).

According to some authors, a very important part has been played by braided streams in developing extensive plains by lateral planation.[1] The theory is applied in particular to the planation of zones peripheral to mountains, where "the flood plains of adjacent streams coalesce to form continuous plains" (Gilbert). Gilbert figured an "ideal sketch" of a landscape with such a continuous plain bordering a mountain front. He describes the streams responsible for the planation as flowing in shifting channels. Variation in the supply of waste to a stream sometimes fills its

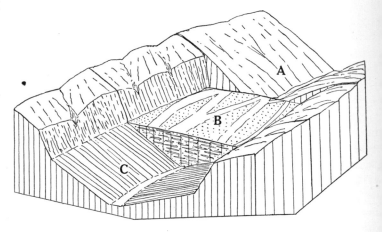

Fig. 106. Lateral corrasion accompanying aggradation.

channel to such an extent that it spills over into a new one. "Th abandoned courses remain plainly marked....Where a series o streams emerge from adjacent mountain gorges upon a commo plain their shiftings bring about frequent unions and separations and produce a variety of combinations."

The "pediments" of arid and semi-arid regions—sloping plain bordering dissected mountains in a late-mature stage of landscap dissection—are thus accounted for by Johnson, while othe observers agree that lateral corrasion at least takes part in the formation, though perhaps not the dominant process. It is we

[1] G. K. Gilbert, *Geology of the Henry Mountains*, pp. 126–31 (1877); Dougl Johnson, Planes of Lateral Corrasion, *Science*, 73, pp. 174–7 (1931); Ro Fans of Arid Regions, *Am. Jour. Sci.* 23, pp. 389–416 (1832); Rock Planes Arid Regions, *Geog. Rev.* 22, pp. 656–65 (1932).

understood that running water, ephemeral as streams may be in a desert, does an important part of the work of erosion in most if not in all deserts. So reference to the theory of lateral planation in arid and semi-arid regions is not out of place here, though a more complete discussion of "pediments" cannot be attempted without consideration of the whole desert landscape. Johnson has made the further suggestion that many high-level now-dissected surfaces generally thought to be parts of uplifted peneplains would be more correctly explained as plains of lateral planation,[1] and his reference to high-level benches in the South Island of New Zealand as possibly the inner margins of once vast plains of lateral corrasion[2] necessitates consideration of the process of wide planation in its possible application to humid as well as arid and semi-arid regions. The benches referred to are, without doubt, those bordering the mountains of South Canterbury, at the rear of the southern end of the Canterbury Plain.[3]

The essence of the theory of efficient lateral planation producing plains, as developed by Johnson, is that, where streams are actively eroding in their headwaters, deepening their valleys there and gathering loads of waste, and in their lower courses are depositing waste and aggrading their floors, as streams must do, for example, in arid deserts, there is a middle portion of their courses in which they are neither downcutting nor upbuilding to a cumulative extent, and in which, therefore, lateral corrasion will take place at a fixed level, so that in this middle part of their courses the streams are competent for, or capable of, planation. Where adjacent streams from mountains are similar in this respect there may be a "zone of lateral planation", as Johnson terms it, in their middle courses, in which the streams cut through and later obliterate the divides between them, so as to develop a continuous plain. Across this plain the rivers will continue to flow, each on a radius of its own rock fan. Considerable irregularity of surface, one may note, is to be expected in the early stages of development of a plain made up

Loc. cit., Am. Jour. Sci. 23, p. 410 (1932).
Loc. cit., Science (1931).
Johnson has also attempted to explain a bench that borders the sea near Wellington, New Zealand, as confluent rock fans truncated by marine retrogradation (loc. cit., Am. Jour. Sci. p. 397 (1932)). In this case, however, the theory has a strong competitor in marine erosion followed by emergence and warping, for the fanlike convexities of the bedrock surface that are figured (loc. cit. Fig. 2) seem to be illusory.

of coalescing rock fans, for adjacent large and small streams will be at different levels and have different gradients. Abstraction of the smaller streams when divides are breached, followed by their regrading to lower local base-levels, will interrupt the continuity of the process of lateral planation, and much of such integration of drainage will be permanent, at least if it takes place in humid regions.

In an arid climate, it has been pointed out, the streams of a theoretical zone of lateral planation, though not actually aggrading, are intermittent in their flow, and when they flow, or flood, bring down much coarse alluvium. They do not, therefore, flow in swinging, sweeping meanders, but, on the contrary, "accumulation of debris tends to block the channel, the stream spreads, cross currents are set up, and braiding develops rather than meandering. The heavy load favours lateral planation...by favouring...lateral displacement through accumulation of debris along and within the channel. Since there are a multitude of interlacing channels, no one of them need shift very far in order that lateral planation should take place...".[1] The veneer of alluvium on the cut surface is thin, discontinuous, and composed of coarse, largely unsorted gravel, and is thus very different in character from that covering the flood plains of meandering rivers.

There is in New Zealand a plain of considerable size, the Maniototo Plain, which has been formed by coalescence of valley plains of lateral planation developed by a group of parallel streams from the northern highland of Otago. It has been described as a "local peneplain" on soft rocks.[2] Though the streams that cut the plain have since excavated shallow valleys in it (Fig. 107), the southward slope of the whole feature is conspicuous to the eye (Fig. 108), and suggests alluvial fans, but the plain is a surface of planation, though cut on very weak materials only, and not extended back into the hard-rock mountains at the rear, which are separated by faults from the weak sediments underlying the plain.

Rock fans and plains made up of confluent rock fans, like all other cut surfaces, must be subject to renewed dissection when local base-levels are lowered. Such lowering may be brought about

---

[1] Douglas Johnson, loc. cit., Geog. Rev. 22, p. 660, 1932.
[2] C. A. Cotton, Block Mountains in New Zealand, Am. Jour. Sci. 44, p. 29 (1917).

by general or local uplift, but its occurrence does not necessarily imply uplift of the land or lowering of the general base-level. Under arid and semi-arid conditions the graded parts of the streams concerned in the planation of such a surface have steep gradients on account of the great loads of waste they are bringing down from

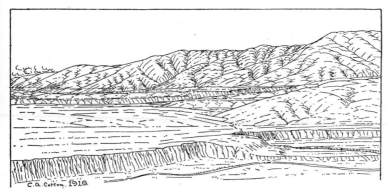

Fig. 107. The Maniototo Plain, a plain of lateral planation slightly modified by renewed erosion. The rear boundary of the plain is defined by the fault-boundary of the northern highland of Otago, which is composed of relatively very resistant rocks.

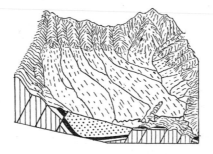

Fig. 108. The Maniototo Plain. (After Benson, redrawn.)

their headwaters (in the case where these are dissecting mountains that are still of strong relief), and under the postulated climatic conditions there is not a very large volume of water to carry this load. These steep gradients are subject to reduction in the course of the cycle as less waste becomes available for transport from the mountains of dwindling relief in the headwater zone. Downcutting to weaker gradients lowers local base-levels along the streams, and must result in planation at successively lower levels. With uniformity of conditions the lowering of gradients will be very gradual, and the entire surface of the plain of lateral planation may be lowered simultaneously. Local circumstances, however, such as small climatic oscillations sufficient to affect the vegetation and through it the rate of erosion on the mountains, may cause surges of erosion resulting in terracing due to alternation of phases of vertical and lateral corrasion. Terrace development and survival of mesas and bench remnants of higher plains due to this cause may be indistinguishable from the effects of upwarping, of lowering of local base-levels owing to changes in river courses, and of major climatic oscillations. The benches between the New Zealand Alps and the Canterbury Plain are possibly, as Johnson has suggested, of some such origin.

CHAPTER XIII

River Terraces

GILBERT has warned us against "the error of supposing that river terraces in general are the records of sedimentation, when in fact they record the stages of a progressive corrasion".[1] "River terraces", he tells us, "as a rule are carved out, and not built up. They are always the vestiges of flood plains, and flood plains are usually produced by lateral corrasion." In addition to *river* terraces, to which Gilbert alludes, there are also, of course, structural terraces (Chapter x), terrace-like stranded lateral moraines of glaciers of a bygone age, and remnants of shore-line platforms and deltas of former lakes, which may now border river valleys, as well as, possibly, bench-like relics of former plains of lateral planation bordering mountains (Chapter XII), and of emergent wave-cut platforms parallel to the sea-margin.

River terraces may, however, be defined (following Gilbert) as terraces that border river valleys and mark former levels of flat valley floors such as have resulted from either corrasion or valley

[1] G. K. Gilbert, *Geology of the Henry Mountains*, p. 132 (1877).

filling. The latter must be rare, however. The materials out of which terraces are cut have, indeed, frequently been formed by valley filling, and are then in some cases river-laid; but terrace formation is essentially, as Gilbert insisted, an accompaniment of valley formation by corrasion, alternately vertical and lateral; and the material filling a former valley is best regarded merely as a part—a softer part—of the rock out of which a new valley has been cut. The "treads" or tops of terraces, except where burial beneath

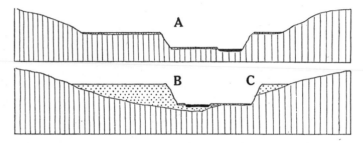

Fig. 109. Terraces cut on bedrock, *A*; and on valley-filling gravel, *B*, *C*.

alluvial fans and screes has taken place, are almost always parts of flood plains cut by lateral corrasion, though sometimes in bedrock and sometimes in valley-filling alluvial gravels or lake silts.

In so-called "rock terraces" (from which structural terraces[1] must be excluded as irrelevant to the present discussion of river terraces) the former flood plain that has been reduced to a terrace has been cut across bedrock by lateral corrasion, and is only thinly veneered with alluvium (Fig. 109, *A*; Pl. XXII, 2). These are "valley-plain terraces" equally with those underlain by thick gravel beds (Fig. 109, *B*, *C*), though not included under that heading in Wright's classification.[2]

In New Zealand—a land of terraced landscapes—terraces both of bedrock with thin alluvial veneer and of thick alluvium are common. The abundant terraces in the valleys of the rivers of western Wellington are cut on soft bedrock (Pl. XXXIV, 1). Equally abundant are the terraces of Canterbury, cut in the thick

[1] Termed "rock terraces due to differential erosion" in a somewhat unsatisfactory classification of river terraces by F. J. Wright (The Physiography of the Upper James River Basin in Virginia, *Virginia Geol. Surv. Bull.* 11, pp. 35–41 (1925)).
[2] *Loc. cit.*

gravels of the Canterbury Plain (Frontispiece), and gravel terraces are present in many inland valleys that have passed through phases of deep aggradation—for example, a great series of terraces in the Esk valley (Fig. 110), the terraces of the Shotover valley (Figs. 116, 117), and those of the extensive Clutha valley system.

While all ordinary river terraces are in a sense valley-plain terraces, this term has been applied[1] particularly to those that are

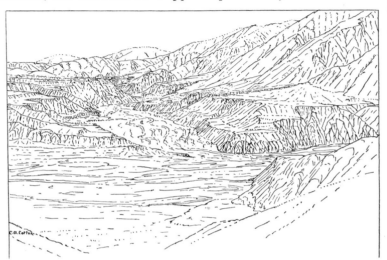

Fig. 110. Terraces bordering the Esk River, a tributary of the Waimakariri, Canterbury, New Zealand. (Drawn from a photograph by V. C. Browne.)

remnants of the broader valley floors developed by rather wide planation (generally in soft materials) in what are generally regarded as partial cycles of erosion, or rather long halts in discontinuous uplift of the land, as contrasted with the narrower or discontinuous flood plains developed in relatively short pauses in discontinuous vertical corrasion (perhaps brief *epicycles*). *Valley-plain terraces*,[2] as thus defined, are surviving parts of formerly continuous valley floors cut by rivers to widths often very much greater than those of the immediate present-day valleys that have been incised in them in more recent episodes of vertical corrasion, followed frequently by renewed lateral corrasion. If such has been

[1] C. A. Cotton, River Terraces in New Zealand, *N.Z. Jour. Sci. Tech.* 1, pp. 145–52 (1918).

[2] "Principal erosion terraces" of J. Hanson-Lowe, *Geog. Jour.* 93, p. 65 (1939).

the sequence of events, valley-plain terraces of matched height may be present facing each other on opposite sides of a valley [1] (Fig. 111); but if, on the other hand, the former valley has been little, if any, wider than the inner or immediate valley of the river is now, the cutting of the latter will have very largely destroyed the higher valley plain, though remnants of it may be preserved here and there on both sides of the valley, and those on one side may be matched with those on the other, and isolated remnants correlated as parts of the same once continuous flood plain.

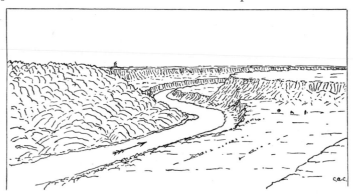

Fig. 111. Valley-plain terraces of the River Adda, near Suisio, north Italy (After a drawing by Ricchieri.)

Valley-plain terraces of more than one episode of lateral plana-tion may border a valley, and have a fair chance of partial preserva-tion if the later planations were successively less extensive. Even brief halts in at least the last episode of vertical corrasion may be recorded by terraces; but these generally escape preservation except on the slip-off slopes of spurs facing the undercut amphitheatres in expanded curves of the inner valley. Such spur ends are commonly broken by a number of *slip-off slope terraces*, as they may be called (Figs. 112, 113). Even in such a situation, however, some terraces are nearly always destroyed as lower ones are cut, and correlation of the patterns of terraces from spur to spur becomes uncertain. The convex fronts of terraces on a slip-off slope are related very simply to the convexities of the spur ends on which they are cut.

[1] Two very well-defined valley-plain terraces cut in hard bedrock border the Yellow River in Kansu (G. B. Barbour, "Pleistocene History of the Huangho, *Bull. Geol. Soc. Am.* 44, pp. 1143–60 (1933)).

Terraced slip-off slopes may perhaps be regarded as the rule, not the exception. Where they are smoothly sloping and apparently unterraced, this condition may be regarded as the result of integration of a large number of small terraces. Thus a smooth slip-off slope

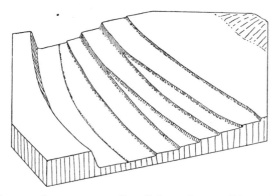

Fig. 112. Pattern of terraces on a slip-off slope, Awatere River, New Zealand.

Fig. 113. Slip-off slope terraces, Jackson River, Virginia.
(Described by F. J. Wright, *loc. cit.*)

is termed by Chaput[1] a "polygenetic terrace" (*terrasse polygénique*).

Slip-off slope terraces can survive no longer than the spurs on which they are cut, and are, therefore, ephemeral. Valley-plain terraces may be longer lived, though in constant danger of destruc-

---

[1] J. E. Chaput, Le rôle des surfaces polygéniques dans le modelé, *Union Géogr. Internat., Second Report of Commission on Pliocene and Pleistocene Terraces,* pp. 78–82 (1930). The idea is applied also to forms resulting from glacial and marine erosion.

tion as valleys are opened out to greater width. All river terraces are, indeed, definitely features of landscape youth. *Rock-defended terraces*, even though they may be narrow, stand a chance of much longer survival, however, than those whose preservation is purely fortuitous in that they are at the mercy of the capricious swinging of an uncontrolled meander belt. Terraces in this category are generally defined as those having hard bedrock (underlying alluvial gravels or other easily eroded valley filling) exposed at the base of the terrace front in such manner as to have stopped, or at least

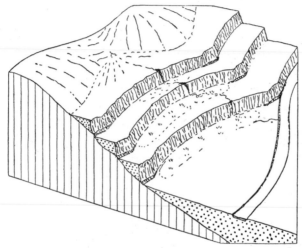

Fig. 114. Terraces of easily eroded valley-filling gravels protected by re-exposed outcrops of buried spurs.

restrained, the lateral stream corrasion that has at some time threatened to undercut and destroy the terraces (Fig. 114), together, of course, with all other valley-side forms;[1] but similar exposure of outcrops of more resistant members of a bedrock sequence may be equally effective in checking lateral planation, and so preserving as terraces parts of flood plains cut on easily eroded softer members. Thus, a favourable position for terrace preservation is the dip-slope side of a homoclinal valley (Fig. 115), and this is a case where preservation of terraces may be expected to occur on one side only of the valley. Outcrops that are most effective in defending terraces

[1] W. M. Davis, River Terraces in New England (1902), *Geographical Essays*, pp. 514–86 (1909).

occur most commonly, however, at valley constrictions, or gorges. At such a point, where a river crosses either a spur buried in alluvium, from which the river is superposed upon the spur

Fig. 115. Profile of terraces on the dip-slope side of a homoclinal valley.

(Fig. 114, and Pl. XXIII, 1), or a resistant bedrock outcrop (Pl. XIX, 1), sideward swinging meanders upstream and downstream from the gorge take concave bites out of the terrace fronts, and such concave fronts are characteristic of rock-defended terraces, two concave fronts meeting in a cusp on each defending rock outcrop (Fig. 114).

Convergence of concave-fronted terraces on a defending gorge in the Broken River intermont basin, New Zealand, is shown in

Fig. 116. Terraces in the Shotover valley, Otago, New Zealand.

Pl. XXIII, 2; these are "rock terraces". Pl. XXIV, 1, shows terraces at the point where the Waimakariri River (N.Z.) escapes from its mountain gorge on to the trenched Canterbury Plain. A peculiar example of defended terraces in alluvium is afforded by a "flight" in the upper valley of the Shotover River, New Zealand (Fig. 116). The river has been superposed from its own alluvium on to hard bedrock to one side of a former valley filled with gravel. It has cut the flight of terraces on the gravel valley-fill when swinging between two gorges (Fig. 117).

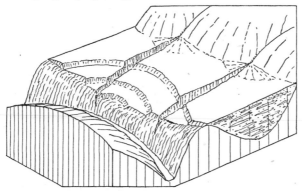

Fig. 117. Diagram of the superposed course of the Shotover River and rock-defended terraces developed by swinging across gravels filling a former valley of the river.

Any constriction in a valley may have an effect similar to that of a rock gorge in defending terraces. Such constrictions may be formed in mountain valleys by fans of alluvium built by tributary streams, which may maintain their position, if the supply of gravel is sufficiently copious, while the level of the main valley floor is being lowered. By forcing the main stream towards the opposite side of the valley they prevent its wide swinging, and form nodes in a manner similar to gorges; or, at least, they prevent swinging towards their own side, and thus defend terraces. Examples have been noted in the Rakaia valley, New Zealand.[1]

The conditions of structure that provide terrace-defending rock outcrops may also determine a very slow rate of vertical corrasion. The superposition of the stream on bars of hard rock where it encounters buried spurs in a filled valley (Fig. 118), or its transverse course through hard-rock strata or other barriers, may so slow down the rate of vertical corrasion that in adjacent areas of softer materials it maintains during the slow process of valley deepening

[1] R. Speight, Terrace-development in...Canterbury Rivers, *Trans. N.Z. Inst.* 40, pp. 16–43 (1908).

a continuously graded, fully mature, and broadly opened valley. A similar result may conceivably be brought about by extremely slow uplift of the land. In such cases a river, in its graded reaches, must continue during downcutting to maintain a meandering course on a flood plain; the meanders will migrate downstream, and the meander belt will swing from side to side of the valley floor. Since, however, the stream is continuously cutting downward, each time the meander belt approaches the valley side its floor is at a lower level than that of the previous time. If it quite reaches the

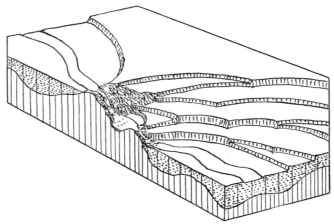

Fig. 118. Terrace development in soft alluvium where discovery by the stream of a buried spur of resistant rock has restrained vertical corrasion. (After a diagram by W. M. Davis, redrawn.)

valley side, it will completely cut away the former flood plain, but if not it will leave a remnant of it as a terrace[1] (Fig. 119). Terraces such as these are not commonly found in valleys of rivers that are excavating in homogeneous material, even though it be soft, for in this case there is no limit to the lateral swinging of the meander belt at the lower levels, and so the higher floors are destroyed as new ones are developed. Remnants of the higher-level flood plains do commonly survive, however, where defended by hard-rock outcrops in the valley sides (Fig. 114) or in gorges (Fig. 118), and some members at least of most flights of concave-fronted terraces have originated thus as *terraces of continuous valley excavation during restrained downcutting.*

[1] W. M. Davis, *loc. cit.*

In some cases it is possible to distinguish terraces of this kind from those marking halts or discontinuities of vertical corrasion, for, unlike those of the latter kind, they will fail to match, where present on both sides of a valley. Instead of matching (Fig. 120 *A*), successively lower terraces will alternate (Fig. 120 *B*) on opposite sides owing to the fact that an appreciable interval of time has

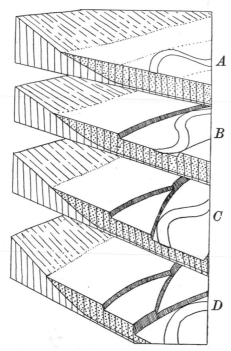

Fig. 119. Terrace development by a river that is deepening its valley very slowly in soft material. Stage *B*, the highest terrace, is a remnant of the valley plain, *A*; *C* and *D*, later stages, in which lower terraces are cut at successive flood-plain levels. Between each stage and the next the meander belt swings away towards the other side of the valley and returns at a lower level.

elapsed during each swing of the meander belt across the valley, allowing it to be cut to a lower level. Where there is an appearance in opposed flights of terraces of matching of some terraces and alternation of others, it is probable that the flights are of composite origin, some being cut during halts and others during slow down-cutting.

Probably the commonest cause of a renewal of vertical corrasion

in rivers, such as results in the development of terraces, is upheaval, or lowering of the general base-level relatively to the land
—that is, either regional uplift or eustatic emergence owing to
lowering of sea-level. Equally effective where it occurs, however,
is local uplift, which will be accompanied by warping or dislocation
and tilting of the surface. A river may be shortened (betrunked)
by rapid cliff recession at its mouth due to marine erosion, and this
accident also will result in revival of vertical corrasion in the river.
The process is not necessarily continuous at a uniform rate, and if
intermittent it may result in terrace formation in the valley
of the river. Small rivers with short courses to the sea are most
readily affected by this cause of terracing.

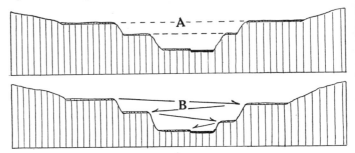

Fig. 120. *A*, valley-plain terraces matching in level on opposite sides of a valley;
B, alternate terraces developed during continuous valley excavation; arrows
indicate swinging of the meander belt.

A change of climate from less to greater humidity has also an
important effect on the regimen of streams. Even a small change
not only provides more water, but also may appreciably reduce the
load of waste to be transported by encouraging increased growth
of protective vegetation in the catchment areas of the streams; and
every change in the ratio of waste to water in a river demands
a considerable adjustment of the gradient of its graded profile
resulting, especially far inland, in great changes in local base-levels
In this case the adjustment is brought about by an episode of
vertical corrasion, which may isolate portions of an earlier flood
plain as terraces. Still another possible cause of terracing is a
general reduction in river loads, with consequent flattening of rive
gradients, that results from the wasting away of mountains in the
course of a cycle of erosion. This may go on not uniformly but in

surges, if accompanied by a succession of appropriate climatic oscillations, and will in such a case be accompanied by terrace development.

From the foregoing considerations it will be clear that the correlation of terraces—even of well-marked valley-plain terraces—from one valley or valley system to another, or even in reaches of the same valley that are separated by gorges, may be a matter of uncertainty, and may even present insuperable difficulties. Far inland, for example, it will be very unlikely that surges of vertical corrasion resulting from regional elevation or eustatic emergence will have worked their way an equal distance upstream in different valleys;[1] while the effects of warping and tilting of the surface are necessarily local and sporadic; and so a fair degree of agreement of terrace patterns, if found in separate valleys, points to a climatic as the only probable general cause of terracing.

The slopes of terrace surfaces, or treads, may be considered both transversely to the river and longitudinally. Transversely to the valley-direction terrace treads are initially the surfaces of former flood plains, but may be more or less maturely dissected (Pl. XXIV, 2). Where they have escaped dissection they may still preserve the irregularities of flood-plain surfaces.[2] Traces of cut-off meanders are found especially at the rear of a terrace along the base of the concave embayment in the front of the next higher terrace, where the last swing of the former river channel was cut off and abandoned.[3] On certain terraces, on the other hand, especially in mountainous and semi-arid regions, and especially on the highest terrace (Fig. 110), there is a thick covering of alluvial gravel in the form of fans spread by tributary streams, as has been noted in the case of the terraces of the Shoshone River, in Wyoming.[4] Such fans may be confluent with talus slopes from a high valley side between tributaries, so that the terrace surfaces have strong across-valley slopes. These accumulations, though found on terraces, are really valley-plain features, and were present in some cases before the valley plains were reduced to terraces.

[1] G. B. Barbour, Kalgan Area, *Mem. Geol. Surv. China*, A 6, p. 108 (1929).
[2] "Bars and swales, abandoned channels, natural levees..., meander scars, and minor depositional features." (D. St Clair, *Science*, 86, pp. 399–400 (1937).)
[3] W. M. Davis, *loc. cit.*
[4] J. H. Mackin, Erosional History of the Big Horn Basin, Wyoming, *Bull. Geol. Soc. Am.* 48, pp. 813–94 (1937).

They imply, however, that lateral planation on what is now the terrace has long been ineffective, and this condition may date only from the incision of the valley to a lower level.

Longitudinally the profiles of terraces, though not strictly parallel with the gradients at which rivers now flow below them, slope generally in the same direction, as they were determined by the gradients of the same rivers at the time the terraces were parts of their valley floors. Warping of the land surface may, however, have steepened, weakened, or reversed their slopes; and even where no warping has occurred, a terrace may be either less steep than the present-day river gradient, where the inner valley has developed as a result of lowering of base-level and is still very young, or steeper, as may be expected where the surges of erosion that have caused terracing have been the results of climatic fluctuations during the general lowering of the land surface. Terraces of this latter kind may, indeed, be expected to converge on sea-level at a river mouth, as do the terraces of the rivers that cross the Canterbury Plain in New Zealand.

CHAPTER XIV

Maturity of the Landscape; Subdued Relief-forms

ON the sides of young valleys and gorges and on the slopes of escarpments, where slopes are steep, waste is removed as rapidly as it is produced by weathering, the waste-mantle is thin, and there are many outcrops of bare rock, generally of jagged and irregular forms, so that the slope is not only steep but uneven. It may be broken by more or less irregular structural terraces, where heterogeneous strata outcrop. Such slopes are analogous to the uneven profiles of young rivers, and, like them, they may be described as not yet graded (Pl. XXV). Later, when rivers are no longer cutting downward so as to undercut the slopes, valley sides are worn back to gentler declivities, as weathering, creep, sliding, and streaming down of waste continue. Outcrops of bare rock, at first almost continuous, are gradually replaced by slopes of waste. These are at first short, discontinuous, and broken by rock outcrops, but outcrops are weathered away, and the waste slopes become *graded* in a manner analogous to the grading of a water stream, though the gradient of a waste stream when it is graded is necessarily very much steeper than that of a water stream, because of the relative immobility of the material of which it is composed and the greater retardation of its flow by friction. In this way are developed the smooth hillside slopes of full and late maturity (Fig. 121).

Much steeper slopes become waste-covered and smoothly graded under the protection of a forest covering than under more open or discontinuous vegetation. In New Zealand, especially in the northern part of the country, and in many other regions also, though these are for the most part intertropical, the virgin forest consists of large trees together with a dense undergrowth, and this affords the ground beneath it complete protection from raindrop impact.

The forest and its attendant litter layers absorb much rainfall. Thus the run-off is low and so impeded that it has little power to erode. The roots of forest trees anchor together the soil and subsoil. On the steeper hillsides the curiously curved lower trunks of trees, with their deeper roots trailing uphill, evidence the forest's effort to remain anchored, and the forces tending towards the downhill creep of the soil. (TAYLOR.)

Though creep is thus active, actual mass movements seem even more effective in the downhill transfer of waste. "Everywhere throughout the forest hill lands arcuate scarps indicate the sites of former slips" (Taylor). The whole process of downhill migration is slow, however; "ground bared by slips has time to be invaded by vegetation before another slip appears; bare rock has time to weather" (Taylor);[1] and under such conditions of retarded erosion and soil accumulation very steep slopes become graded.

When the dissected landscape first enters on the stage of maturity, the crest lines of ridges and spurs are formed by the intersection of valley sides that are for the most part still steep, so that the ridges are sharp and their crests are uneven. They may be described as *serrate* (Fig. 121). Later, however, they become less sharp, with rounded crests, the change taking place earliest in areas of moderate

---

[1] Quotations from N. H. Taylor, "Some Aspects of Erosion of Farm Lands", read at Grasslands Conference, Hamilton, N.Z., 6th October, 1938.

relief and on the flanks and among the foothills of mountain ranges, but eventually also among the mountain peaks, as these are lowered by erosion. When slopes have become moderately gentle, broadly convex hills and mountains are developed, which are described as *subdued* forms (Davis). The majority of salient forms are subdued when the landscape cycle has attained full maturity (Fig. 121).

Fig. 121. A landscape in early maturity (left) compared with the same landscape (right) subdued in full maturity. (After diagrams by W. M. Davis, redrawn.)

The subdued or broadly convex summit forms referred to in the preceding paragraph are those of normally developed, mature, soil-covered landscapes. Under special conditions of weathering that affect unjointed granitic rocks, some large smooth domes of bare rock (Pl. XXVI, 1) have been developed from initial forms with presumably rugged outlines by a process of large-scale exfoliation taking place in the main probably as a phase of weathering in which hydration of feldspars is important. The explanation of convexity of summit forms that fits these is, however, obviously not of general application. Conspicuous examples of such domes occur on the Sierra Nevada of California,[1] and a similar explanation is applied to granite domes and sugarloaves in Brazil[2] (Fig. 122).

The actual processes involved in the development of ordinary convex summit forms are not thoroughly understood, but there must be in operation some agency or agencies working in a manner

[1] G. K. Gilbert, Domes and Dome Structure of the High Sierras, *Bull. Geol. Soc. Am.* 15, pp. 29–36 (1904).
[2] J. C. Branner, Decomposition of Rocks in Brazil, *Bull. Geol. Soc. Am.* 7, pp. 255–314 (1896).

different from the general process of grading valley sides and the reduction of such graded slopes of waste to gentler declivities incidentally to the wasting away of the land surface as a whole. This must be the case, at any rate, if all graded valley-side slopes and all slopes resulting from rain-wash transportation assume concave profiles, as Gilbert[1] believed to be the case from analogy

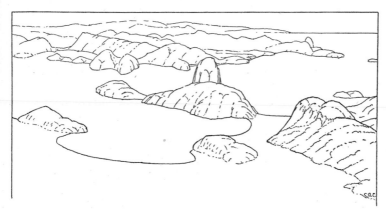

Fig. 122. Granite domes and sugarloaves of exfoliation, Bay of Rio de Janeiro. (Drawn from a photograph.)

with graded profiles of rivers; for divides, or ridge crests, formed by the intersections of concave slopes, however gentle the slopes may become, must remain angular and quite unlike the familiar convexly rounded forms of hilltops and ridge crests.

A suggestion of Davis,[2] accepted and elaborated by Gilbert,[3] in explanation of the convexity of ridge crests, is that this results from dominance of soil creep over other transporting agencies in the process of lowering the land surface by removing the waste-mantle produced by weathering on and in the vicinity of divides. For the purpose of developing this hypothesis, it may be assumed that soil creep acts alone—that is, unaided by rain-wash, etc.—in removing a surface layer from the crest of a ridge or the top of a hill. The amount of material so creeping past given points increases progressively with the distances of the points from the crest or summit.

[1] G. K. Gilbert, *Geology of the Henry Mountains*, pp. 122–3 (1877).
[2] W. M. Davis, The Convex Profile of Badland Divides, *Science*, 20, p. 245 (1892).
[3] G. K. Gilbert, The Lowering of Hilltops, *Jour. Geol.* 17, pp. 344–50 (1909).

So slopes of increasing steepness in both or all directions from a horizontal summit are required, and will be developed, to facilitate transportation by creep.

It is improbable, however, that soil creep ever acts alone, and on some broadly convex summits the soils are very thin, and there is no evidence that effective creep is in progress at all. It seems very doubtful, therefore, whether creep is always the most important factor in rounding summits, and Lawson[1] concludes that the chief agent lowering hilltops is rain-wash, running off the surface during heavy rain, when the soil is saturated, as a "film " or shallow sheet flood, or a "network of rills" not yet concentrated or collected into definite channels. The process he regards as merely transportation, without corrasion, and a necessary preliminary is complete rock decay, which produces fine soil particles suitable for transportation by this agency. In contrast with water flowing as streams in definite channels, where the moving water is "underloaded", and for this reason corrades and develops the characteristic concave stream profile, the film, or shallow sheet flood, "is continually loaded to capacity for the grade of material available". It "is always in contact with its load, and the latter is at all points free and ready to be picked up, or moved". The fully loaded condition prevents corrasion, such as would lead to the development of gullies.[2]

A characteristic feature of valley-side profiles of youth and very early maturity, before summit convexity appears, is a straight slope (rock material being assumed homogeneous). At first the straight slope is too steep to retain a mantle of weathered waste, or soil; but when deepening of adjacent valleys ceases, such slopes become less steep, and carry a layer of residual soil of progressively increasing thickness. Razor-back divides and pyramidal peaks now have their sharp angles and points replaced by convex forms, which gradually become broader and more extensive. The summits acquire "curvature of greater and greater radius.... The maximum lowering of the surface of the hill, measured in the direction of the vertical, is at the summit, where, paradoxically, the volume of water, the agent of erosion, and also its velocity, are always at a minimum"

[1] A. C. Lawson, Rain-wash Erosion in Humid Regions, *Bull. Geol. Soc. Am.* 43, pp. 703–24 (1932).
[2] This process is termed "sheetwash" (J. L. Rich, *Bull. Geol. Soc. Am.* 46, p. 1003 (1935)); also "sheet erosion" (Snyder and Paschall, Report of Subcommittee on Erosion Terms, *Am. Soil Surv. Ass. Bull.* 17, p. 97 (1936)).

(Lawson). At the same time what remains of the earlier straight slope (tangent to the summit curvature) recedes either (as Lawson assumes) parallel to itself or with diminishing declivity, and, sooner or later, concave lower valley-side profiles also gradually replace the earlier straight slopes until a profile that is a compound curve, convex above and concave below, has been developed, which is characteristic of full and late maturity.

Beneath the surface in the concave lower slopes when they first develop tangent to an early position of the remnant of the primitive straight slope, there is some accumulation of soil washed down from above, which has accumulated as a fringe of small fans and talus slopes, but these lower slopes are, in the main, slopes of transportation rather than of accumulation when valleys have become fully mature, and their soil is derived in part from "local subsoil weathering" (Davis). Their concavity (diminishing declivity down the slope) is ascribed by Davis[1] to progressively increasing fineness of the grade of waste on them down the slope, which is a result of progressive weathering during its gradual downhill transportation. In late maturity the lower, concave valley sides are reduced to gentler slopes and become side strips of the valley floors.[2]

When valley plains have become broad relatively to river size, their further expansion by lateral planation under normal humid climatic conditions generally becomes extremely slow, as the river in its meandering course more and more rarely swings against bedrock in the valley sides. The stage at which steep bluffs bordering a flood plain testified to its rapid lateral growth is long past. The last traces of bluffs are fading out of the landscape, and it is obvious that lateral stream corrasion, though it cannot be said to cease, assumes a minor role. The general erosional lowering and grading of the land surface, always in progress, assumes now relatively greater importance, especially in its function of developing very gently sloping valley-side profiles that take the place of the bluffs of an earlier stage. At the stage of late maturity of transverse

[1] W. M. Davis, Rock Floors, *Jour. Geol.* 38, pp. 1–27, 136–58 (1930).
[2] In this discussion uniformity of rock character in the terrain has been assumed. A case may be complicated, however, by juxtaposition or alternation of weak and resistant rocks. At a rock boundary the point of inversion from convexity to concavity of slope may ascend or descend. "Convex slopes are common on rocks yielding coarse permeable debris, while concave slopes are more frequent on fine-grained, more or less impervious material" (H. Baulig, Sur les "gradins de piedmont", *Jour. Geom.* 2, p. 303 (1939)).

profile, the middle portion of the valley thus assumes a very broad U-form (Fig. 123).

The continued removal of the finer soil from the valley-side slopes causes them to recede from the banks of the graded stream to which they previously descended; and as they do so narrow strips of valley floor...will be developed at their base, back of whatever flood plain... is simultaneously formed by the stream. As these slopes widen, the concavity of the profile across the valley bottom...is given broader expression....The lateral strips will be everywhere covered by detritus, partly derived from local subsoil weathering, partly washed down from the valley sides; and the detrital cover will, in time, constitute a large part of the valley floor....Each lateral strip of the valley floor will have ...a...transverse slope from the valley side toward the stream or its flood plain, so that fine soil washed down from the valley side can be transported across the strip by the agencies, rill wash chiefly, available for that duty.[1]

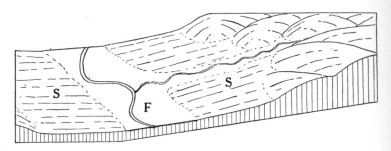

Fig. 123. An advanced stage of valley-floor widening in late maturity. *F*, flood plain; *S*, valley-floor side strips. (Based on a diagram by W. M. Davis.)

Notwithstanding the fact that lateral corrasion by the river will usually continue to widen the flood plain by cutting back the lower edges of the valley-floor side strips, these "will be developed [at the expense of the upper valley-side slopes] to greater and greater width independent of the flood plain".[1]

In time valley-floor side strips develop in tributary as well as in main valleys. They encroach more and more on the dissected interfluvial areas, and eventually coalesce to form a great part of the peneplain that takes form in the old-age stage of the landscape cycle as residual salients waste away to smaller and smaller dimensions.

[1] W. M. Davis, *loc. cit.* pp. 136–7.

The level on the valley side at which the concave curve of the valley-floor side strips merges into the upper, or ridge-crest convexity at full maturity, is determined by that at which waste that is subject to continued weathering, as it is carried down the slope, reaches a certain degree of fineness. The debris of weathering on the higher parts of the convex slopes is relatively coarse, and transportation of such material both by wash and creep, as it increases in quantity downhill, requires a steepening declivity downhill, that is, convexity of slope. As it is reduced gradually by weathering to a finer texture and becomes less permeable, though increasing still in quantity, it can be transported (mainly by wash) down a slope of increasingly gentler declivity, that is, with a concave profile.[1]

The proportions of convexly rounded crests and concave lower slopes in mature landscapes vary very widely, but, if conditions of climate and the nature of the rocks favour deep weathering, and, especially, if the rainfall and temperature are such as to encourage dense forest growth, very broadly convex (*subdued*) forms dominate the landscape.

Where rock composition and texture and other weathering conditions do not favour formation and accumulation of thick soils, or lead to the early production of a fine grade of waste, and this is not protected by a close growth of vegetation, so that it is subject to sheet erosion, late survival into the mature landscape of razor-back divides is favoured, where the convexity is reduced to minimum dimensions. The feldspathic sandstones, or greywackes, of the mountain axis of New Zealand, for example, when reduced to moderate relief and maturely dissected yield soils containing a large proportion of fine sandy clay; and on these the characteristic ridge profiles are somewhat sharp, especially in districts that have not been clothed with dense forest, though there is always some convexity of summits (Pl. XXV).

The sharpest razor-back forms are found in hot and wet regions, and more especially where basic igneous rocks are present at the surface, on which chemical weathering takes place even on outcrops of bare rock, and rain-wash scours away the soluble and fine-grained products of rock decay.

In torrid lands of rapid weathering and heavy rainfall the ridges that rise between broadly opened valleys are so extraordinarily sharp that,

[1] See J. L. Rich (*loc. cit.*) on "sheetwash" erosion.

in proportion to their breadth, they realise the knife-edge acuteness which Gilbert believed ought to result from degradation by running water; and the meaning of their sharpening appears to be that, under the extra heavy rainfall they receive, they really are sharpened chiefly by running water rather than by soil creep, in spite of the rapidity with which soil is there produced.[1]

According to Lawson[2] excessive rainfall is the determining factor. "If the rain-wash be excessive, the soil is removed, or does not form, and the conditions are then those which characterise degradation in wet climates as distinguished from humid climates" [in which convexity of summits is developed].

Examples of very sharp razor-back ridges separated by broad

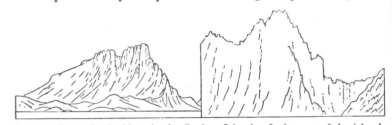

Fig. 124. Razor-back ridges in the Society Islands. Left, part of the island of Borabora (after Davis); right, Dana's sketch of Mt Orohena, Tahiti.

valleys with concave profile occur commonly in dissected volcanic islands of basalt in the tropical seas, notably in such islands in the Hawaiian and Society groups (Fig. 124). Perhaps the most conspicuous of the sharp divides are those of Raiatea, where one such arête has attained such thinness that a window has developed in it. In Tahiti

the larger...valleys abut at their heads against the central peaks in lofty precipices—precipices of two to nearly four thousand feet. Some of the larger valleys are widest at the centre of the island and terminated under the peaks in vast amphitheatres. The ridges...are...very narrow. Above an elevation of 3000 feet or so (as I found in my ascent), the top edge of the ridges for much of the way is but three or four feet wide...; and in some spots it diminishes to a foot, and even, at times, to a thin edge of bare rock; and from the crest the declivities either side pitch off steeply 1000–2000 feet.[3]

[1] W. M. Davis, The Cycle of Erosion and the Summit Level of the Alps, *Jour. Geol.* 31, p. 21 (1923).
[2] A. C. Lawson, Rain-wash Erosion in Humid Regions, *Bull. Geol. Soc. Am.* 43, p. 706 (1932).
[3] J. D. Dana, A Dissected Volcanic Mountain, *Am. Jour. Sci.* 32, p. 250 (1886).

This kind of ridge-and-valley profile has been observed and studied in detail in the Hawaiian Islands (Fig. 125), where Stearns[1] has found valley heads (of amphitheatre form) and valley walls retreating after the manner of escarpments in the gently dipping beds of alternating lavas and tuffs of which the mountains are

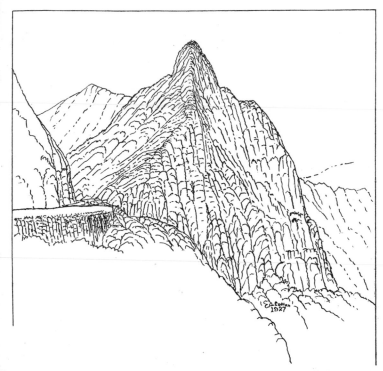

Fig. 125. Sharp divide at the "Pali", near Honolulu, Oahu.

composed. Retreat of the nearly vertical walls of the valley heads especially is greatly accelerated by plunge-pool erosion (Pl. IX, 2) at the many points where abstracted consequent streams enter a master valley as tributaries (compare Fig. 29), and narrow spurs left standing between the plunge pools "fail by their own weight" (Stearns) and collapse as rockfalls or slides. Another observer,

[1] H. T. Stearns, Geology and Ground-water Resources of the Island of Oahu, *T.H. Division of Hydrography*, Bull. 1, pp. 24–6 (1935).

157

Wentworth,[1] has attributed considerable importance to the unusually great depth of the water table, which is a result of the porous nature of the volcanic rocks. The whole of the surface undergoing erosion in the mountainous parts of the islands is, indeed, far above the water table, and is thus weakened by chemical weathering. The combination of tropical weathering conditions with initial mountain forms built of porous basaltic rocks (resulting in a water table far below the surface) is obviously a special case favouring the development of broadly concave valley profiles with the side walls, as well as the amphitheatre heads (Pl. IX, 2), retreating more or less parallel to themselves and sharpening the ridges. In a post-mature stage the ridges are destroyed and the land surface is reduced to small relief, as has taken place as a result of this process (to some extent aided by others) along the whole windward (north-east) side of the island of Oahu[2] (p. 70). Somewhat similar valley development is observed in limestone regions, where also the water table is deep (because of the presence of open underground passages due to solution) and chemical weathering is active.

The explanation of compound (convex-and-concave) landscape profiles in general as mature forms implies that such profiles are, or, at any rate, may be, derived by normal processes from characteristically young profiles in the course of a cycle of erosion. It is sometimes maintained, however, that the assumption of such a history for them is not in accordance with facts. It is, indeed, probable that some similar profiles have been developed without their passing through an anterior condition typically young; and such may be described in a Davisian phrase as "mature-born".[3] Their inclusion in the cycle scheme presents no difficulties; but a special case must be envisaged in which elision of the stage of youth takes place.

To explain the forms of youth, that is, to deduce the development of forms to match those regarded as young in natural landscapes, it is generally convenient to assume that, as a result either

[1] C. K. Wentworth, Principles of Stream Erosion in Hawaii, *Jour. Geol.* 36, pp. 385–410 (1928).
[2] H. T. Stearns, *loc. cit.* p. 28.
[3] W. M. Davis, Peneplains and the Geographical Cycle, *Bull. Geol. Soc. Am.* 33, pp. 590–1 (1922); see also *Die erklärende Beschreibung der Landformen,* p. 147 (1912).

of the resistant nature of the rock material to be eroded or of the rapidity of the uplift introducing erosion, the amount of erosion taking place *during* the initial uplift is relatively so unimportant that it may be neglected as compared with the erosion that follows completion of the uplift. Such an assumption is unwarranted, however, when erosion is working on very weak materials or when uplift takes place very slowly. In either of these cases complete elision of the stage of youth in the landscape cycle may be expected to occur, or, at any rate, profound modification of the typical forms of youth must take place.

Even though mature-born, convex-and-concave landscape forms have generally passed through later stages of their development after cessation of the initial uplift in the manner outlined in the early part of this chapter. An alternative deductive explanation of some such forms has, however, been proposed. Walther Penck[1] has explained hill- and valley-side features on the basis of an assumption that the development of mature landscape forms commonly accompanies (instead of following) the incision of valleys, which means that it takes place while uplift is still in progress. His explanation of the origin of combinations of convex and concave profiles assumes that the landscapes containing them have passed through successive phases of "waxing" and "waning" valley development, the former characterised by valley incision by vertical corrasion (due to uplift) taking place at an increasingly rapid rate, and the latter by a later slowing down and perhaps eventual cessation of the process (along with the uplift that has caused it).

From an analysis of straight-sloping valley sides of "uniform" development—i.e. development accompanying vertical incision at a uniform rate—in which V-shaped valleys are formed (steeper sided the more rapidly they are cut), a conclusion is reached that all uniformly sloping elements of land slopes, once they are developed, continue thereafter (in homogeneous rocks) to retreat from the valley axis perpendicular to themselves at rates depending on their steepness, the steeper slopes migrating back much more rapidly than those of gentle gradient. The argument for retreat of elements of compound slopes without altering in steepness is that, where any such element has below it one of greater or less declivity, the point at which the declivity changes is a local base-level for the

[1] W. Penck, *Die morphologische Analyse* (Stuttgart, 1924).

element of the slope immediately above. From this hypothesis of retreat of each element of a slope at right angles to itself follows the argument that waxing development (accelerated incision) produces convex valley-side slopes, and waning development (incision at a diminishing rate) concave valley sides. Thus a valley side convex above and concave below *may* have resulted from waxing followed by waning development of the valley.

It might be pointed out that migration in their entirety of slopes of convex, concave, or compound form, if it can take place according to the law announced in this hypothesis, can be a strictly horizontal retreat from the valley axis only if the rate at which each element of the slope migrates in a direction at right angles to itself varies as the sine of its angle of slope. Obviously, if the rate of retreat increases with the angle of slope more rapidly than the sine, changes of slope

Fig. 126. Profiles of a widening valley; left, according to W. Penck; right, according to W. M. Davis. (After Davis.)

(convexities and concavities) will migrate upward as well as outward from the valley axis (as shown in Penck's Figs. 3 and 6), and the convexities of valley sides will sooner or later pass upward out of the landscape, which will eventually consist of broad concave valleys separated by razor-back divides. If, on the other hand, in any case the rate of slope retreat should increase with the declivity less rapidly than the sine of the slope angle, the theoretical migration of slope elements will be downward as well as outward, and convex forms will assume an increasing share of the landscape after the cessation of valley incision. Possibly investigation along this line will bridge the gap between the Davisian and Penckian conceptions of peneplain profiles (Fig. 126).

If Penck's deduction could be adopted as a working hypothesis, it might afford an explanation of upper valley-side convexity in the valleys of main streams and some of their larger tributaries; but to attempt to apply this explanation to all surface convexities would be to imply that all streams, including minor tributaries and ultimate dissecting ravines, had deepened and shaped their valleys simultaneously, and that the entire pattern of streams in a landscape had been in existence throughout its dissection. This would be incompatible with any theory of progressive dissection of a land surface by insequent and subsequent streams.

It seems very doubtful, however, whether Penck's hypothesis of migrating slopes can be accepted.[1] Each element of slope, considered as a straight slope, is a slope of transportation for material from above it. When smoothly graded it may be regarded as analogous to the graded profile of a river in which a condition of equilibrium exists between gradient and load. Just as a graded river profile may become steeper or less steep with changing load, so, it would seem, may a hill slope, without change of local base-level. This argument is independent of the relation between the steepness of a slope and the grade (coarse or fine) of waste that can be transported down its declivity. Both diminishing load and increasing fineness of waste with progressive maturity of the landscape would seem to require that an element of slope as it retreats in the course of landscape erosion *shall become less steep*.

In deference to those who consider long-continued still-stand an exceptional or impossible condition, and prefer to deduce the forms of landscapes under postulates of continued movement, an analysis may be introduced here of a special case considered by Albrecht Penck to be of importance for the explanation of the land forms of the European Alps.[2] A sharp ridge-and-valley landscape (mature-born) develops during preliminary uplift. Uplift continues at a uniform rate, and during its progress the rivers are constantly reinvigorated, so that they continue to cut down through the rising land mass. Development of a stable and characteristic valley-side slope now induces a condition of constant relief, in which valley deepening and ridge lowering continue at the same rate, though for a time the land mass as a whole rises at such a rate that absolute elevations continue to increase.

See H. Baulig, *Jour. Geom.* 2, p. 303 (1939); also J. L. Rich, Recognition and Significance of Multiple Erosion Surfaces, *Bull. Geol. Soc. Am.* 49, pp. 1695–1722 (1938); O. Jessen has postulated special conditions for horizontal retreat of steep valley walls (*Zeits. Ges. Erdk. Berlin*, pp. 36–49 (1938)).
A. Penck, Die Gipfelflur der Alpen, *Sitzungsb. pr. Akad.* 17, pp. 256–68 (1919); see also W. M. Davis, The Cycle of Erosion and the Summit Level of the Alps, *Jour. Geol.* 31, pp. 1–41 (1923).

Next, according to Penck's deduction, the rivers, constantly invigorated as they are carried higher and higher above sea-level, must cut downward more and more rapidly. Without change of characteristic ridge-and-valley forms and slopes, or of relief, there will now be an approach to a stable condition, in which the lowering of the whole surface by erosion just keeps pace with the uplift of the land; so that an apparently unchanging, though in reality continually eroded, landscape persists for an indefinite period.

Such an accident of uplift at a rate neither too slow nor too rapid may, therefore, introduce a phase of stability of landscape forms that will temporarily interrupt the continuous panorama of changes envisaged in the presentation of the ideal cycle. The delicate adjustment that must be assumed makes this necessarily an exceptional case, but the analysis will serve to remind the reader of the infinite variety of nature.

A hypothetical case involving slower, though continuous, uplift has been analysed by Davis,[1] where "the stage of youth would have been elided and that of maturity would have prevailed from the beginning". Features of the landscape prevailing while uplift was in progress would be

broadly open valleys, whose gently sloping evenly graded sides descend to the stream banks leaving no room for flood plains.... The absence of flood plains would show that the streams had not yet ceased deepening their valleys, and the graded valley sides would show that the downward corrasion by the streams has not been so rapid that the relatively slow processes of slope grading could not keep pace with it.

Changes in the relief of an eroded landscape may be briefly considered, attention being confined to the case of a landscape eroded during a single normal cycle in which initial uplift has been completed early, and in which no renewal of uplift has occurred to introduce complications. Relief, as measured by the depth of valleys below ridge crests, or, in youth of the landscape, below doabs or residual interfluves, increases while the rivers are young and are deepening their valleys, and until these become graded. At this stage, or when rivers become mature, relief reaches maximum, at any rate in the usual case where the upland surface has not as yet been appreciably lowered by erosion. If dissection

[1] W. M. Davis, Complications of the Geographical Cycle (1905), *Geographical Essays*, pp. 279–95 (1909).

of the upland has not been completed by this time, relief will remain practically constant until landscape maturity has been reached, for the rate of further valley deepening will be negligible. Thenceforward, when the upper slopes of adjacent valley sides intersect in ridges, further valley erosion—which will result in widening, scarcely, if at all, accompanied by deepening—will involve retreat of the valley sides and lowering of the ridge crests formed by their intersection (Fig. 126, right). Such lowering must be more rapid than any simultaneous valley deepening that may occur in the fully mature to senile stages of the cycle, and so in these later stages relief will continuously diminish. Any departure, of course, from the postulate of still-stand implies interruption of the cycle (Chapter XIX), and the occurrence of any earth movement will eventually affect the relief.

CHAPTER XV

Constructional Land Forms; Aggraded Plains

DURING the course of a cycle of erosion some features are built as a result of terrestrial accumulation of the waste of the land. Most of these are doomed to suffer dissection during the later stages of the cycle in which they appear, and in some cases the materials of which they are built will be afterwards completely removed. Deposits of rivers, either in initial hollows of the land surface or in valleys cut by youthful streams and afterwards subject to aggradation, are, in general, less permanent than marine deposits, for they are laid down above the general base-level, and are liable to be removed by erosion in the general lowering of the land surface that takes place in late maturity and old age of the cycle of erosion. Where still-stand does not continue until a cycle runs its full course, interrupting earth movements of subsidence may not only cause aggradation, but also carry river-laid deposits below base-level, where they will be preserved indefinitely; but such deposits are buried, and, having no longer an exposed surface, are of interest only as geological formations and not as land forms. The shorter-lived deposits that remain above base-level, while they survive, present prominent and characteristic surface forms of great areal extent in some landscapes.

Among forms resulting from accumulation may be placed the nearly continuous mantle of residual surface waste, streaming, creeping, washing, and sliding downhill, and thus smoothing out irregularities of the surface, accumulating locally to fill hollows, and flowing around the more prominent rock outcrops until these eventually crumble and disappear and, the waste-mantle becoming continuous, the slope is graded. *Talus slopes*, or *screes*, are a phase of the waste-mantle at its early, discontinuous stage. They are formed by the actual streaming, rolling, and glissading of rock fragments, generally newly broken by mechanical weathering, and therefore unworn and angular. The surface slopes at the angle of repose[1] and the talus material has accumulated in layers parallel with the present surface, but stratification is absent or very imperfect, as the material is quite unsorted.

Talus slopes are common features on mountain sides, where the fragments broken by mechanical weathering from bare-rock outcrops on peaks and high slopes stream down through funnel-like eroded couloirs, or "chimneys", of the steep rocky surface. Confined thus for some distance, they spread out lower down in conical shape, delivering their surplus waste into streams of water that carry it away down the valleys. Talus slopes of this kind are particularly abundant among mountains that have been sharpened by glacial erosion, and they fringe the oversteepened sides of glaciated valleys in post-glacial times, when these precipitous sides have become exposed to the weather, as, for example, in "the Screes", a vast, continuous talus apron along the side of the English lake Wastwater. There is widespread development of screes also on every slope of the rapidly crumbling Southern Alps of New Zealand, where, on the Canterbury (eastern) side of the ranges, the monotonously uniform "greywacke" formation yields enormous quantities of coarse, mechanically weathered boulders on slopes recently steepened by glacial erosion (Pl. XXVI, 2).

Talus slopes occur fringing cliffs, however these may have been formed, provided that the rate of removal of fallen material from

[1] "Angle of repose", see footnote on p. 11.

the base of the cliffs is not sufficiently rapid to prevent its accumulation there. Near Wellington, New Zealand, sea cliffs are not at present being undercut, for a small uplift has caused the shore-line to retreat from the cliff base. Since 1855, when the uplift took place, conspicuous screes have been formed of rock material that would in the normal course of events have been washed away by the sea as fast as it came down.

The angular fragments of broken rock forming the surface of a talus slope do not, as a rule, remain long enough in place to become weathered and allow of the formation of a soil covering, for the stream of rolling and glissading boulders from above continues, and so surface layers are either quickly buried as the thickness of the accumulation increases or else the surface is simply a chute down which fresh supplies of material continue to stream as it is swept away by running water at the toe of the slope. Vegetation is, therefore, generally absent from rapidly growing or vigorously active talus slopes. Where accumulation is slow enough, however, there may be a fairly close covering of forest or other vegetation.

On more gentle, graded slopes, where the waste-mantle includes much chemically weathered waste, and is not actively streaming downhill, vegetation flourishes. In fact, the stability of most of these slopes depends on the natural vegetation. A slope may be steep and yet the soil may be so bound together and protected by the vegetation, perhaps forest, that streaming and vigorous sheet wash, or sheet erosion, are prevented and only creep and a certain amount of mass movement permitted (see p. 149), so that a state of balance has been arrived at between the rate of removal of waste and the rate of supply of new waste by weathering of the underlying rocks.

When the natural vegetation, whether in a forested or grass-steppe region, is interfered with, erosion, with the formation first of gullies (Pl. XXVII, 1, 2) and later the complete removal of the waste-mantle leaving bare rock, may take place on surfaces previously graded. In a land of virgin forests, such as the greater part of the North Island of New Zealand was until the middle of the nineteenth century,

with the coming of the farmer forests are felled and burnt; the hillsides sown in grass, and thus begins the process of changing a forest soil into a grass soil.... The strong roots of the forest trees are replaced by the finer and generally shallower roots of the grasses....Under the grass cover less rainfall is absorbed, causing increased run-off and wider fluctuations in the moisture-content of the soil. With more water passing over the surface of the soil sheet erosion becomes important wherever the soil is unprotected by vegetation. In dry periods the soil becomes more parched than it had normally done under forest cover, and cracking of the ground becomes more pronounced. The alternate wetting and drying of the soil, with its seasonal cracking and swelling, weakens the soil mantle and tends to speed up the processes of soil creep and slipping. Under the forest cover slipping was slowly taking place. Indeed, the shape of the hills themselves was due largely to the forest. However, a hillside in balance under forest is not necessarily in balance when clothed in grass. The soil tends to move into the valleys more quickly, forming easier slopes which can be grass-controlled. This causes the upper slopes of the hills to become steeper. More bare rock is exposed and the run-off further increased. The scars we see disfiguring the steeper hillsides are thus seen to be due to the acceleration of the process normally taking place as part of the erosion cycle under forest. The cause of this acceleration is our interference with the plant cover.[1]

Reversion of hill slopes from a graded to a rough, ungraded state is a condition for which apparently there is no cure. In Italy, in China, in the Appalachian province of the United States, and elsewhere, where great quantities of soil have been lost by cultivation of slopes that are too steep, affected slopes have become barren areas of bare rocks or have been sculptured into bad-land forms. Regrading of such surfaces is an inevitable natural process, but the graded slopes of the future will be less steep than those that have been destroyed and the surface must be lowered considerably by erosion before they are developed, and no one can guess how many thousand years will elapse before the process is complete. The critical slope, above which it is dangerous, or impolitic, to clear forest from hillsides, varies widely with the nature of the underlying rocks and with the climate, and is discovered only by experience. It has been found, in most parts of New Zealand, that good turf protects slopes very well, though probably not so well as the forest it has replaced; but failure to maintain a continuous cover of grass, where a farm is overstocked or neglected, may lead to serious erosion, with irreparable loss of soil and gullying and destruction of the graded surface.

[1] N. H. Taylor, "Some Aspects of Erosion of Farm Lands", read at Grassland Conference, Hamilton, N.Z., Oct. 6, 1938.

Not only are hill slopes rendered barren where erosion has been accelerated by deforestation, but neighbouring valleys are also injuriously affected. The supply of waste to streams is increased to such an extent that they become overloaded and are caused to aggrade, filling up and reducing the capacity of their channels so that they become subject to frequent floods, and also depositing waste over the valley plains. The first of the soil washed down from eroded head-water slopes may be a welcome addition to that already on the valley plains, but as the process of slope destruction gains momentum this is followed by coarser rock waste, and fertile lowland plains are buried beneath layers of coarse gravel and boulders. The tendency of rivers to flood is increased also as a greater proportion than formerly of the precipitation runs off immediately from the surface, causing greater fluctuation of stream volumes. This is owing to loss from the hill slopes not only of the forest and its absorbent litter but also of the waste-mantle, which has, when present, a great capacity for absorbing rain water and storing it as ground water. From the mature landscape surface shown in Plate XXVII, 1 much soil has been removed by accelerated wash, and the talus cone below the newly cut gully indicates how the supply of coarse waste to streams is augmented.

The actual surface of a flood plain or valley plain developed by lateral corrasion of a river, whether with meandering or braided course, consists of deposited material, but this may be only a veneer of no great thickness covering an abraded rock surface. In the case of the flood plain of a meandering stream, the upper layer (consisting of fine silt) grows in thickness during every flood, but in streams that are not aggrading this upbuilding of the valley floor is only temporary, for the flood plain is cut away as meanders change their form and sweep downvalley, and silt accumulation must begin again on the gravel flats left by the swinging channel of the stream. The surface of such a valley plain is not quite level. In addition to slight across-valley convexity of the whole plain (see p. 130), there is stronger convexity as the river channel is approached. During floods the river may be, to some extent, confined to its ordinary channel by *natural levees*, as the low ridges of alluvium it has built along its banks are termed.

Where a river has aggraded its valley, the gravel deposits underlying the valley floor are thicker at least than the depth of the stream channel, and the valley may have been filled to a depth of hundreds or even thousands of feet. The effects are similar whatever the cause of aggradation. The river may be very young and still engaged in filling up so as to build a bridge for itself across a hollow of the initial surface, which may be irregular owing to the occurrence of warping as an accompaniment of the initial uplift, or, perhaps, owing to the streams of the present epoch having to grade courses across the irregular slopes and excavated hollows left by the vanished ice of the Glacial Period (Pl. XXVIII, 1). Various causes of possible temporary aggradation during the course of a normal cycle have already been suggested (p. 53), and deeper aggradation may result from interruption of a cycle by earth movements involving tilting or warping (Chapter XIX), may follow in the train of events resulting from general subsidence (Chapter XX), or may be consequent upon a climatic change in the direction of lower rainfall, or upon deforestation and other interference by man with natural vegetation. Reduced rainfall induces aggradation by increasing the proportion of waste to water in streams: the effect is twofold, for not only is there less water, but almost certainly there is more waste to be transported, as forests may die out, or, at least, become less luxuriant and so protect the ground less effectively under drier conditions.

During a glacial epoch heavy aggradation takes place in valleys the heads of which are occupied by glaciers. The abundant waste originating as a result of valley-head glacial erosion—waste which must be carried away by the melt-water from the glaciers—as compared with the smaller loads formerly carried by rivers in the same valleys, seems to have been the cause of the aggradation and formation of plains termed "valley trains". Later substitution of normal for glacial erosion at valley heads commonly leads to such restriction of river loads that trenches are cut by the rivers through the valley-train deposits, and a succession of glacial epochs alternating with interglacial epochs of normal erosion may be expected to be accompanied by successive aggradational fillings and re-excavations of the lower valleys. A nice adjustment of glacial intensities and a diminuendo of duration of both glacial and interglacial epochs may result in survival of remains of a succession of valley-train aggraded plains as matched terraces on valley sides,[1] such as are found in valleys of the Alps[2] (Fig. 127). The surfaces, or treads, of such terraces are constructional gravel-built forms, and thus distinctly different in origin from the cut valley-plain terrace forms generally developed both on solid rock and alluvium. The higher terraces of a fluvio-glacial series are somewhat ancient and may be expected to be submaturely dissected.

Fig. 127. Successive fluvio-glacial valley fillings surviving in terraces.

Where alternating aggradation and degradation due to other causes have occurred, terrace remnants of the plains built during aggradation may survive. Most terraces bordering European rivers in flights have been thus described as remnants of aggraded plains,[3] but alternatively they are ascribed to progressive excavation of alluvium.[4]

Though it is most obvious that aggradation is in progress where stream courses are braided, meandering rivers may aggrade also. Lateral corrasion accompanying sweeping and the cutting-off and redevelopment of meanders does not in such cases cut the flood-plain deposits entirely away so as to lay bare bedrock in the river channel, but, on the contrary, the building of each new flood-plain strip or scroll starts at a higher level than before, and the meander-belt is built up, and so eventually is the whole flood plain. In the lower

[1] " Terrasses emboîtées" of French authors, translated "inset" terraces (Barbour).
[2] Penck and Brückner, Die Alpen im Eiszeitalter, p. 107 (1909).
[3] C. Depéret, Essai de chronologie, C.R. Ac. Sci. (1900–2).
[4] Douglas Johnson, C.R. Cong. Int. Géog. Paris, 2, pp. 202–3 (1933).

Mississippi valley, for example, "the flat floor...is a surface built as a result of thick alluviation.....Meandering is certainly a process to be associated with filling...."[1]

Aggraded valley floors that are built up by streams in braided courses spreading unsorted waste over the whole surface are in humid climates stony and infertile if built of coarse waste, but under semi-arid conditions of weathering and deposition unsorted gravel may contain a sufficiently large proportion of fine unleached rock debris to give it great fertility. Vegetation has little chance, however, of establishing itself on the temporary islands between distributing branches of a braided course.

Should an aggrading river change its habit and cease building up the surface of its plain, entrenching itself perhaps in a new, young valley, such parts of the upbuilt plain as escape dissection have an opportunity to develop a soil-covering and become fertile. The productive Waikato River basin, in New Zealand, owes the formation of its broad valley plains to aggradation, which affected rivers flowing from the central volcanic district of the North Island during a phase of copious supply of fragmentary pumiceous volcanic ejectamenta.[2] This specifically light load can be carried by rivers down very gentle gradients, but over-supply of the material led in this case to aggradation, with development of extensive plains of very gentle declivity. That of the Waikato valley has an average fall of 6 ft. per mile. It is 500 sq. miles in extent, spreading out northward and westward over the middle valley basin of the river in fan-like form from an apex at the Maungatautari gorge (M, Fig. 128), at which point the river spilled from another aggraded course into this lowland during the aggradational phase. The aggraded basin is surrounded by hills, and the river leaves it by way of the Taupiri gorge (T, Fig. 128). The surface of the plain is broken by the emergence of incompletely buried hills, which are parts of a maturely dissected sheet of volcanic material similar to the alluvium of the aggraded plain. The Waikato River, having now a diminished load owing to a slackening of the volcanic activity at the source of the load material, has cut a trench in its aggraded plain of a depth increasing to 200 ft. near the head of the basin.

[1] R. J. Russell, Physiography of Lower Mississippi River Delta, *Louisiana Dep. Cons. Geol. Bull.* 8, p. 123 (1936).
[2] N. H. Taylor, Water Supplies of Farms and Dairy Factories in Hamilton Basin and Hauraki Lowland, *N.Z. Dep. S.I.R. Bull.* 48 (1935).

Aggradation in a main river raises the local base-levels to which tributaries must adjust their courses, and so they also are com-

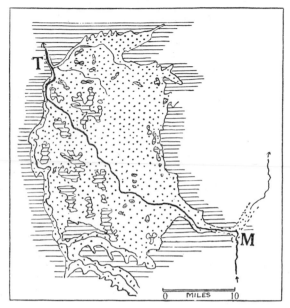

Fig. 128. The aggraded plain of the Middle Waikato, New Zealand. (For locality see Fig. 131.)

pelled to aggrade their valley floors. If a tributary brings down insufficient waste to allow it to build up as rapidly as its main is doing, its outlet is blocked by the alluvial deposit built by the main across the mouth of its valley, and it spreads out to form a lake (p. 42). In the lower valley of the Waikato River, New Zealand, aggradation has thus ponded a number of shallow lakes in tributary valleys (Fig. 129). The Wairarapa Lake (Fig. 17) is a larger example. Lakes so ponded may spill out through new outlets, which become permanent if the rivers entrench

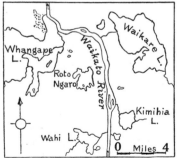

Fig. 129. Lakes formed as a result of ponding of tributaries by aggradation of the Waikato River, New Zealand.

171

themselves in a phase of renewed vertical corrasion. At a late stage of the growth of the aggraded plain of the Middle Waikato basin described on p. 170, the Waikato's largest tributary, the Waipa, had its course thus permanently changed.[1]

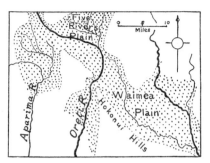

Fig. 130. Alternative courses of the Oreti River, New Zealand, across aggraded plains of its own construction.

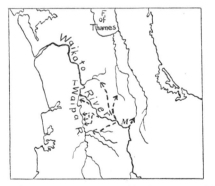

Fig. 131. Some former courses of the Waikato River, New Zealand. (After Taylor.)

Main rivers may themselves take entirely new courses by spilling out of valleys they have aggraded through the lowest gaps in their valley walls, being thus "diverted by alluviation" (Gilbert). Generally such a new course will be at first too steep for the diverted river, which must grade a new valley for itself, and as this involves cutting downward, the diverted river becomes fixed in its spill-over course. Diversion in some cases, however, is only

[1] Taylor, *loc cit.*

172

temporary. The newly cut outlet may be filled again if the river continues to be well supplied with waste, and, when the new course is built by aggradation higher than the original course, the river will spill back into that again, and thereafter (while aggradation continues) it will occupy and build up the two courses alternately.

A number of clear cases of diversion by alluviation are known among the rivers of New Zealand. The Oreti River, for example, has reached the stage where it has alternative routes to the sea, one directly southward by its present outlet and the other south-eastward across the Waimea Plain (Fig. 130). The Waikato River (Fig. 131) also, when building the aggraded plain of the Middle Waikato Basin (Fig. 128), spilled over temporarily north-eastward to an east-coast outlet in the Firth of Thames. An earlier diversion of this river, which was permanent, resulted when it spilled into the present "Middle" valley (at M, Fig. 131) from a former northward course with another east-coast outlet.[1] This change took place early in the aggradational phase and led to the building of the aggraded plain of the Middle Waikato (p. 170).

CHAPTER XVI

Fans; Bahadas; Basin Plains; and Deltas

As rivers emerge fully loaded from eroded valleys, in which they may be degrading, into broad depressions or basins where slopes are so gentle that the streams are compelled to aggrade in order to prolong their graded profiles—or to build up courses sufficiently steep to give them their needed velocity—they deposit part of their load in such a manner as to build *alluvial fans*.[2] The surface of a fan resembles a portion of a low cone with its apex in the mouth of the valley from which the fan-building stream emerges (Frontispiece and Figs. 132, 133), the slopes being the same from this

[1] L. Cussen, *Trans. N.Z. Inst.* 26, pp. 398–407 (1894).
[2] F. Drew, Alluvial and Lacustrine Deposits and Glacial Records of the Upper Indus Basin, *Quart. Jour. Geol. Soc.* 29, pp. 441–71 (1873).

point down every radius of the fan. The front or toe of the fan is roughly semicircular if built over level ground (Fig. 132), but necessarily varies in outline according to any irregularity of the underlying surface, and outlines of confluent fans are modified by interference of each with the free growth of its neighbours. Over a growing fan the stream that builds it flows in the braided channels generally characteristic of aggradation, and as one set of channels

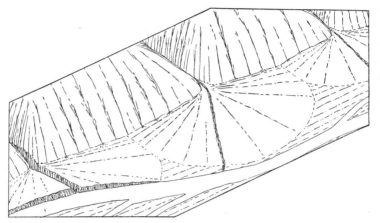

Fig. 132. Diagram of alluvial fans built by tributaries entering the wide valley of a large river.

after another is filled up and abandoned the stream flows by turns down every radius of the fan, completion of each set of radial "spokes" adding a new layer to the fan surface, so that the fan grows symmetrically. Any transverse profile of an alluvial fan, like a section of a cone, is convex, and this convexity, though more strongly marked, is of the same nature as the slight transverse convexity of valley plains, for the floor of an aggraded valley may be regarded as a long narrow fan prevented from extending laterally by the valley sides. Very steep fans have been called *alluvial cones*,[1]

[1] Otherwise, *alluvial cone* has been used in the same sense as *alluvial fan* (G. K. Gilbert, *Geology of the Henry Mountains*, pp. 133–5 (1877)). The differentiation was suggested by Gilbert. The term "fan" was used in 1864 by Haast, in New Zealand (J. Haast, *Report on the Formation of the Canterbury Plains* (Christchurch, 1864)). He restricted it, however, to the subaerial parts of the confluent deltas—in part, probably, true fans—forming the Canterbury Plain, and employed the term "half-cone" for the majority of what are now called "fans", because of their greater steepness.

and there is a transition through these from alluvial fans to talus slopes.

Fans are abundant in mountainous regions where a normal cycle following a period of glacial erosion is still in its early youth, for example, in the broad aggraded valleys of the Himalayas and of Canterbury, New Zealand, where every small tributary builds a fan (Fig. 133). They are common features also in early stages of the

Fig. 133. Truncated and partly reconstructed ("two-storied") fan, Rakaia Valley, New Zealand.

cycle in regions of strong initial relief (especially block-faulted regions), and wherever streams flow from dissected higher country into broad depressions, whatever their origin, more especially under conditions of semi-aridity, which result in a high proportion of waste to water in the streams, with consequent steepness of aggraded slopes. Under more humid conditions fans, though present, may be less conspicuous, because their slopes are gentler.

A fan built by a vigorous tributary may extend across a main valley so as to dam the river in it and form a shallow lake, which overflows in rapids across the toe of the fan. Without actual ponding taking place, the fan of a tributary may force the main river against its valley side, where lateral corrasion perhaps develops an amphitheatre. Where the growth of fans is less vigorous, or the main river more energetic, a swing of the latter to the far side of a broad valley may allow a large fan to be built by a tributary, and when the river swings back the fan may be truncated, cliffed, or almost entirely cut away (Fig. 132). Truncation of the fan, if it shortens the course of the fan-building stream, will compel it to regrade its profile by cutting a trench along that radius of the fan it happens to be flowing on when truncation occurs, becoming fixed in this course for the time being; but another swing of the main stream away from the truncated fan will lead to the growth of a new fan in front of it (Fig. 133), making a "two-storied" or compound fan,[1] and the newer fan may grow to such dimensions as completely to envelop the remnant of the earlier. Fans built in front of the cliffs of a steep coast when the sea has retreated owing to coastal emergence or progradation may be truncated by wave-cut cliffs during subsequent retrogradation of the coast (Pl. XXVIII, 2).[2]

On rapidly growing steep fans of coarse waste in humid climates there is little soil and vegetation is generally scanty, for all parts are liable to have fresh layers of clean-washed gravel spread over them. Where, however, the growth of a fan has ceased for a time owing to the depositing stream's becoming entrenched and, at least temporarily, fixed in position, soil may be formed by weathering of the surface layer of gravel, to which wind-borne dust may add a quota. In arid and semi-arid regions much fine waste as well as gravel is incorporated in fans, as the streams of water dwindle and sink into the ground, and the material of such fans forms fertile soils. Water for irrigation is obtainable from the stream at the apex of the fan, or may be drawn from the ground water in the fan, the supply of which is maintained as the fan-building stream sinks into the porous ground. The ground water may emerge as a line of springs at the toe of the fan; it is nowhere far from the surface, and may be tapped by sinking shallow wells, or even in some cases by driving tunnels horizontally into the alluvium.

Where a number of streams emerge from mountains undergoing dissection and build fans along their front, the fans if large become laterally confluent, and thus form a continuous apron built of waste bordering the mountains, the surface of which is a *piedmont alluvial*

---

[1] F. Drew (*loc. cit.* p. 454) figures a "triple" fan.
[2] In Southern California the sea cliffs of Santa Monica furnish an example (W. M. Davis, *Bull. Geol. Soc. Am.* 44, Pl. 47 (1933)).

plain or *bahada* (thus pronounced, and now generally written, but originally the Spanish form *bajada*).[1] It has an appreciable slope away from the mountains, and is made up of a number of convex portions, each of which is one of the component fans (Fig. 134). The directions of the ever-changing courses of streams on a growing bahada are obviously consequent on the slopes of the fans they have built, and they may become fixed in position if, as is the case with the great fan-building rivers of the Canterbury Plain, in New Zealand (Fig. 134), they enter on a phase of vertical corrasion, and cut trenches across the plain (Frontispiece). Smaller rivers either follow consequent courses down the slopes of the fans

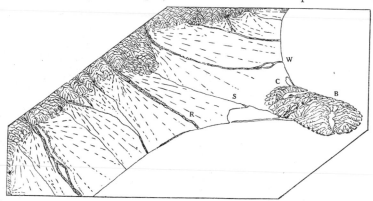

Fig. 134. The Canterbury Plain, New Zealand, a large piedmont alluvial plain.

of their larger neighbours or are found in *intersequent* positions[2] in the re-entering angles of the surface between adjacent large fans—e.g. the course of the Selwyn (*S*) between the fans of the Waima-kariri and Rakaia (*W* and *R*) on the Canterbury Plain (Fig. 134).

Basin plains, which are closely related in origin, structure, and form to bahadas, are widespreading alluvial plains made up of confluent fans built by streams entering from various directions the *intermont basins* that have resulted from pronounced warping or faulting of the land surface on a large scale, or from some combination of the two. Though plains, they are far from plane, if composed of contiguous gravel-built fans of steep-grade streams,

C. F. Tolman, *Erosion and Deposition in Southern Arizona Bolson Region, Jour. Geol.* 17, pp. 136–63 (1909).
J. P. Buwalda, *Intersequent, a New Type of Stream, Bull. Geol. Soc. Am.* 43, p. 228 (1932).

but large basin plains that are built in part of broad fans of finer waste are more nearly level in their central or axial portions. The Vale of Kashmir is an example of a large-scale basin plain with an area of about 5000 square miles; like most others it has suffered a certain amount of dissection as the outlet gorge of the Jhelum River has been deepened.

Commonly the alluvial deposits built into basin plains have been more or less eroded, and throughgoing rivers easily cut them down to valley plains of lateral planation, bordered for a time by terraces which are remnants of the aggradational surface (Fig. 135), or, more commonly, by flights of terraces cut in the alluvial material.

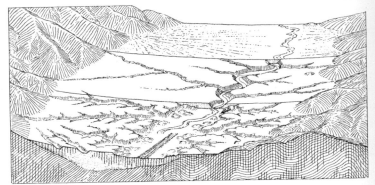

Fig. 135. Three stages in the history of a basin plain. (After Davis.)

Large gravel-filled intermont basins in the North Canterbury district of New Zealand (Fig. 83) have been extensively planed down and terraced, but the Mackenzie Plains of the large intermont basin of the upper Waitaki valley, in the South Canterbury district retain the aggradational basin-plain surface only slightly modified. The dissection to youth and to submaturity of a basin plain traversed by a throughgoing river is illustrated in Fig. 135, taken from a description by Davis[1] of the Valdarno, a basin plain in an intermont basin of the Apennines, traversed by the upper Arno, and dissected to the submature stage figured.

Deposits of gravel in fans and bahadas and underlying aggraded plains exhibit a rough stratification parallel to the surface. Each

[1] W. M. Davis, Der Valdarno, eine Darstellungsstudie, *Zeits. Ges. f. Erdk. Berlin*, 68 pp. (1914).

layer has been built up, however, by the filling of a great number of separate channels successively occupied, and so, where seen in section, the beds are lenticular, thickening and thinning irregularly, and passing laterally by rapid transition into coarser or finer material (lens-and-pocket stratification). There is nothing here comparable to the complete sorting of material that takes place during deposition in the sea or a lake, where waste of different grades of fineness is deposited in different places, so that the deposit in a particular portion of any stratum is of even size; but there is generally a certain amount of rough sorting, and some lenses of sand or sandy clay may accumulate in abandoned channels that have become backwaters, to be covered later by gravel lenses. Coarser and finer gravel lenses may be present also, but there is generally much mixture of coarse and fine gravel with some fine material throughout. In fans built by vigorous mountain streams large boulders may be present scattered through the gravels. Under humid climatic conditions the gravel is cleaner-washed and more thoroughly freed of admixture of fine material than in the case of the unsorted waste built into the fans and bahadas of arid and semi-arid regions.

Great piedmont plains of finer waste and of gentler slopes than these gravel-built bahadas have been spread out by rivers in various parts of the world. Two of the best-known examples, the plains of northern India and those bordering the Rocky Mountains on the east, are somewhat dissected, but the vast south-eastern plain of Turkestan is still in course of aggradation. Here

very grain of sand and silt that the Tejen and Murg-ab bring from the mountains of their upper courses must be deposited on the plains, where their lower courses wither away. The plains are dead-level to the eye; yet the muddy rivers detect a slope.... The habit that these rivers have of flowing on the plains, instead of in valleys eroded somewhat below the plains, is highly suggestive. Such a habit is easily explained as a necessary consequence of the formation of the plains by rivers; it would be difficult to explain it if the plains had been laid down in a sea or lake basin and then laid bare by uplift.[1]

Where waste is deposited at the mouth of a river in a body of standing water, either the ocean or a lake, the shore-line may be

W. M. Davis, A Summer in Turkestan, *Bull. Am. Geog. Soc.* 12 pp. (1904).

built forward, some new land being formed. Where such natural reclamation takes place, the new land formed is the emergent part of a *delta*.[1] A delta is built only when the river supplies more waste than can be carried away by tidal or other currents assisted by wave action. Thus deltas are commoner in lakes than bordering the ocean, for in lakes there are no appreciable tides, and currents and wave action are generally weaker than in the ocean. Deltas are common at the heads of, or quite filling, estuaries, into which rivers have discharged as a result of a late partial submergence of the land margin. Such *bay-head deltas* do not exhibit the triangular

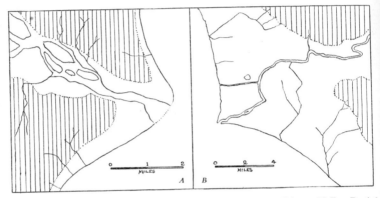

Fig. 136. Typical salient deltas; *A*, delta of the Clarence River, N.Z.; *B*, delta of the Tiber.

outline of the Greek capital letter from which they are named; but vigorous rivers fill their estuaries with deposited material (Pl XXIX, 1) and then build out coastal salients of true delta form which is assumed also by the deltas of rivers that afford no evidence of having filled up embayments of the coast (Fig. 136).

The small deltas built by steep-grade streams carrying gravel into lakes serve as a type of all deltas. Not only are the subaerially formed surfaces of such deltas visible, but also, very frequently the parts laid down under water have also emerged as land form owing to lowering of lake-level. The internal structure, which is o great interest because of its relation to the form of the surface, may often be seen, moreover, where the stream that built a delta ha

[1] Term used by Herodotus, in the fifth century B.C., for the delta plain of th Nile.

afterwards cut a trench in it as a result of the lowering of the level of the lake (Pl. XXIX, 2). The upper or subaerial surface of one of these small deltas resembles an alluvial fan, having been formed in an exactly similar way by an aggrading stream flowing in shifting channels and forced to add layer after layer to the upper surface, in this case in order to maintain a slope sufficiently steep to keep it flowing and transporting its load as the width of the delta increased, prolonging the stream course. Aggradation extends, indeed, far upstream, forming an aggraded valley plain that is an inland extension of the delta (Pl. XXX, 1). The aggraded slope is the

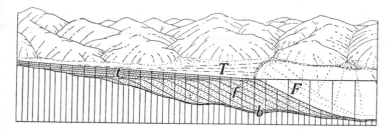

Fig. 137. The structure of a delta of coarse material at the head of a lake or bay.

top-set slope of the delta (Fig. 137, *T*), and the materials of which it is built are top-set beds (*t*). The subaerial top-set slope is continued with little change as a subaqueous top-set slope below lake-level for a short distance, until it descends to the limiting depth to which wave action stirs the lake waters. Here it gives place rather suddenly to a very much steeper slope, the *fore-set* slope (*F*), that forms the front of the delta. The bulk of the gravel forming the delta and underlying the top-set beds is stratified in fore-set beds (*f*) parallel with this slope. These entirely subaqueous beds may dip at an angle of about 20°, and the surface of each marks a former position of the fore-set slope of the delta, which was continuously built forward as gravel was poured over its edge and came to rest in the still, deep water at the angle of repose (Pl. XXIX, 2).

The mud that is brought into the lake does not accumulate with the gravel in the fore-set beds, but remains long enough in suspension to be carried by lake currents to a considerable distance. It eventually sinks and forms a layer of silt all over the bottom of the lake, smoothing out its irregularities to some extent, and lying more or less horizontally. Thus lake-floor plains are deposited, and may be exposed as subaerial plains of great fertility if the lake waters are drained off. Some of the silt layers are incorporated in the growing delta as fore-set beds are built over them, and thus become its *bottom-set* beds (Fig. 137, *b*).

The deltas built by large rivers of low gradient, which carry finer waste, are similar in a general way to the gravel deltas that have been described, with the important exception that their top-set and fore-set slopes are very much less steep, the former being almost perfectly horizontal and very liable to flooding.[1] Near the margin accumulation of sediment may take place in lagoons enclosed by sand bars thrown up by waves along the seashore, as occurs conspicuously in the case of the Nile delta. Swamps are thus formed, but, as a delta continues to grow, these areas, the filling of which is a phase of top-set deposition, may have their level raised by the addition of layers of ordinary top-set alluvium. In the case of the Mississippi, which builds the extreme type of digitate, or "birdfoot", delta, alluvial deposition prevails over wave action, with its attendant beach and sand-bar construction, so that the mouths of distributaries of the aggrading stream are extended into the shallow marginal sea between seaward extensions of their natural levees.

The marginal zone of shallow water has beneath it the very gently inclined subaqueous extension of the top-set slope. In all deltas built into the ocean or large lakes, this continues seaward into water of considerable depth (to the level of "wave base", below which the water is not stirred by wave action), and gives place somewhat suddenly, at a fairly definite line, to the steeper fore-set slope (with an inclination of 2 or 3°) of the delta front, down which sediment may slide, or on which, settling from suspension, it remains permanently at rest.

The subaerial parts of the top-set portions of the deltas of the great rivers that carry fine waste are *delta plains* of rich land. The great plains of the Huangho delta, with an area of 100,000 sq miles, and supporting a vast population, are an example. The river

[1] R. J. Russell (Lower Mississippi River Delta, *Louisiana Dept. of Conservatio Geol. Bull.* 8, p. 9 (1936)) doubts whether fore-set *beds* occur to any importan extent in the deposits of which great deltas are built, their absence bein accounted for as a result of subsidence accompanying delta growth; but th statement in the text is based on observed surface slopes of delta plains an delta fronts.

frequently changes its course, and there are historical records of many disastrous floods, as well as of major diversions of the main stream resulting from its own aggradation. It has found its way to the sea sometimes north and sometimes south of the Shan-Tung Peninsula, formerly an island, but joined to the mainland by growth of the delta (Fig. 137 A).

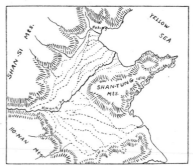

Fig. 137 A. The Huangho delta, showing former courses of the river. (After Blackwelder.)

Another illustration of the instability of river courses on deltas is afforded by the delta of the Colorado, at the head of the Gulf of California. The delta extends right across a deep fault-bounded depression, so as to divide it into two parts, the Imperial Valley to the north and the Gulf of California to the south. The former had been a lake whenever the Colorado had flowed into it, but when man came on the scene the Colorado was flowing directly to the Gulf, and the lake had been dried out by evaporation leaving an extensive lake-floor plain of fertile soil, 2200 sq. miles of the basin floor being below sea-level. Left to itself the Colorado River would one day have again taken a more northerly course and refilled the lake basin with water. Man, however, hastened the process by attempting to lead a stream of water from the Colorado into the Imperial Valley to irrigate its fertile soil. The river enlarged the irrigation canal, abandoned its former course for this new one, and poured a vast stream into the valley until again diverted by a feat of engineering, though not until it had succeeded in recreating the "Salton Sea" with an area of 410 sq. miles, since reduced again to small dimensions by evaporation.

The city of Christchurch, New Zealand, is somewhat insecurely situated on the delta of the Waimakariri (Fig. 134, *C*), and in its vicinity are some recently abandoned beds of that river—wastes of bare gravel, with braided channels and occasional sand dunes—which indicate that the river has had its outlet sometimes north and sometimes south of Banks Peninsula (Fig. 134 *B*).

CHAPTER XVII

Peneplains

P RESENT-DAY landscapes belong, as a rule, to one of the earlier stages of the geomorphic cycle. There have been so many earth movements in recent times that the current cycle has scarcely anywhere advanced beyond the stage of full maturity, except locally on very weak rocks; but, though young and mature forms now commonly occur, forms developed in late-mature and senile stages of earlier cycles have not been entirely obliterated. Some have been uplifted, with the result that they have become the initial surfaces on which erosion has begun to cut landscape forms of newer cycles. Others have been submerged at various periods during the long past history of the earth, and preserved beneath sedimentary deposits. From evidence afforded by relics of imperfectly dissected uplifted surfaces and by resurrected parts of buried landscapes of the past, it is known that many extensive surfaces of very small relief truncating diversely folded and dislocated rock structures were developed by erosion in bygone periods; and it is for the explanation of the origin of landscapes of former cycles, rather than for the description of the rare examples in which the slow processes of late-mature and post-mature erosion may still be operating, that the deduced scheme of the features of senility of the cycle has its chief importance; and the deduction must be made with extreme care, for this hypothesis of destruction of relief is only one of a group of hypotheses that have to be considered as possible explanations of the formation of the plains and plateaux of past ages. Other hypotheses are, for example, that of lateral planation (Chapter XII), that of development as desert "pediments", and that of marine erosion.

The inevitable result of the uninterrupted action of the normal processes of landscape erosion, working under unchanging climatic conditions, widening the already flat floors of river valleys and lowering the land surfaces between them, is the reduction of the whole, or in a penultimate stage almost the whole, of a region to very faint relief. In the stages of late maturity and old age graded valley floors will be cut down to levels lower than those of early maturity owing to the reduction in the supply of waste to rivers when the heights and slopes of the interfluves have been lowered. Such lowering takes place so slowly, however, that widening out of valley floors must go on continuously with it, the general result being a flattening down of, or destruction of relief over, the whole surface. The surface of small relief that results in the senile, or old-age, stage of the cycle—not quite a plain, but nowhere far from level—is a *peneplain*.[1]

As old age comes on, the mounts and hills, already well subdivided and subdued, are reduced in area and worn down to so moderate a relief that no sharp line of demarcation can be drawn between their slopes and the margin of the ever-widening and slowly lowering valley floors; but a zone of transition may be recognised where the convex profiles of the residual hills gradually become concave as they are continued down to the broad valley floors, which slant very faintly toward their streams. By this time the rainfall, increased at the time of original upheaval, has lessened in consequence of loss of mountain altitude; and the discharge of rainfall in rills is also decreasing, not alone because of diminishing supply but also because a greater share of the rain that falls soaks into the ground, now that the slopes are weaker and the soils are deeper. Hence the direct run-off is decreased and a larger proportion of the rainfall is delivered to the streams as ground water emerging in channel-side springs. The brooks and rivulets may, therefore, lose some of the headwater length that they enjoyed earlier, when slopes were steeper; and with this loss the widely opened ravine heads may be somewhat obscured by soil creep.[2]

Slopes are now so gentle that there is no longer any possibility of headward erosion, such as might lead to the development of new subsequent valleys. The process of adjustment to structure has, indeed, long ago slowed down and ceased, and some of the adjustment attained in the stage of early maturity may even have been

[1] The term was invented to define this concept by W. M. Davis (The Topographical Development of the Triassic Formation of the Connecticut Valley, *Am. Jour. Sci.* pp. 423–34 (1889)). Douglas Johnson uses the spelling *peneplane* (Plains, Planes, and Peneplanes, *Geog. Rev.* 1, pp. 443–7 (1916)). Davis translated "peneplain" into German as *Fastebene*, which was rejected by W. Penck in favour of *Endrumpffläche* (*Die morphologische Analyse*, p. 125 (1924)), though Davis had made it quite clear that he had in mind a penultimate and not an end form, which—a theoretically perfect plain (or plane)—requires infinite time for its development by the processes of the normal cycle, and is, therefore, only an abstraction. ·
[2] W. M. Davis, Rock Floors in Arid and in Humid Climates, *Jour. Geol.* 38, p. 142 (1930).

later lost at places where lateral planation, extending valley plains, has cut through the now deeply weathered outcrops of resistant rock strata that were formerly the sites of strike ridges.

Near the sea the land surface will now be nowhere far above the general base-level, but, "if a peneplain, thus worn down, extends a thousand miles from its ocean border into a continental interior, its old rivers with a fall of one or two feet to a mile will not reduce its interior parts below an altitude of 1000 or 2000 ft.; hence, while a peneplain is a surface of low relief, it is not necessarily a lowland over all its extent ".[1]

Unlike a valley plain, which is a true plain of lateral river planation, a peneplain is not an almost perfectly flat surface throughout. It does indeed consist in part of the wide valley plains bordering the larger rivers and the narrower flood plains of smaller streams, but between these are extensive areas of low undulating relief with very gentle graded slopes and no rock outcrops.[2] "A small difference of altitude must long remain between broad hill arches and broad valley floors, even though it is a diminishing difference. The main divides between the larger, opposing rivers of the region will be reduced to low and broadly convex swells, delicately diversified by wide-open and shallow valley heads of branching streams. Minor divides will be of similar but less pronounced form."[1]

The conception of peneplanation by gradual expansion (simultaneously with the gradual reduction of surviving salient forms) of systems of branching nearly flat valley floors, so that these become eventually a major feature of the senile landscape, distinguishes the peneplanation process from that of plain development by lateral planation, however effective the latter may possibly be in levelling extensive plains in zones bordering mature mountains (p. 132). Should such a zone of lateral planation have been developed in late maturity of the cycle of erosion, it must persist as a fringe around the peneplain that later takes the place of the mature mountains. Thus peneplains and plains of lateral planation are closely related, and may be very closely associated.

[1] W. M. Davis, *loc. cit.* p. 143.
[2] A quarter of a century ago the late Professor Davis for the author's benefit defined the limiting steepness of the slopes of a peneplain as such as one might lay out a straight road on in any direction "and trot on it". In these days this would be a high-gear road.

Above the general level of a peneplain a few isolated groups of hills, or even subdued mountains, may rise, to which the name *monadnocks*[1] is given (Figs. 138, 146). They are the remnants of dividing ridges, or of the mountain knots where several divides meet, and are composed of the more resistant rocks of the region, for on the outcrops of these the divides have become fixed in an earlier stage of the cycle of erosion.

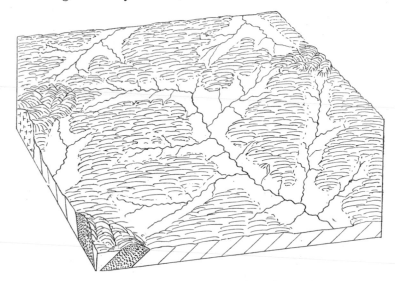

Fig. 138. A peneplain with monadnocks.

The time required for the change from mature to senile relief must be many times greater than that which elapses during dissection to the stage of maturity, for the rate of erosion on slopes becomes exceedingly slow as the slopes become gentle. So slow does the mechanical removal of waste from the gentle slopes of a senile surface become that chemical erosion, relatively unimportant on most rocks in the earlier stages of the cycle, when mechanical erosion was more active, is now responsible for a great part of the lowering of the surface, as the soluble products of rock decay are

[1] "Taking the name from a typical residual mountain which surmounts the uplifted peneplain of New England in south-western New Hampshire." W. M. Davis, The Seine, the Meuse, and the Moselle (1896), reprinted in *Geographical Essays*, p. 591 (1909).

removed in solution.[1] "Chemical weathering is believed to play the largest part in maturing the almost stationary soil cover, even to the point of decomposing feldspars, extracting their silica, and leaving the residue as hydrated alumina or bauxite" (Davis). For the development of a peneplain across resistant rocks, therefore, an enormous period must be required, certainly millions of years, but, on the other hand, so great are the differences in rates of erosion on different rocks that a district of very weak rocks may be reduced to a peneplain in a very small fraction of the time required to produce a similar result even on rocks of average resistance, or on a mixed assemblage of weak and resistant rocks. So slow must be the process of peneplanation on resistant rocks that the probability of the occurrence of a sufficiently long still-stand, or period of immunity from earth movements, for the full development of extensive peneplains is sometimes questioned, and Passarge has denied the possibility of sufficiently long continuance of uniformity of climatic conditions for the fulfilment of the cycle.

In the present unstable condition of the earth's crust and of sea-level, when landscape evidence of recent movement is of general occurrence, examples are very rare of peneplains in an undisturbed and undissected condition. Even landscapes with wide valley floors of late maturity, such as have been described as transitional to a senile surface, or peneplain, are of rare occurrence in a condition where they are still progressing towards senility in an uninterrupted cycle. It is very exceptional, that is to say, to find them traversed by rivers at levels which, as local base-levels, still control the uninterrupted development of a peneplain. The existence of an actual undisturbed peneplain still undergoing uninterrupted development as such has been recorded, however, by Davis near Semipalatinsk, in Siberia. Traversed by the Irtysh River it is "a great steppe of small relief, a worn-down surface of crystalline and greatly deformed stratified rocks; by far the best undissected peneplain I have ever seen".[2]

The inevitability of the destruction of all prominent relief forms

---

[1] "The degradation of the last few inches of a broad area of land above the level of the sea would require a longer time than all the thousands of feet which might have been above it, so far as this degradation depends on mechanical processes;...but here the disintegration by solution and the transportation of the material by the agency of fluidity come in to assist the slow processes of the mechanical degradation, and finally perform the chief part of the task." J. W. Powell, *Report on the Geology of the Uinta Mountains*, p. 196 (1876).

[2] W. M. Davis, A Summer in Turkestan, *Bull. Am. Geog. Soc.* 12 pp. (1904).

by long-continued erosion is accepted alike by those who agree that normally landscapes pass through the cycle stages of youth and maturity, leading on to old age, and by those who do not. Some of the latter stress the possibility of very slow uplift continuing for a vast period, throughout which erosion proceeds. Valleys are deepened about as fast as the land is raised, but the rate of uplift is assumed to be so slow that valleys are widened more rapidly than they can be deepened, with the result that interfluves of the pre-existing surface (possibly flat) are worn down almost as fast as they are raised, and no sharp forms are ever developed, however long uplift continues. A surface so degraded will be always practically a peneplain during the continuance of a vastly prolonged uplift, which must be accompanied in the case of an upheaval of some magnitude by an enormous amount of erosion.

Such, possibly, may be the origin of some locally developed peneplains or, more probably, plains of lateral planation, confined to the limits of very soft rock formations; but it is a highly improbable explanation of extensive peneplains truncating resistant rocks. This conclusion cannot be avoided when the extreme slowness of erosion and transportation of waste down the weak slopes of a peneplain, and the extreme slowness, therefore, of the rate at which such a surface can be lowered, are taken into account. Slowness of erosion is confirmed, if such confirmation be necessary, by the great thickness of weathered waste which overlies the bedrock of a peneplain, and by the advanced stage of chemical weathering to a bauxitic or lateritic residue often found. An eternity would, apparently, be required for the removal by erosion under these conditions of the vast thickness of rocks which, it cannot be doubted, have been cut away from above peneplains that truncate folded and other formerly deep-seated rock formations, especially some metamorphic rocks the presence of which at the present-day surface must indicate that a rock layer at least 10 miles thick has been eroded from it. The arguments showing that this theory makes an extravagant demand on time are so obvious that it is hard to imagine the reasoning behind an opinion expressed by one geomorphologist (quoted by Davis) that this mode of peneplanation is, on the other hand, economical of time as compared with the rival theory of transition of the surface to old age through young and mature stages.

Where slow uplift of a district of extremely weak rocks does lead to wasting away of the surface during uplift without development of any forms of strong relief, the conditions may be considered to constitute a special case of the cycle of erosion in which the stages of youth and maturity are both elided. A landscape with such a history is described as "old from birth".[1] Almost the only suggestion that has been made of a means of distinguishing an "old-from-birth" peneplain from one that has passed through a condition of mature dissection is that the former may be expected to exhibit less complete adjustment to structure than the latter.

In some of his later writings devoted to the rehabilitation of the cycle theory after it had been adversely criticised and discarded by one of its former supporters (Albrecht Penck), Davis drew attention to the way in which the case of "old-from-birth" peneplains and various other special cases could be fitted in with the general theory. Some criticisms of the applicability of the cycle scheme as the basis of a system of nomenclature of landscape types has been offered on the ground that so-called "young", "mature", and "old" landscape forms may make their appearance in an order different from that required by the general theory and suggested by their names, being perhaps developed even in reverse order. Such criticisms are met by taking into account those special cases, or variants, of the ideal cycle in which slowness of uplift or weakness of the rock materials undergoing dissection makes erosion during uplift important because relatively rapid, and by taking into consideration also the effects of changes in the rate of uplift during a long erosional history. Examples are known (the central plateau of France is cited by Davis) of uplifted peneplains in a cycle of renewed erosion on which headwater streams flow in shallow, open valleys, apparently mature-born in the new cycle, though larger rivers have cut narrow, deep, young valleys; that is to say, old forms (of an earlier cycle) seem to have been replaced by mature-born forms, and these in turn are being replaced by young forms.

The following is a selected special case of varying rate of uplift imagined and deduced by Davis, and described in terms of the cycle stages:

One may conceive of a region that, after a first very slow uplift, is uplifted more rapidly, but eventually stands still for an indefinite period;

[1] W. M. Davis, Peneplains and the Geographical Cycle, *Bull. Geol. Soc. Am.* 33, p. 591 (1922).

and in such a case the expression of the first-developed valleys would be "old"; then, as the rate of uplift increased, the "old" valleys would be first incised by "mature", and then by "young" valleys; and finally the "young" valleys would, during the ensuing still-stand period, gradually gain the appearance of "mature" and "old" valleys.[1] Even in such a case the first-developed, or "infantile" valleys should be distinguishable, at least theoretically, from old valleys, as their gentle lower side slopes may be expected to be convex instead of concave. "These so-called old and mature forms of early development are merely peculiar kinds of young forms."[2]

The theoretical distinction between "infantile" forms developing on a peneplain as it is slowly uplifted and the "senile" forms it exhibited before uplift was first made by Walther Penck.[3] Davis agreed with him in attributing convex valley-side slopes to infantile as well as to later more deeply cut valleys developed during accelerated uplift. Penck has termed an undisturbed peneplain an *Endrumpf*, but distinguishes from this the surface that has begun to feel the effects of uplift as a *Primärrumpf*.[4] It is a surface which, according to Davis's deduction, should exhibit infantile profiles. An "old-from-birth" surface, provided uplift has not yet ceased, should be similar in form, and is also termed by Penck a *Primärrumpf*.

In Penck's scheme of accelerated uplift, introducing renewal of vertical corrasion as a preliminary to mountain sculpture, the *Primärrumpf* is merely an abstraction, for continued erosion has destroyed it. Davis has, however, compared the ideal profiles of the *Primärrumpf* and *Endrumpf* (or peneplain) copied from Priem,[5] who obviously had enormously exaggerated the vertical scale (Fig. 139). The peneplain profile, it will be noted, assumes a surface without any convexities, but with sharp ridges separating broad, concave valleys. This is a deduction from Penck's[6] theory of

[1] W. M. Davis, Peneplains and the Geographical Cycle, *Bull. Geol. Soc. Am.* 33, p. 591 (1922).
[2] W. M. Davis, Piedmont Benchlands and Primärrümpfe, *Bull. Geol. Soc. Am.* 43, p. 428 (1932).
[3] W. Penck, *Morphologische Analyse*, p. 177 (1924).
[4] Davis, in his discussion of this concept, in which he described its valley forms as infantile, did not suggest an English equivalent for *Primärrumpf*. It is translated "primary peneplain" by C. Sauer (*Univ. Cal. Publ. Geog.* vol. 3, no. 4 (1929)). Penck's *Endrumpf* is indistinguishable from a peneplain.
[5] *Geogr. Anzeiger*, pp. 373–81 (1927).
[6] W. Penck, *Die morphologische Analyse*, p. 125 (1924). *Einrumpfung*: "Sie ist bis auf ihr theoretisches Endergebnis in allen Phasen durch konkave Hangprofile ausgezeichnet."

horizontal valley-side retreat in a phase of waning development (p. 160, and Fig. 126), and is incompatible with the more widely accepted idea of dominance of broadly convex forms and ill-defined divides on the interfluvial parts of peneplains.

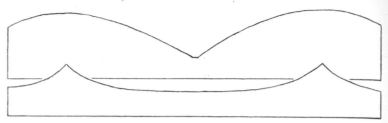

Fig. 139. Priem's profiles of a *Primärrumpf* (above) and a peneplain (below). (After Davis.)

Dissection of a peneplain may generally be attributed to uplift, with the possible alternative, in cases where uplift appears to have been uniform, of eustatic withdrawal of the ocean to a lower level. Domed or broadly undulating uplifts are the most common; and dissection without uplift may result from lowering of the neighbouring land surface by down-warping, as pointed out by Philippson.[1] Should the central, higher part of a continental peneplain have the sea margin brought nearer to it, or have a steepened slope formed along its border, by subsidence of a down-warped or fault-bounded marginal portion without itself moving either up or down, it will be subject to dissection as though it had been uplifted.

A climatic change may also result in some dissection of an inland peneplain, as in the case of plains of lateral planation, but river gradients are weaker on peneplains, and probably no deep dissection or production of sharp forms of relief need be explained in this way. An hypothesis of changing climate ought to be considered, however, along with other possible causes of the development of "infantile" features, if such should be recognised on a peneplain.

Local dissection will begin on any warped peneplain wherever an earth movement steepens the general slope; but where quite uniform uplift or eustatic sinking of sea-level has taken place, the lowering of base-level relatively to the land surface does not

[1] A. Philippson, Zur Morphologie des rheinischen Schiefergebirges, *Verh. XIV. deutsch. Geographentag*, pp. 193–205 (1903).

immediately stimulate renewed erosion and dissection of the whole surface.

The old-age processes of peneplanation continue their action unchanged in the early stages of the new cycle of erosion introduced by the upheaval, hence the central peneplain suffers no significant change of form, except that it becomes an older and older peneplain, in spite of being now in the infantile stage of the new cycle instead of in the senile stage of the former cycle. So it continues until news of the upheaval is brought to it by the retrogressive erosion of peripheral streams; then it is more or less sharply dissected.[1]

It is noteworthy that characteristic "infantile" profiles (p. 191) do not make their appearance in this case of an uplifted but as yet undissected peneplain. Another view that may be taken of it is that the former cycle is still current, and will remain so until the "news of the upheaval" is brought to it, when the new cycle will begin. Other difficulties arise, however, if uplift is not regarded as interrupting the cycle simultaneously in the various parts of a region affected, and Davis has cut the Gordian knot by ruling that it does so,[2] and "similarly a uniform depression should be taken as introducing a new cycle".

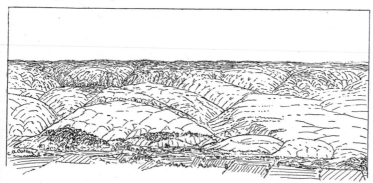

Fig. 140. The Longmynd, Shropshire. The plateau surface was cut by erosion (probably as a peneplain) across the varied structures of ancient resistant rocks. (Drawn from a photograph.)

Remnants, large and small, of many uplifted peneplains still survive in dissected plateaux, where resistant rocks outcrop over wide areas (Fig. 140), and as occasional flat-topped mountains and

W. M. Davis, Piedmont Benchlands, *Bull. Geol. Soc. Am.* 43, p. 419 (1932). *Loc. cit.* p. 420.

ridges in submaturely dissected regions of mixed rocks. In such cases it may be possible to imagine a restoration of the originally continuous peneplain if a sufficient number of remnants of it survive, and such a restoration may show that, instead of remaining level as it was uplifted, the peneplain has suffered deformation, being perhaps warped into a smooth elongated dome, or perhaps warped irregularly, or even broken by faults.

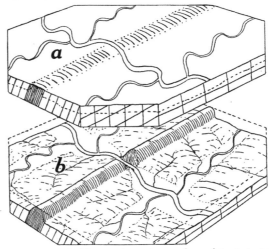

Fig. 141. An even-crested ridge on the outcrop of a resistant stratum preserving a remnant of the peneplain *a* at a later period, *b*, when weaker formations have been worn down to lowlands.

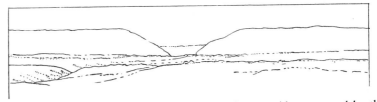

Fig. 142. Even skyline of the Schooley peneplain on a ridge traversed by the water gap of the Delaware. (From a drawing by W. M. Davis.)

Peneplain surfaces last for a vastly longer time on highly resistant rocks than on weak rocks or even those offering moderate resistance to erosion. Thus perfectly even-crested, flat-topped though possibly narrow, ridges of the most resistant rocks may be found separating subsequent lowlands of quite small relief and considerable breadth developed in a later cycle or cycles (Figs

141, 142). In the Appalachian plateau of the United States, for example, the "Schooley" peneplain is only submaturely dissected over an area of regional extent in which all outcropping rocks are resistant; farther east, however, in the Allegheny ridges, it survives only on the even crests of subsequent ridges of the most resistant rocks (Fig. 142); and farther again east it is recognised as a continuous plateau on resistant rocks in the Piedmont belt.[1] This

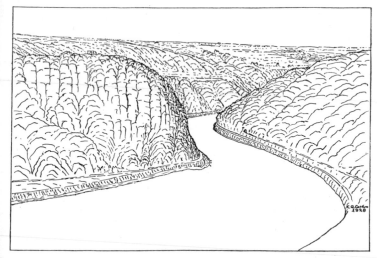

Fig. 143. Highland peneplain cut through by the gorge of the Rhine at the Loreley bluff.

widespread and almost perfectly planed surface, which evenly truncates the most resistant rocks of the region, and which was formerly ascribed to Cretaceous erosion, is now regarded as of much later date. Its uplift has been accompanied by warping into an elongated dome diversified by smaller domes, the forms of which are still traceable in districts in which the peneplain is well preserved, some having been mapped as a result of field and map studies.[2] In the region of the Allegheny ridges, subsequent lowlands that have been excavated below the Schooley level on the broad outcrops of the weaker formations exhibit relics of partial

Douglas Johnson, *Stream Sculpture on the Atlantic Slope*, see especially Figs. 5–9 (1931).
F. J. Wright, Physiography of the Upper James River Basin, *Virginia Geol. Surv. Bull.* 11 (1925); see also H. M. Fridley, Identification of Erosion Surfaces...New York, *Jour. Geol.* 37, pp. 113–34 (1929).

peneplains developed in two later and successively shorter periods of still-stand.[1]

A partly dissected peneplain still well preserved as plateau remnants on mountain ranges of resistant ancient rocks is recognised over a wide region of north-western and western Europe—for example, in the mountains of Germany cut through by the gorge of the Rhine (Fig. 143), in the Ardennes, in the central plateau of France, in Brittany, and in the plateau of Norway[2] (Fig. 144). In

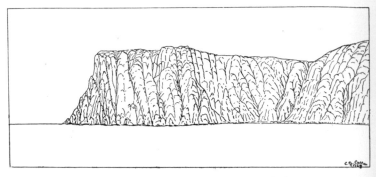

Fig. 144. The plateau of Norway, at North Cape.

Britain it is apparently present in the surface bevelling the cuesta of Mesozoic rocks in England, where it is definitely a surface of late Tertiary erosion not uplifted until the Pliocene,[3] on the uplands of Devon and Cornwall,[4] at heights of 1500–2000 ft. in Wales, and at 2000–3000 ft. in Scotland.[5]

[1] Johnson, *loc. cit.*
[2] This is perhaps more strictly part of the resurrected fossil peneplain of Fennoscandia. See V. Tanner, *Die Oberflächengestaltung Finnlands* (Helsingfors, 1938).
[3] Wooldridge and Linton, Influence of Pliocene Transgression on the Geomorphology of South-east England, *Jour. Geomorph.* 1, pp. 40–54 (1938).
[4] J. F. N. Green (Anniv. Addr., *Quart. Jour. Geol. Soc.* 92 (1936)) adheres to the English theory of marine terraces, rejecting Sawicki's identification of a peneplain in southern England (*C.R. Soc. Sci. Varsovie*, 5 (1912)).
[5] Statistical study has convinced S. E. Hollingworth (*Quart. Jour. Geol. Soc.* 9, pp. 55–84 (1938)) of the presence of many marginal benches at various levels developed by marine erosion during eustatic emergence of Britain. This excludes the possibility of explaining any but the highest parts of the summit plateaux of Britain as parts of the great peneplain that is supposed to have attained regional development mainly in the Miocene period. The last word has not been spoken on the subject yet, however. Contrast the view of S. Ting (*Geografiska Annaler*, pp. 62–83 (1937)) that Scotland has very recently been tilted to the west.

High standing, deeply dissected peneplains are described by de Martonne in the Transylvanian Alps; Daneš, Cvijić, and others have found lower standing peneplains in the Dinaric Alps....The southern extension of the Ural Mountains is still a low-lying peneplain, undissected over large areas; but farther north uplift and dissection of what seems to be part of the same peneplain produces a topography of submountainous relief. The Tian Shan and the Pamir exhibit numerous and extensive highland peneplains....Lofty highlands of erosion in the north-western Himalayas are described by Oestreich; Loczy and Filchner describe similar forms in Tibet....Willis has given abundant description and discussion of high standing, dissected peneplains in the mountains of China....Bornhardt, Uhlig, and Jaeger describe highland peneplains, more or less dissected, in equatorial east Africa, Passarge and Hassert in south-west and west Africa. Keidel reports uplifted peneplains in the eastern members of the Argentine Andean massif....Bowman describes a lofty peneplain in the Bolivian Andes....[1]

Nearly the whole surface of Australia is a great peneplain, the development of which continued until late in the Tertiary, and large parts of it have suffered little modifications since because of the small magnitude of the uplifts that have affected it, though smaller parts, and especially a strip near the eastern coast, have been uplifted with warping, and are more or less thoroughly dissected.

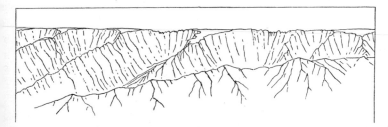

Fig. 145. The flat-topped Bural-bas-tau Range, in the Tian-Shan. (After a drawing by W. M. Davis, *Appalachia*, p. 279 (1904).)

Probably all well-preserved (i.e. not thoroughly dissected) peneplains are of geologically modern origin, if we exclude consideration of such as have, at some stage of their history, been preserved by burial and long afterwards re-exposed by removal of a cover. Even the great peneplain of central Asia (Fig. 145), which is preserved on the crests of the Tian-Shan Mountains and on the Pamirs at

W. M. Davis, *Ann. Ass. Am. Geog.* 1, p. 46 (1911).

heights of over 12,000 ft., was developed, according to a reliable authority,[1] at the end of the Tertiary era; and Davis has suggested that this is part of the peneplain that remains at a low level and undissected where it borders the Irtysh in Siberia. Where parts of extensive erosion surfaces of small relief are known or believed to be of greater age, the regions in which they occur have generally remained lowlying until the end of the Tertiary era, as was the case in the uplifted and dissected parts of the great Australian peneplain.[2] The significant date is the date of interruption of the major cycle of erosion in which the peneplain was formed, however

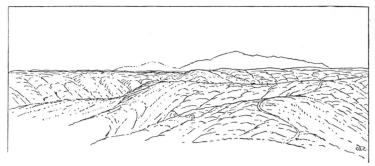

Fig. 146. The Rocky Mountains peneplain (about 10,000 ft. above sea-level) with a high monadnock (Pike's Peak) standing above it. (Drawn from a photograph by Professor Douglas Johnson.)

vast the anterior period may be during which it was already in existence at a low level, undergoing more and more complete planation. It is well to accept with caution some geological dates of origin, in some cases incredibly ancient—a favourite suggestion being Cretaceous—that have been ascribed to peneplains of which remnants still survive, though they are believed to have been continuously subject to dissection since uplift occurred, terminating the ancient period of their supposed formation. Later revision[3] in most cases has either referred such surfaces of supposedly very ancient development to much later periods of erosion or transferred them to quite another category of land forms, namely, the resur-

[1] E. Huntington, Exploration in Turkestan, *Carnegie Inst. Publ.* p. 168 (1905)
[2] E. C. Andrews, Origin of Modern Mountain Ranges, *Jour. and Proc. R. Soc. N.S.W.* 67, pp. 251–350 (1934).
[3] Even in Africa, a region of large-scale forms and slow erosion tempo, A. C. Veatch now dates the period of most extensive peneplanation as Miocene (Evolution of the Congo Basin, *Geol. Soc. Am. Mem.* 3, pp. 15–29 (1935)).

rected fossil land surfaces (to be discussed in Chapter XVIII) that have emerged very recently or are now progressively emerging as erosion strips away covering strata beneath which the surfaces have been preserved for an indefinite period.

The peneplain that survives extensively as plateau surfaces in the Rocky Mountains (Fig. 146) is now ascribed[1] to a prolonged period of erosion extending from middle into very late Tertiary time, and even this comparatively recently developed surface has been widely mantled with thick alluvial deposits, the presence of which must have contributed to its preservation. In France, also, where extensive plateaux are parts of a peneplain developed in a Miocene cycle of erosion, this ancient surface of erosion has been long preserved as a fossil plain beneath a cover of Miocene strata that has very recently been removed from it.[2]

According to some authorities the duration of the Tertiary era was about sixty million years. A fraction, though perhaps a considerable fraction, of this apparently sufficed for peneplanation of average resistant rocks under average conditions. It is of interest to glance at an attempt made by Davis actually to estimate in years the duration of a cycle of erosion. By comparing incipient erosion of beach features of the extinct Lake Bonneville with ridge-and-valley forms on which these rest, he estimated that the erosion of the latter had taken scores of times as long as the duration of the post-Bonneville epoch; but the ridges and valleys themselves had been eroded in detritus resulting from partial degradation of a fault-block mountain range, which must have occupied scores of times as long as the erosion of the valleys in the detritus. As complete destruction of the range will take many times longer, i.e. "many times longer than scores of scores of post-Bonneville epochs", the length of a cycle of erosion is estimated roughly at from 20 million to 200 million years.[3]

It is not surprising to find the remains of well-developed peneplains in those regions in which there is geological evidence of almost perfect stability of the earth's crust in the later geological periods, but one is inclined to accept with great caution similar evidence of prolonged still-stand in the crustal strips that have

[1] Atwood and Atwood, Working Hypothesis for the Physiographic History of the Rocky Mountain Region, *Bull. Geol. Soc. Am.* 49, pp. 957–80 (1938).
[2] H. Baulig, *Le plateau central de la France*, pp. 451–63 (1928).
[3] W. M. Davis, The Basin Range Problem, *Proc. Nat. Ac. Sci.* 11, p. 391 (1925).

suffered strong deformation in late geological times. Relics of peneplains have been credibly described, however, in most of these, even in the European Alps and in New Zealand. In the latter region widespread river planation, accompanied by peneplanation of interfluves, affected weak formations at a very late date—Pleistocene—subsequently to the Kaikoura paroxysm of block faulting accompanied by folding that brought Tertiary deposition to a close,[1] and in the vicinity of the city of Wellington a late mature to senile surface, perhaps developed in the same late period, is represented by remnants on ridge crests of rather resistant rocks.[2]

In the southern part of the South Island of New Zealand—notably in the Western Otago district, which appears to have escaped deformation in the Kaikoura, or end-of-Tertiary, orogenic epoch—there are relics of a peneplain dating back to a late Tertiary cycle of prolonged erosion.[3] This surface, which elsewhere has been much warped and in places strongly dislocated by great faults, in Western Otago suffered only uplift to form the initial surface that has been dissected into the high residual mountains of that district[3] (Fig. 147); and it is possibly present as undissected plateau remnants on at least some of the level-topped block mountains farther east in the Central Otago district (Pl. XXX, 2).

Where no flat remnants of a peneplain actually survive, *accordance of summit levels* (Fig. 147) may indicate that such a surface has been dissected and destroyed by erosion; many peaks will still reach to about a common level, or to levels accordant with a domed or warped surface passing over them, though the top of each sharpened peak must have been lowered at least a little below the level of the initial surface. From such evidence it has been inferred that a peneplain (referred to above) extended formerly over the residual mountains of Western Otago, though no actually flat summits have survived its mature dissection (Fig. 147). Some peaks rising above the general level are believed to have stood out as monadnocks on the former peneplain.

Even occasional monadnocks rising to equal heights above a

[1] C. A. Cotton, *Geomorphology of New Zealand, Part I: Systematic*, pp. 129–30 (1922).
[2] C. A. Cotton, Some Peneplanations in...New Zealand, *N.Z. Jour. Sci. and Tech.* 20, p. 6 b (1938).
[3] W. N. Benson, Some Land Forms in Southern New Zealand, *Australian Geographer*, 2 (7), pp. 4–22 (1935).

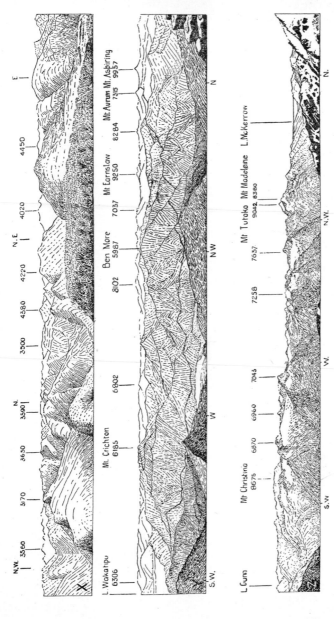

Fig. 147. Panoramas showing accordance of summit levels in Western Otago. (After Benson.)

peneplain may sometimes be interpreted, as is done in eastern Australia, as preserving in the level of their summits a trace of a more ancient peneplain (Fig. 148), an inference there confirmed in some instances by the preservation of lava-capped gravels on the summits of the monadnocks.

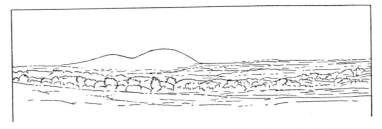

Fig. 148. The great Australian peneplain, near Yass, New South Wales, sur-mounted by a monadnock, the summit of which is a remnant of a more ancient peneplain believed to have been in course of destruction by erosion since about the close of the Cretaceous period. (After a photograph by Süssmilch.)

Mere accordance of summit levels, unless particularly well marked, in which case survival of at least a few flat-topped peaks may be looked for, does not indicate former peneplanation (or development of a plain of erosion of some other kind) with certainty, for a rough accordance may be expected in the heights of peaks carved by erosion on mountains of folded rocks in a first cycle.[1] Anticlines that are lifted to an exceptional height must tend to sink again isostatically. Also, mechanical erosion is most active on the highest peaks, and, provided that the resulting waste can slide away down steep slopes as fast as it is supplied by weathering, to be then removed by streams, differences in height must in this way be reduced; while from Gilbert's law of equal declivities—the tendency to develop slopes of equal steepness—it follows that, if streams are evenly spaced and have cut downward to the same depth, the ridges between them must be reduced to the same height. So it appears that a mountain range made up initially of a concourse of blocks and arches differentially elevated, the whole forming—as it probably would—an elongated dome with a very irregular surface, might tend to develop such a measure of accordance of its summit

[1] R. A. Daly, The Accordance of Summit Levels among Alpine Mountains, *Jour. Geol.* 13, pp. 195–205 (1905).

levels that it would resemble the mountains carved by erosion from the smooth dome of a warped, uplifted peneplain.

Another possible cause of accordance of summit levels, and even of the development of an extensive upland surface of small relief independent of the general base-level, has been pointed out by Lawson.[1] This is the exposure of a structural surface of relatively resistant rocks, such as the more or less regular, but not quite smooth, upper surface of a batholith, when erosion has removed from it a roof of weak sedimentary rocks. Lawson suggests this origin for the highest, or "summit upland", surface of the granite terrain of the Sierra Nevada of California. "That differential degradation does actually effect the results here ascribed to it is finely demonstrated on the northern flanks of the Caucasus, on the route from Kislowodsk to Elbrus. Here the stripping of soft Cretaceous clays down to a thick stratum of hard Jurassic limestone gives rise to gently sloping plateaux of great expanse, which are high above the streams of the region."[2]

CHAPTER XVIII

Resurrected Fossil Land Surfaces

A FOSSIL is a thing "dug up", and for the palaeontologist the term "fossil" signifies some part or some trace of an animal or plant buried in the distant geological past and either dug up or exposed by erosion very recently. A *fossil erosion surface* is, in a similar way, an erosion surface, whether young, mature, or old, and whether produced by normal subaerial erosion or other agency, that has been buried beneath a cover of sedimentary deposits and long afterwards exposed to view again by renewed erosion. Some fossil erosion surfaces can be seen only in quarries, cuttings, or natural sections, where the covering strata still lie on them; but others have been partly *resurrected* owing to stripping away of a cover that is relatively very weak as compared with the resistance

[1] A. C. Lawson, The Geomorphogeny of the Upper Kern Basin, *Univ. Cal. Publ. Bull. Dep. Geol.* 3, pp. 291–376 (p. 312) (1904).
[2] A. C. Lawson, *loc. cit.* p. 313.

offered to erosion by the undermass, so that parts of an ancient relief, perhaps very little modified by the erosion that accompanies their resurrection, again appear in the land surface after having been buried for geological periods.

An ancient landscape of hilly relief has been exhumed in places in the North-west Highlands of Scotland after having remained buried since late pre-Cambrian times. It was developed on hard gneissic rocks, while its cover consists of relatively weak sandstone (Fig. 149). As is commonly the case where mature landscape forms

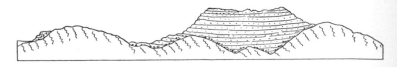

Fig. 149. A surface of late pre-Cambrian erosion emerging again as a cover of Torridonian sandstone is stripped from it, in the North-west Highlands of Scotland. (After a published section.)

have been buried, the cover is of non-marine origin. Similar resurrection of a hilly surface developed in the Triassic period on very ancient rocks is taking place in Charnwood Forest, in Leicestershire.

Another example of a surface of considerable relief exhumed by removal of horizontal covering strata has been described from the "central plateau" of Morocco, west of the Atlas Mountains, though in this case the resurrected surface, described as the post-Hercynian "peneplain", has been "modified somewhat" by later erosion.[1]

In compound structures, where a cover of relatively young sedimentary formations rests unconformably on an eroded under-mass, a lapse of time—in some cases an enormous interval—has occurred between the formation (and commonly also deformation) of the undermass and the ensuing submergence (or combination of other circumstances) that has led to the deposition of the cover. It is during this time interval that deep erosion, and generally more or less perfect planation, of the undermass takes place, preparing a floor on which the cover subsequently rests.

Such is the origin of fossil erosion surfaces. Young and mature

[1] A. C. Lawson, The Atlas Mountains of Morocco, *Scientific Monthly*, 32, p. 105 (1931).

surfaces are only rarely found buried: fossil surfaces are commonly plains of erosion, and sometimes clearly peneplains, on which an ancient soil may still be recognised, with vestiges of vegetation, covered by gravels of terrestrial origin, though these are generally followed by marine sediments. In other cases, however, marine sedimentary formations rest directly on the eroded surface of the undermass, which consists of fresh rock evidently planed by marine erosion. Even in such cases the surface prior to submergence may quite probably have been a peneplain, for during progressive sub-mergence of a land surface *of low relief* the waves of the advancing sea could break up and remove the deeply weathered soil, exposing and planing the underlying unweathered rock. In many profile sections of sedimentary strata these may be seen lying unconformably on a flat floor that was horizontal at the time the beds were deposited, as is shown by the fact that it is now parallel to their stratification. If this relationship of cover to undermass is seen in a number of scattered sections, it is known that the fossil plain underlying the cover is of wide extent.

One of the best-known regions in which fossil-plain profiles are clearly revealed in many natural sections is that intersected by the Grand Canyon of the Colorado and the canyons of some tributary rivers (Fig. 150). A cover of Cambrian and other Palaeozoic rocks, still quite horizontal in spite of their advanced age, lies on a floor that has been interpreted as a buried peneplain, for, instead of being quite plane, it rises in low monadnocks that interrupt the continuity of the Tonto sandstone—the lowest member of the Cambrian cover.

Fossil peneplains, and fossil erosion surfaces generally, are not necessarily found in their original attitude: some have been tilted and warped, or folded, along with the strata that lie on them. Where, as is usually the case, the beds of the cover were laid down horizontally on a horizontal floor, the parallelism of at least the lower beds of the cover with the floor has been retained, however, though both are warped or tilted. In some of the sections revealed in the walls of the Grand Canyon (Fig. 150), a series of beds older than the Cambrian, and forming part of the undermass beneath the Cambrian peneplain (the strata of the "Algonkian wedge") appear, and are also well-bedded formations—tilted, however, in this case —and these have beneath them still older, crystalline rocks, on which they lie unconformably. Here the contact is made at a floor that is another fossil plain, tilted along with the beds that rest upon it, and so perfectly planed by ancient erosion that unlike the Cambrian fossil plain this more ancient (Proterozoic) one must be regarded as having been levelled off finally by marine erosion as the sea advanced over it to deposit the Unkar series now preserved in the "wedge".[1]

Fig. 150. The "Algonkian wedge", with fossil plains below and above it, in the Grand Canyon of the Colorado River. (After Davis.)

Fossil plains have a chance of emerging again, or being resurrected, as surface forms if the cover overlying them is relatively very weak and is, therefore, readily removed by erosion from such parts of the fossil surfaces as are raised by modern earth movements above the base-level—below which, however, they will continue to be preserved indefinitely. Only such surfaces can be extensively exposed as have escaped severe distortion accompanying folding of the cover. A crumpled surface such as that illustrated in Fig. 151, even if stripped of a weak cover, would be destroyed by erosion as it emerged.

[1] W. M. Davis, An Excursion to the Grand Canyon of the Colorado River, *Bull. Mus. Comp. Zool. Harv.* 38, pp. 173–5 (1901).

Extensively resurrected fossil peneplains, in various stages of destruction by erosion and in many places traceable only in isolated remnants, are now recognised in various parts of the world. In many cases "peneplains" formerly described as though they had survived, or, at least, in parts escaped complete destruction, though continuously subjected to subaerial erosion following uplift in Cretaceous or early Tertiary times have more recently been given a more easily credible interpretation as fossil surfaces comparatively recently resurrected.[1] In the central plateau, or highland, of France, for example, the surface is now regarded as in great

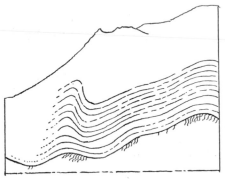

Fig. 151. Folds in Table Mountain sandstone and the floor on which it lies unconformably, Worcester, South Africa. (Drawn from a photograph published by Rogers and Du Toit.)

part a peneplain of pre-Miocene age that has been extensively buried under a cover of late Tertiary strata and resurrected later; and bordering this there is a strip of a much more ancient (post-Hercynian) surface resurrected from beneath Mesozoic strata.[2] Farther north in western Europe a wide extension of late Tertiary deposits is known or suspected to have been present, covering areas that are now upland plateaux of resistant rocks[3] alternatively regarded simply as continuously emergent parts of the great west-European peneplain. In south-eastern England resurrected strips of fossil surfaces both of early Eocene and Pliocene age are now

[1] The peneplain of Fennoscandia has been shown to be a very ancient fossil surface resurrected (see footnote, p. 196).
[2] H. Baulig, *Le plateau central de la France*, pp. 91, 102 (1928).
[3] J. Cornet, Études sur l'évolution des rivières belges, *Ann. Soc. Géol. Belg. Mem.* 31, pp. 260–500 (1904). Facets of fossil surfaces of various ages have since been found by H. Baulig.

recognised. In eastern North America the Fall Zone peneplain, of Johnson, is known in a resurrected strip, in South Australia resurrected relics of a surface of pre-Miocene erosion[1] now occur as facets in the Mount Lofty ranges, and in east-central Africa a fossil plain is emerging from beneath a Cretaceous cover.[2]

In New Zealand extensive strips of the land surface in Otago and other districts of the South Island and smaller areas in the North Island are resurrected parts of fossil plains. The majority of the upland surfaces so interpreted in this region have not remained horizontal, but are tilted, arched, and even folded in gentle undulations. Some horizontal, gently tilted, and even, in exceptional cases, quite strongly tilted portions of the fossil plains, though stripped of weak cover "as mud is washed from a board", are but slightly dissected, while others have been destroyed by mature dissection, especially where strongly tilted or corrugated or otherwise deformed during uplift.

Smooth slopes of appreciable steepness have escaped dissection to a remarkable extent in the semi-arid district of Central Otago, where not only is the annual rainfall low but rain is light and generally well distributed through the seasons, though some local cloudbursts have been reported. Whether the climatic conditions have contributed appreciably to their preservation or not, it is true that in this district smooth tilted strips are so stable, or so long-lived in the landscape, that they constitute important and conspicuous features that make up a considerable proportion of the uplands and highlands. The differential uplifts of the ranges on which these slopes have been exposed and survive cannot be regarded as of very recent occurrence, but must be ascribed to a period of uplift and deformation at the end of the Tertiary era, which has been followed throughout most parts of New Zealand by an enormous amount of erosion. On the other hand, there is no reason why it should be thought, on *a priori* grounds, that the uplifts of various ranges were quite simultaneous. The cover that has been stripped away has generally been very weak, and it has probably long ago been removed from most of the exposed surfaces, but it must be true

[1] "The prevailing highly resistant Cambrian and pre-Cambrian complex..., which was planed down to a remarkably widespread level surface in pre-Miocene times." C. Fenner, The Major Structural and Physiographic features of South Australia, *Trans. Roy. Soc. S. Aus.* 54, p. 17 (1930).
[2] F. Dixey, *Quart. Jour. Geol. Soc.* 95, pp. 75–108 (1939).

that some of the slopes have been exposed to erosion, and subject to dissection, much longer than others. The delay of dissection on the slopes longest exposed, whichever they may be, has resulted in an accumulation of similarly developed forms, or, to put it in another way, indicates the stability, or longevity, of forms at this stage of development under the conditions here prevailing. Such stability marks these forms as a definite type, and calls for investigation.

Special resistance to erosion in the undermass rocks of the Otago district cannot be appealed to. The commonest material is a mica schist that cannot be regarded as an exceptionally resistant rock, and somewhat shattered greywackes similar to those of the mountain axis throughout New Zealand underlie some of the slopes. Granted that the rocks underlying a tilted fossil plain—or, indeed, any other tilted surface—are somewhat resistant to erosion, though perhaps not exceptionally resistant, the next important condition making for long preservation of slopes in an undissected condition after exposure seems to be that there shall be little run-off. It is well known that slopes of very absorbent, even though unconsolidated, materials are relatively indestructible, and the paradox has been announced that "gravel is a resistant rock". In the case of the resurrected plains referred to, however, the surface is not very absorbent, but small run-off results from the nature of the climate, already described. The initial slope must also be smooth and uniform, so that the consequent drainage on it, or drainage superposed on it from a cover on which it has been consequent, shall run off as numerous small parallel streams among which none is likely to become a master.

The back slope of Rough Ridge (a tilted uplifted block) is one of the best examples of these well-preserved resurrected inclined surfaces in New Zealand (Fig. 152). There seems to be in this case such an agreement between the slope of the surface and the volumes of numerous small streams that drain it that the latter have become graded without being deeply incised in the surface, and it is obvious that any smooth surface, horizontal or inclined, that is traversed by shallow ravines which are no longer being deepened, and which do not contain streams sufficiently large or permanent to be capable of lateral corrasion, will escape rapid dissection, and so be a stable form. As the ravine sides become graded, the sharp shoulders which at first may bound the flat doabs between the ravines will early disappear, and so in the stable condition of the slope these interfluves are broadly convex, subdued forms; but the inclined crest-lines of the flat spurs, which they have become, are accordant with one another, allowing the eye to reconstruct the somewhat worn tangent surface of the emergent plain.

An extensive resurrected surface on the Hunter's Hills (South Canterbury, N.Z.), with similar slope to that of Rough Ridge has

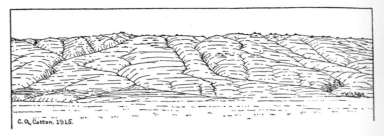

Fig. 152. The north-westward slope of Rough Ridge, New Zealand, a resurrected portion of a fossil erosion surface that descends in the foreground beneath covering strata.

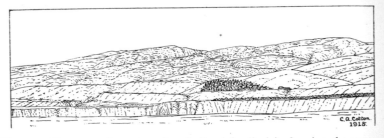

Fig. 153. Resurrected portion of an inclined fossil plain forming the western slope of the Hunter's Hills, New Zealand. In the middle distance the slope of the fossil plain descends beneath marine covering strata in the valley of the Waihao River.

streams more deeply incised in it (Fig. 152), perhaps because of more abundant rain in that district; and in north-west Nelson, which is a wet district, similar slopes are well dissected. There, however, particularly well-preserved resurrected surfaces *that have remained horizontal* occur as rather extensive plateaux, notably the Mount Arthur Tableland and that known as the Gouland Downs, each at an elevation of 3000 ft. The Gouland Downs plateau (Pl. XXXI, 1 and Fig. 213) is very slightly undulating, in part swampy, with a sour waterlogged soil, and is drained by streams that are sluggish and but little below the plateau level near their headwaters, though downstream they are beginning to cut V-shaped young valleys. Though this is a very wet district, the presence of particularly resistant slates and quartzites in the undermass has resulted in delaying the destruction by erosion of those parts of the resurrected surface that are nearly level. Resurrection of a fossil surface is here well attested by survival

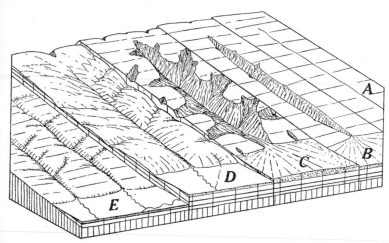

Fig. 154. Development of the surface of a gently tilted strip, the land surface of which is initially a sloping plain on a weak cover lying over a resistant undermass with planed surface. *A*, initial form; *B*, *C*, and *D*, intermediate sequential forms; *E*, stage at which a fossil plain has emerged as a stable form.

on the plateau of small mesas,[1] which are remnants of a cover of Tertiary limestone in course of removal in solution (the bush-clad "islands" in Pl. XXXI, 1 and Fig. 213).

Among general conditions favouring conspicuous survival of resurrected plains, obviously the first essential is that the undermass shall be contrastingly resistant as compared with the unconformable cover that may be removed from it. Erosion of the cover is hastened by tilting of strips or earth blocks during differential uplift; but survival—as compared with progressive destruction by dissection as it emerges—of the surface of the undermass itself can take place

[1] Or "hums" (see p. 283).

only when the strip or block is tilted at a moderate angle, the permissible slope being somewhat steep, as discussion of some examples has shown, in a dry climate with well-distributed rainfall. On the surface of a compound block with uniformly weak covering strata uplifted with tilting (Fig. 154), numerous consequent streams will come into existence, and if the tilting is uniform these will be approximately parallel and closely spaced, and throughout the dissection and degradation of the cover (Fig. 154, *B*, *C*, *D*) the stream pattern will change but little. Degradation of a uniformly weak cover will take place rapidly (though, of course, it will be necessary in applying the analysis to special cases to take into account erosion on covering beds of varying resistance). When, however, the streams cut through the cover and are superposed on the resistant rocks of the undermass, their vertical corrasion is checked, and becomes very slow. After the streams have become superposed and the upland is maturely dissected, the relief of the surface, previously increasing, is reduced again as the interfluvial strips waste away. Even if the streams, or some of them, have become graded without cutting through the cover in the early stages of dissection, after the cover has been largely removed from the higher parts of the area they will be forced to degrade and will become superposed. Later, when the removal of the cover is nearly complete, all the streams will be incised to some extent in the undermass. In the resistant rocks of the undermass, however, the ravines will for long remain V-shaped, with convex side slopes, *simulating* youth, while on the spurs of the upland, between the streams, flat areas will survive, where the ancient eroded floor has been stripped of its cover (*E*; see also Fig. 152, and Pl. XXXI, 2). This stage will be attained earliest at the middle parts of even slopes, for there stream corrasion has deepened the valleys most; upstream and downstream from such points, owing to smaller depth of stream corrasion, undissected interfluvial areas will be larger and survive longer.

In the New Zealand examples that have been described there is convincing evidence of their origin as resurrected fossil plains: either the surface slopes down so as to plunge beneath similarly inclined beds of the cover still resting on it in an adjacent depression, or outliers of the cover still survive here and there on the plateau or upland surface.

On the plateaux of the Otago province, *sarsen stones* also lie about. These are relics of some exceptionally resistant bed in the cover that has broken up as softer material on which it formerly rested has been washed away. The fragments which, though generally reduced by long-continued weathering to small dimensions, still litter the surface of the exposed undermass on the Otago plateaux, consist of quartzite from well-cemented layers or lenses in the cover of quartz gravels. In a few places, where the sarsen stones are exceptionally large, they are very conspicuous (Pl. XXXII, 1); but much more numerous and widely scattered small boulders testify to the former presence of a widespread cover.

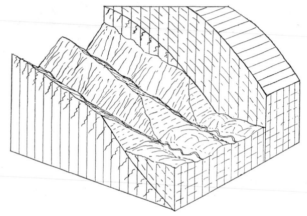

Fig. 155. Dissection of a rather steeply sloping surface by vigorous streams.

Survival of sarsen stones does not, however, prove that plateau surfaces on which they now lie are parts of a fossil plain; for they are so resistant to weathering that they might survive while a peneplain was in course of development below the floor of the original cover, either with or without an intermediate phase of resurrection of the fossil plain forming the floor. The sarsen stones and "grey wethers" of the South of England and the Ardennes have survived in a similar way from a former cover, but, though those of the south of England are derived from a cover of Eocene age, their presence does not prove any plateau surface on which they lie to be the Eocene floor resurrected.

The survival of irregularly or slantingly uplifted plains, whether of fossil, peneplain, or other origin, must be regarded as somewhat exceptional, depending on special conditions such as have been suggested in this chapter. In more commonly occurring circumstances surfaces strongly warped or tilted during uplift are short-lived. If, owing to abundant rainfall, to steepness of initial slope (Fig. 155), or to initial irregularities of the uplifted surface that have resulted in concentration of consequent drainage into large streams, the graded profile for the dissecting streams lies far below the uplifted surface, its mature dissection will not be long delayed. Remnants of the stripped surface may long survive on spur ends, however, between bottle-necked ravines on either side that are not cut far below it (Fig. 155), and a strip at this level may be almost continuous if the dissecting valleys are widely spaced, perhaps having been reduced in numbers in the struggle for existence. At the top of a slope that is sharply cut off in that direction, perhaps by the scarp of a faulted block, there is not much concentrated wash, ravines are not deeply cut, and another nearly continuous strip may survive (Fig. 156), possibly even capped by residuals of the cover. Examples of such features are found in New

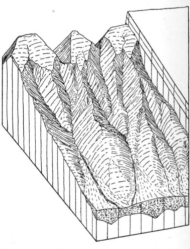

Fig. 156. Dissection of the middle of a slope, with survival of flat remnants at its top and bottom.

Zealand, and there are a number of cases where long accordantly sloping, parallel spurs from one side of a mountain range suggest reconstruction of a smoothly sloping surface above them that has been maturely dissected—e.g. the slopes of the Seaward Kaikoura range (Fig. 82, left) descending to the Middle Clarence Valley.

Occasional association of fossil plains, some resurrected and others merely observed in profile, with remnants of peneplains of later development, necessitates consideration of the problems presented by "intersecting peneplains". Two fossil erosion surfaces of different ages may intersect and be observed in profile sections, as exemplified in the "Algonkian wedge" of the Grand Canyon section (Fig. 150); and many examples may be found of intersection of a relatively young summit peneplain, generally little deformed, with profile sections of an inclined or folded fossil plain, or with more or less discontinuous strips or facets of it, resurrected and emergent as a surface feature. A notable example of such intersection is present in the Piedmont Plateau of the eastern United States, where, at the Fall Zone, Johnson has differentiated facets of an inclined resurrected surface (termed by him the Fall Zone peneplain) from the more nearly horizontal upland overstretched by the Schooley peneplain.[1] Another notable example is the intersection in south-eastern England of the upland peneplain of late Tertiary development with sloping facets of a resurrected surface from which Eocene strata are in course of removal.[2]

Where, in such cases, a fossil plain is extensively exposed by erosion, it may be difficult to distinguish between isolated parts of this ancient resurrected surface and of the newer peneplain that intersects it. In the central plateau of Morocco, for example, Lawson records that "the exhumation of the old pre-Permian surface has produced a post-Alpine peneplain which in part happens to almost coincide with the post-Hercyninan one".[3]

A complex of landscape forms in which two intersecting erosion surfaces occur was termed a *morvan* by Davis, who took the name from the Morvan of central France. Another example of a morvan, which has been described in detail by Davis, is the Front Range of the Rocky Mountains, in Colorado (Fig. 157).[4] In this case the morvan explanation stresses the modern age of the Rocky Mountain peneplain as compared with the floor underlying the Mesozoic strata arched up over the range and preserved along its monoclinal front. In any morvan the rocks have compound structure, with an undermass planed by erosion and over this an unconformable cover or overmass; the whole compound mass, after being tilted

[1] Douglas Johnson, *Stream Sculpture on the Atlantic Slope*, Fig. 9 (1931).
[2] Wooldridge and Linton, The Influence of the Pliocene Transgression on the Geomorphology of South-eastern England, *Jour. Geomorph.* 1, pp. 40–54 (1938).
[3] A. C. Lawson, The Atlas Mountains of Morocco, *Scientific Monthly*, 32, p. 105 (1931).
[4] W. M. Davis, Relation of Geography to Geology, *Bull. Geol. Soc. Am.* 23, p. 117 (1912); The Colorado Front Range, *Ann. Ass. Am. Geog.* 1, pp. 21–83 (1912); A Geographical Pilgrimage, *ibid.* 2, pp. 93–5 (1912).

or deformed by folding, has had a peneplain developed across it; and later erosion has taken place, stimulated by uplift, resulting in dissection and partial destruction of the peneplain. In simple types of morvan the summit peneplain has suffered no deformation

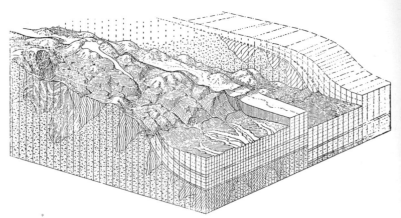

Fig. 157. Condensed diagram of the Colorado Front Range. (After Davis.)

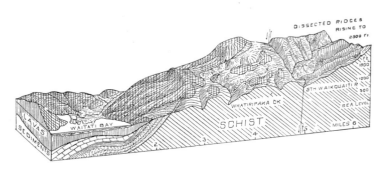

Fig. 158. Margin of the Dunedin lava massif, New Zealand, showing folded intersecting peneplains, both buried at left, appearing as surface forms in centre, and dissected at right. (After Benson.)

beyond doming or a limited amount of warping that has accompanied its uplift, but further complication may result from less regular uplift.

The eastern part of the Otago district of New Zealand, from which examples of resurrected fossil-plain remnants have already been described in this chapter, is a somewhat complex morvan.[1] Here the compound mass has been peneplained after the occurrence of a pre-Pliocene movement of uplift accompanied by slight deformation, and, after a long rest, has suffered another and more severe deformation at the initiation of the present major cycle of erosion. Thus the very extensive plateau of eastern and south-eastern Otago (Pl. XXXII, 2), broken by faults and somewhat warped and in places thrown into irregular undulations, is in parts a peneplain, though elsewhere a resurrected fossil plain; and in many places it seems impossible to distinguish between these intersecting surfaces. At some localities the younger peneplain is buried beneath lava flows. Besides appearing in profile section in some lava-capped buttes and small mesas it forms the floor on which rest the thick lavas of the Dunedin massif, and here both the lava flows and the floor on which they rest are quite strongly folded. The lavas overstep successive strata of the cover and lap over thence on to the undermass (Fig. 158).

CHAPTER XIX

Interruption of the Normal Cycle; Effects of Uplift and Warping

THE course of the normal cycle of erosion may be cut short at any stage by *accidents* and *interruptions* (as Davis called them) of various kinds. Some minor modifications of the normal cycle that may result from small changes of climate have been noted in earlier chapters. Greater changes than these rank as accidents, such as refrigeration, bringing on glacial conditions, and the change to extreme aridity, introducing a complex of erosive processes working independently of base-level. Such accidents, and also volcanic outbreaks, which bury pre-existing landscapes, terminate the slow and orderly succession of normal events such as have been outlined, and introduce special landscape types. Interruptions of the cycle, which must be considered now, are due to substitution of one base-

---

[1] W. N. Benson, Some Land Forms in Southern New Zealand, *Australian Geographer*, 2 (7), pp. 2–22 (1935); C. A. Cotton, Some Peneplanations in Otago..., *N.Z. Jour. Sci. and Tech.* 20, pp. 1–8b (1938).

level for another—i.e. to a movement of the base-level plane to a new position in the land mass either as a result of an actual (eustatic) rise or fall of ocean-level or because the part of the land we are concerned with has moved while the level of the ocean surface has remained approximately as it was. Small changes in the relative levels of land and sea, of which many shore-lines give evidence, are negligible in the long run if they are merely oscillations about a mean position. If, on the other hand, they are cumulative in one direction, the result is that the former base-level, which may for long have controlled the development of landscape forms, is replaced by another. Base-level may have simply moved parallel to itself, up or down. If due to earth movements, this is really a very special case, perhaps quite rare, but there has probably been an approximation to such a condition in recent times in parts of the world remote from ice-caps, when the ice-caps, or continental glaciers, of the late Pleistocene melted and added their melt-water to the ocean. Earlier very considerable fluctuations of the ocean level must have accompanied the alternation of glacial and interglacial epochs.

The more general case is that in which the land, and with it the surface that was formerly the base-level plane, has undergone some deformation, and the new plane of base-level may intersect the former one, which is now a tilted, warped, folded, or fault-broken surface. The same interrupting movement may result in an upward (positive) movement of base-level in one district and a downward (negative) one in another, such movements being, of course, relative to the land mass and not necessarily upward and downward in the sense of increasing or diminishing the distance from the centre of the earth. It is often convenient to speak of negative movement of base-level as emergence of the land, and of positive movement as (partial) submergence.

It is sometimes necessary to take carefully into consideration the effects of erosion of the land and of aggradation that go on during the progress of slow movements, or of a slow succession of small movements (Chapter XIV). Commonly, however, when studying their effects in regions of somewhat resistant rocks, one may safely assume that interrupting earth movements and eustatic changes of base-level take place rapidly as compared with the rate at which erosion works. Experience in matching deduced forms with actual landscape examples also teaches that movements, or spasms of movement, are separated by relatively long rests, or still-stands.[1]

As a result of the change in the position of base-level the former cycle of erosion has been cut short, and a new cycle is immediately inaugurated, which runs through at least some of its stages in the period of still-stand that ensues. Though of the same general type, the landscapes of successive cycles may differ considerably in details. Adjustment to structure, in particular, may be expected to be perfected only in a succession of cycles, proceeding vigorously only in the early stages of each cycle, in which streams are deepening their valleys and extension of these or development of new valleys by headward erosion is possible.

The assemblages of land forms that are to be regarded as characteristic of interruption are those in which a new-cycle landscape is, as it were, superimposed on the older landscape of the former cycle, considerable areas of the actual surface being attributable to erosion in each cycle. In the descriptions already given of uplifted and dissected peneplains, the concept of landscapes composed of erosional forms developed in successive cycles has already been introduced. A cycle may be interrupted, however, long before the landscape has become senile, and a *composite* landscape—i.e. one exhibiting "composite topography" (Davis), or forms developed in two (or more) cycles—quite commonly comprises summit forms that are relics of a partially destroyed mature landscape. A cycle has been interrupted at the stage of maturity, and its mature forms may be seen in course of replacement by somewhat younger forms of a new cycle, more advanced development of which will eventually destroy all traces of the mature summits, the landscape then ceasing to be composite. Some parts of the land surface of the earth have been emergent and subject to erosion for vast periods and have been uplifted from time to time, so that, in the aggregate, very great thicknesses—measurable in miles—have been removed from them. They have passed through many cycles, but traces only of the later, perhaps latest, of these will be found in their landscape forms. The gradual replacement of landscape forms of an interrupted cycle by young forms of the cycle that succeeds it is termed *rejuvenation*, and a composite landscape may also be described as rejuvenated (Figs. 159, 160). A characteristic feature of rejuvenated landscapes

[1] H. Baulig, *Le plateau central de la France*, p. 513 (1928).

Fig. 159. Composite landscape forms of Vancouver Island, resulting from "mature dissection of an uplifted subdued surface". (After C. H. Clapp.)

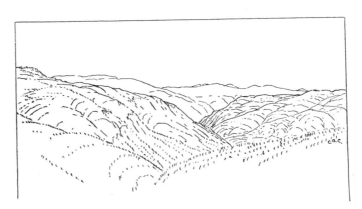

Fig. 160. Composite landscape forms, Franklin Valley, British Columbia, a late-mature upland surface dissected to a depth of 1000 ft. by younger valleys of a later cycle. (Drawn from a photograph published by C. W. Drysdale.)

is the shoulder, or break of slope, separating the gentler slopes of an older landscape above from steeper and younger valley sides below (Pl. XXXIII, 1, 2).

Where the shoulder is about midway down a valley side, as it may be in an early stage of rejuvenation of a mature landscape, the effect is produced of an inner valley with steeper sides cut within a more open valley, sometimes termed "valley-in-valley".

According to W. Penck's [1] method of explaining landscape forms (p. 159), a valley-side shoulder indicates the occurrence of a rapid acceleration of valley incision, or of uplift controlling this vertical corrasion—a quick change might take place, for example, from very slow uplift to rapid uplift at a uniform rate.

Rejuvenated features of the Alps have been thus described by A. Penck: [2]

The whole surface of that mountain region was in a state of orographic maturity. At the north-eastern end of the Alps, especially in Styria, these mature surface features still exist. At other places they are dissected by very deep valleys. Thus, for example, in the southernmost parts of the Tyrol west of Lake Garda and south-east of Trient. Here the highlands have the soft rounded forms of a mature landscape. Those mountainous parts are separated from each other by valleys with very steep slopes. The slopes are evidently cut into the older formations. Even in the interior of the mountain chain we find remnants of its former maturity. We meet with very broad valleys and mountains, the general outline of which is a rolling one. Even the chain of the Mont Blanc conserves features which indicate that the chain was formerly rounded.

Interior parts of uniformly uplifted upland surfaces remain for a long time unaffected by the rejuvenating effects of interrupting movements. Even in cases of somewhat irregular and differential movement the slopes of upland surfaces, distant from main rivers, may be insufficiently altered in steepness by tilting to affect the rate of erosion on them immediately to any serious extent. So rapid changes in the sculptured forms of the landscape do not necessarily follow immediately on uplift in inland localities unless deformation of the surface has been exceptionally severe; some effects of strong local warping will be described later in this chapter.

[1] *Die morphologische Analyse*, pp. 121–3 (1924).
[2] A. Penck, The Origin of the Alps, *Bull. Am. Geog. Soc.* 41, pp. 65–71 (1909).

However long they may be delayed inland, however, landscape changes inevitably follow any uplift, and forms related to (accordant with) the new base-level encroach, generally little by little, upon the landscape of the former cycle, first along the side of the main rivers near their mouths, then farther inland, up the tributaries, and eventually up to the heads of all the branching headwater ravines. These results all follow, or accompany, regrading first of stream profiles and later of valley-side and valley-head slopes, for, after any interrupting movement the grading processes, degradation and aggradation, come into operation, grading both streams and surfaces with respect to the new base-level.

The larger streams, graded and flowing down gentle declivities in the interrupted cycle, are indeed sensitive to changes of gradient throughout the affected region. Such parts of them as are steepened as a result of warping at once flow more rapidly and now have energy to spare beyond what is required to transport their as yet unaltered loads of waste. They degrade, therefore, reducing their declivities until a graded condition is again established. If, on the other hand, slight headward tilting has made a stream course too nearly level, the stream becomes too sluggish to carry its former load, and therefore deposits part of its load of waste in its valley (aggrades), thus building up and steepening its profile until it is again graded.

When a landscape is rejuvenated by interruption of a cycle, therefore, its valleys develop new features resulting from either degradation or aggradation, or, when warping has taken place, perhaps from both of these. The valley modifications may be produced either rapidly, but in this case sporadically throughout a landscape, wherever warping has been sufficiently pronounced to affect the regimen of streams, or, in cases where positive or negative movement has been sensibly uniform throughout a region, may have to work their way slowly and systematically inland from river mouths. Locally, however, in river valleys, the effects are very similar, in a general way, whether produced immediately by local tilting or making their appearance after long delay as a postponed consequence of a widespread movement of base-level. In the former case, the varying depth to which new inner-valley trenches are cut, or the variable extent to which aggradation has taken place, together perhaps with angles at which regraded river profiles may be observed to intersect restored preinterruption profiles, may give much information as to the extent, direction, and inclination of tilting that has affected the landscape.

Though changes in slope due to warping are very rarely of sufficient steepness to affect hillsides appreciably, conspicuous re-grading takes place in graded rivers when their down-valley gradients are altered even slightly, and this brings in its train important valley changes. Streams accelerated by down-valley tilting begin at once the development of valley-in-valley forms

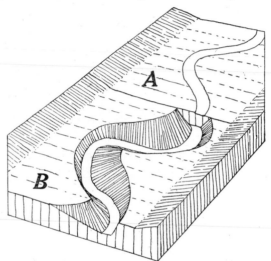

Fig. 161. Incised meanders.

throughout the steepened parts of their courses. The transverse profiles of valleys thus rejuvenated exhibit in some parts of the river courses the simple valley-in-valley, in which an inner valley of youthful aspect broadens out above a more or less distinct shoulder to an open and more mature form (Fig. 160, and Pl. XXXIII, 1, 2). Commonly, however, parts of such valleys are bordered by valley-plain terraces (Fig. 111), and the shoulder of rejuvenation separating the forms of successive cycles is localised at a terrace edge. Multicycle valleys may exhibit several successive valley-plain terraces.

Incised meanders (Fig. 161, *B*) are developed from the curves of a meandering river course on the valley plain of a former cycle

(Fig. 161, *A*), which either guide the headward erosion of a new-cycle inner trench or, where a valley has been steepened by tilting, are deepened more or less simultaneously throughout their length.[1] In many winding valleys the initial curvature has been thus inherited from meanders of a former cycle, though it may be that all other traces of the valley plain on which the meanders were formed have long ago been destroyed; and it is possible that this is the only way in which winding valleys with *symmetrical* curves around interlocking spurs are developed.[2]

Free swinging of meanders on a flood plain must obviously cease as soon as incision begins; but the momentum of the stream still carries it against the concave banks, which are liable to be undercut, and so some enlargement of curves almost inevitably takes place, and there is a tendency, as ever, to push the meanders also down-valley during their incision. The inner valley generally, therefore, assumes an asymmetrical transverse profile, with slip-off and under-cut slopes, like that of any young valley that is increasing its curva-ture while vertical corrasion is in progress, though in plan the curves may be expected to be more symmetrical—"its new valley will be regularly curved, instead of irregularly crooked, as in its first youth".[3]

An attempt has been made to subdivide incised meanders into *entrenched*[4] and *ingrown*, the former exhibiting little or no contrast between the slopes on the inner and outer sides of curves, and the latter having typical slip-off and undercut slopes (Fig. 161). "Entrenched" meanders (Fig. 162) have been developed where, for some reason not usually obvious,[5] no appreciable lateral corra-sion has accompanied the incision of the meander, and where it may be safely inferred that there has been no appreciable increase in curvature or down-valley sweep of the meanders. Very slow

[1] The theory of incised meanders (which were first recognised by Winslow in 1893) was developed by W. M. Davis (Incised Meandering Valleys, *Bull. Geog. Soc. Phil.* 4, pp. 1–11 (1906)).
[2] J. B. L. Hol, Das Problem der Talmäander, *Zeits. Geomorph.* 10, pp. 169–95 (1938); but see also footnote on p. 28.
[3] W. M. Davis, *Physical Geography*, p. 253 (1898).
[4] J. L. Rich (Certain Types of Stream Valleys and their Meaning, *Jour. Geol.* 22, pp. 469–97 (1914)) has thus limited the use of "entrenched" ("intrenched"), a term already in use by Davis (*loc. cit.* 1898) and others as a synonym of "incised". His use of "ingrown" as applied to meanders is new.
[5] "Why the Juniata and the Potomac should differ is these respects is not yet understood" (Davis, *loc. cit.* 1906).

incision, either going on as an accompaniment of slow uplift or tilting, or resulting perhaps from a hold-up of vertical corrasion due to the river's crossing a barrier of resistant rocks somewhere downstream, may encourage development of the extreme type of

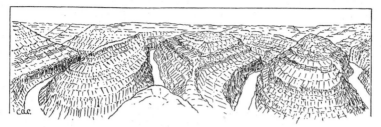

Fig. 162. Incised ("entrenched") meanders. The "goose-necks" of the San Juan River, Utah. (Drawn from a photograph.)

"ingrown" meanders, but rapid incision does not always produce the "entrenched" type. In the case of some New Zealand rivers, very rapid incision has been accompanied by great enlargement of meanders (Pl. XXXIV, 1). Those of the Rangitikei are strongly "ingrown", though incision of the inner valley has been rapid

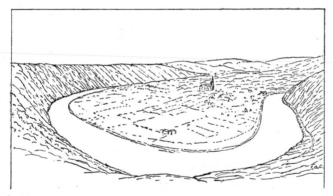

Fig. 163. Incised ("ingrown") meander of the Meuse River, at Fumay, in northern France. (Drawn from a photograph.)

enough to leave tributaries hanging over it with discordant junctions (Fig. 9), even where they are eroding in soft, scarcely consolidated material. Classical examples of large incised meanders that are strongly ingrown are Moccasin Bend, in the Tennessee River, near Chattanooga, and the bend of the Meuse at Fumay (Fig. 163).

The "ingrown" character of the meanders of an incised meandering valley is sometimes strikingly brought out by contrasting views from a high vantage point looking up and down the valley across its interlocking valley-side spurs. In the up-valley direction there may be revealed a succession of slip-off slopes occupied by ploughed and cultivated land, but the view down-valley will show only the steeper undercut slopes, perhaps forested, on the upstream sides of the spurs, "which give the valley an unoccupied appearance".[1]

Some West-European rivers with incised meanders have increased their curvature during the incision to the extent of cutting through the necks of spurs. Well-known examples of such cut-off spurs are those in the valley of the Moselle above Berncastel and in the Neckar Valley at Kirchheim and Lauffen (Fig. 164).

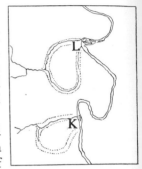

Fig. 164. Cut-off spurs of the Neckar at Lauffen (*L*) and Kirchheim (*K*).

Aggradation accompanying headward tilting of parts of river courses as an accompaniment of surface warping or of differential movements of fault-bounded blocks may result in important modifications of valley forms. These may be quite local in their development, where corrugations or undulations of the surface of no great extent are formed; but very gentle headward tiltings of regional extent may also occur that are capable of producing aggradational effects in large rivers with gentle gradients.

Instances of recent tilting of the surface of sufficient steepness to affect conspicuously the valleys of small and steep-grade streams are found only in parts of the seismic belts—for example, in California and New Zealand. Along the down-warped eastern side of the Port Nicholson and Hutt Valley depression (the Wellington Harbour area) in New Zealand (Fig. 165) recent westward tilting of about 175 ft. per mile has affected an early mature land surface of strong relief, as is indicated by effects produced on land forms of various kinds.[2] Main streams flow parallel to the hinge-line of

[1] W. M. Davis, *loc. cit.* p. 9.
[2] C. A. Cotton, The Warped Land surface on the South-eastern Side of the Port Nicholson Depression, *Trans. N.Z.* 53, pp. 131–43 (1921).

tilting and are not much affected, but grouped tributaries near the headwaters of two of these enter them from the west, and their valleys have been filled to the heads with swampy-surfaced alluvium

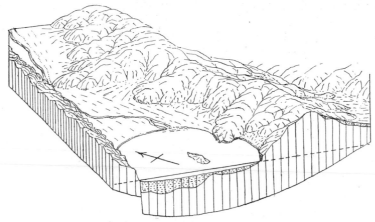

Fig. 165. Generalised diagram of part of the Port Nicholson-Hutt Valley depression (Wellington Harbour basin), New Zealand.

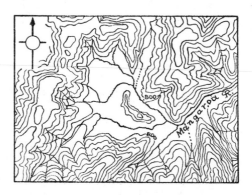

Fig. 166. Backward-tilted deeply aggraded headwater streams east of the Port Nicholson-Hutt Valley depression, New Zealand.

to the extent of partly burying the intervening spurs and converting parts of them into islands (Fig. 166) and peninsulas (Figs. 165, 188; and Pl. XXXIV, 2).

Warping (or deformation involving faulting) transverse to a river may cause headward tilting, even to the extent of reversal of slope, of a part of its course (Fig. 167). This may be the result of upwarping or upfaulting of a belt of country crossed by the river, and through which it may be able to maintain its course as an antecedent. Commonly aggradation proceeds during the continuance of the deformation, and a basin plain is built by the river in an inland or intermont basin, while farther downstream it is cutting an antecedent gorge (Fig. 167, *A*). Reversal of slope of the

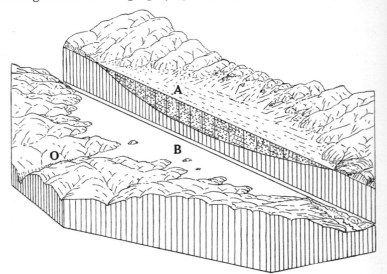

Fig. 167. Results of warping affecting the profile of a river valley. *A*, aggradation, with formation of a basin plain, has gone on *pari passu* with warping; *B*, rapid warping has resulted in the ponding of a lake in the warped valley, with embayments in the valleys of drowned tributaries; *O*, possible new outlet.

former valley floor takes place in this case only after it has been buried, and the river maintains for itself a constant slope in the direction in which it continues to flow by building a bridge of alluvial deposits across the tectonic basin as it is formed.

Should the earth movements that result in the formation of the basin go on sufficiently rapidly, however, ponding of the river, with formation of a lake in the basin, must take place. Though examples are rare of lakes ponded in river valleys by simple transverse warping[1] such as is illustrated by the diagram (Fig.

[1] W. M. Davis, *Die erklärende Beschreibung der Landformen*, p. 175 (1912).

167, B; cf. Fig. 14), many are known to lie in more complex tectonic basins (Chapter v). A lake formed by the ponding of a vigorous river can have but a short life, as it will be rapidly filled by the growth of deltas or drained by erosional lowering of the level of the outlet. The outflowing stream may continue to follow the former river valley as an antecedent, but if a low enough gap is present in the surrounding hills, the lake may overflow through it (as at O, in Fig. 167, B), the river being thus diverted by ponding as a result of warping (or other deformation). As regards the abandonment of the former course, this is a case of *defeat*, and the river in the former valley has been beheaded by warping. The new course taken by the river overflowing from the lake will almost certainly fail to fit the river, which must proceed at once to adapt and grade it for itself. The river will be a misfit of the "overfit" variety, and grading of its course will lower the outlet of the lake and will eventually, and perhaps rapidly, drain it, unless its floor has been warped down below the local base-level.

Basin plains resulting from aggradation over a land surface of considerable relief where a cycle has been interrupted by deformation of the surface will have irregular, embayed outlines very like those of similarly formed lakes, for the component fans of tributary streams will extend up their valleys. After thick alluviation has taken place in a down-warped basin, indeed, fan-filled embayments of the upland, or extensions of the plain, may occupy even valleys opened up or enlarged by rejuvenation during the progress of the deformation. Where a basin has some fault boundaries, however, these are little altered by aggradation, and that little only when movement on the faults has ceased. Peninsulas and islands, either of a pre-existing relief or due to irregularity of deformation, may be partly or wholly buried beneath the accumulating alluvium, but, whatever their origin, they are subject to erosion until they are buried, and so they always underlie the basin-plain deposits "unconformably".

When a land surface of some relief is affected by warping, though diversions of streams by ponding and alluviation may occur, an immediate general transfer of divides to the axes of upwarping is obviously prevented by the fact that rivers are imprisoned in pre-existing valleys; and yet divides will immediately begin to migrate towards these axes, and main divides must eventually come to coincide with them fairly closely, while valley lines shift slowly in a similar way towards axes of downwarping.[1] The explanation of such migration is simple enough. Where two streams that head opposite to each other are affected by an even lengthwise tilting movement, that one whose declivity is increased cuts down vigorously and grows in length headward at the expense of the other. If the tilting that affects them is part of a general warping, the divide migrates towards an axis of upwarping. The general law that axes of up-warping become divides is subject to exception where such axes are crossed by antecedent rivers.

CHAPTER XX

Positive and Negative Movements of Base-level

THE simplest case of composite landscape development may now be examined, in which movement is entirely regional (i.e. simple uplift or depression without any warping), though such is merely a special case of the general problem of cycle interruption by earth movements.[2] Differential (warping and tilting) movement seems to have been so slight, however, in many regions of actual upheaval of the crust that these regions afford a somewhat close approxima-tion to the condition of purely regional movement. This makes an analysis of the effects of such movement worth while; and eustatic rise or fall of base-level (unless complications are introduced by the contemporaneous occurrence of earth movements) fulfils the conditions to the letter.

The simple case of eustatic rise of sea-level or regional subsidence of the land produces immediate effects on the landscape only where it results in partial submergence, with creation of a new shore-line, "drowning" valleys, "betrunking" rivers, "dismembering" river

[1] M. R. Campbell, Drainage Modifications and their Interpretation, *Jour. Geol.* 4, pp. 567–81, 657–78 (1896).
[2] W. M. Davis, Piedmont Benchlands and Primärrumpfe, *Bull. Geol. Soc. Am.* 43, p. 420 (1932).

systems, forming estuaries, harbours, rias, and the innumerable bays and minor indentations that diversify a majority of the coasts of the world. These are shore-line features and do not concern us in this book. Over that part of the land that escapes submergence there may be a slight slowing down of the general wastage of the land surface, but this seems incapable of demonstration, and produces no appreciable changes in the relief. A new cycle has been inaugurated,[1] however, and changes at least in the valleys of the landscape will follow in due course. Rivers, large and small, build out deltas in the still waters of bay heads and estuaries into which they now flow, and the streams that have been betrunked and shortened by submergence thus grow in length again seaward. As delta-building streams, if previously graded, must aggrade inland (see p. 181) in order to continue flowing and maintain grade, it follows that valleys in regions of subsidence and submergence become somewhat aggraded. As there are various other possible causes of aggradation, however, aggraded valleys alone cannot be regarded as proof of subsidence.

A simple regional uplift, or emergence as a result of lowering of sea-level, produces no immediate changes in the relief of the uplifted surface. This is the case where erosion proceeds unchangingly, as though the interrupted cycle were still current, "until news of the upheaval is brought...by the retrogressive erosion of peripheral streams" (Davis) (see p. 193). The region affected lies at the rear of a newly emerged coastal plain, and after its rivers, where they are extended across this strip, have deepened their valleys as far as the fall zone, they are ready to begin the redissection of the hinterland. Though graded farther upstream, the rivers have steepened profiles at the fall zone, and each stream in the over-steep part of its course has again the velocity and energy of youth. Erosion is *revived*, and the stream, itself *rejuvenated*, proceeds to rejuvenate its valley by taking up again the task of vertical corrasion. The falls and rapids that have made their appearance where old rocks are first exposed at the fall zone work their way upstream and inland from this point as the head of a new and young valley guided in its headward erosion by the line the stream is already following—that is to say, the new valley is within that of the former cycle as "valley-in-valley". As there is a ready-

[1] W. M. Davis, Piedmont Benchlands, *Bull. Geol. Soc. Am.* 43, p. 420 (1932).

made stream well supplied with water, erosion is as rapid as the strength of the rocks will allow, and below the headwardly progressing zone of falls and rapids the inner valley eventually becomes graded with respect to the new base-level (Fig. 168). Deepening of the main valley lowers local base-levels as it progresses inland; valley-in-valley development (rejuvenation) begins in tributaries as soon as each of these feels the effect of lowered base-level; and eventually rejuvenation gnaws gradually into the upland.

Fig. 168. Condensed diagram of rejuvenation of a river and its valley proceeding by headward erosion.

Rejuvenations may occur at intervals, and a succession of valleys of revived erosion may be found progressing headward one within the other. As an example of a valley comprising such multicycle forms, that of the Snowy River, of Australia, may be cited. As described by Andrews,

this stream has a course of 300 miles, approximately, from its source in the high fault block of Kosciusko to the Gippsland Lakes, in Victoria. ...Its descent from the subsummit upland...is by means of a series of relatively youthful valleys opening out into each other, the lower being embraced within the higher and outer forms, and the valleys descending to each other by means of rapids and gorges. The rock structures within which these "valley-in-valley" forms occur are more or less homogenous in that they occur in the main within a massive gneissic granitoid rock.[1]

In multicycle valleys the heads of a succession of inner valleys, following each other inland, may be regarded as the messengers bearing the "news of uplift" and setting out one after another after successive uplifts have occurred. In weak rocks, such as the deeply dissected Miocene and Pliocene marine strata of the Wanganui district in New Zealand, the inner valleys even of small streams have rapidly become mature and open (as depicted in

[1] E. C. Andrews, The Origin of Modern Mountain Ranges, *J. and Proc. Roy. Soc. N.S.W.* 67, pp. 334-5 (1934).

Fig. 168). Such a mature valley followed upstream soon narrows, displays youthful features, and steepens, and is discovered to be gnawing headward into the floor of the open, mature valley of the penultimate cycle; but this again may, a few miles farther on, be found to be rejuvenating in a similar way an open valley of an antepenultimate cycle just now receiving news of the last uplift but one, and so on to cycles still farther back from the present.

Just outside the glaciated border of the Alps near Lake Lugano the Colla valley is a stream-eroded valley with a stepped longitudinal profile. Repeated uplifts of the mountains have initiated new systems of downcutting (cycles according to the terminology of Davis), each of which migrated up-valley. Distinct remnants of no less than fifteen such cycles can be recognised, each characterised in longitudinal profile by a stretch of gentle gradient followed up-stream by a steeper gradient, and in cross-profile by valley walls of definite slope.[1]

Accurately plotted profiles of many European rivers show them to be graded only in parts.[2] The profiles as a whole are by no means smooth, and afford proofs of multicycle erosion, for successive nearly level, graded parts are joined by ungraded steeper parts stepping up to the next higher graded reaches by convex "nicks"[3] in the profiles. It is true, of course, that somewhat similar profiles may be developed in the course of a single cycle of erosion, when they are due to the presence of barriers of resistant rock holding up rivers in young, ungraded gorges, which separate graded reaches across weaker rock outcrops; but nicks in a river profile and alternation of mature and open with narrow and young stretches of valley may be independent of structure, occurring where the rocks are homogeneous as far as their resistance to erosion is concerned. Even where nicks occur at resistant outcrops, this is quite commonly a result merely of retardation at such points of headward erosion due to rejuvenation.[4] The most widely accepted explanation of nicks in valley profiles is that they are the effects of successive lowerings of base-level. Regional correlation of such features, which has been carried out in France, has brought out for that

---

[1] F. Jaeger, summarising researches of H. Annaheim, *Jour. Geomorph.* 1, p. 105 (1938).
[2] See e.g. H. Baulig, *Le plateau central de la France*, Pls. I–IV (1928).
[3] German *Knick*.
[4] For discussion of this problem see Douglas Johnson, *Jour. Geomorph.* 1, pp. 178–83 (1938); and H. Baulig, *ibid.* 3, pp. 3–15 (1940).

region such convincing evidence of uniform sinkings of base-level throughout a succession of cycles that Baulig[1] confidently regards these as the results of successive rapid lowerings of the ocean surface without any complications due to crustal movements. Successive river profiles restored by extrapolation are divergent downstream (an arrangement termed "concordant" by Briquet), as would be expected from theoretical considerations. One implication of the hypothesis is that cycles remain current inland long after they have been interrupted near the sea coast. They are, as it were, waves of erosion successively propagated inland, and the only logical method of indicating that land forms belong to any particular cycle is, according to Briquet,[2] to date each cycle geologically according to

Fig. 169. Diagram of the association of flanking benches (inferred from summit-level accordance) on a mountain range with stepped and nicked river profiles.

the date of the base-level that originated each impulse or cycle, though, as pointed out by Baulig,[3] this leads to the anomalous result that a Pleistocene deposit (a glacial moraine) is dissected by erosion of a Pliocene cycle.

Where rivers with nicked and stepped profiles dissect a mountain mass, there may be found traces of benched profiles also on the highland and upland flanks of the mountains, though the only indications of these that have escaped destruction by erosion may be seen in some measure of summit-level accordance (Fig. 169). Their existence has been inferred from studies of topographic maps, in some of which a method of "projected profiles" has been employed. As stated by its originator,[4] "belts of country are selected which stand up highest. That line of sights taken across this belt which is at right angles to the general slope of the topography and

[1] H. Baulig, loc. cit. (1928) p. 513.
[2] A. Briquet, Ann. de Géog. 20, p. 35 (1911).
[3] H. Baulig, loc. cit. (1928) p. 47.
[4] J. Barrell, The Piedmont Terraces of the Northern Appalachians, Am. Jour. Sci. 49, p. 245 (1920).

which gives, therefore, the least concealment of the background by the foreground. It is the direction of sight which is best adapted to show the character of the culminating upland surface, as to whether it was a plane or a series of planes."

Barrell's profile studies seem to show that numerous benches break the continuity of the "Schooley peneplain" of the eastern United States (p. 195), which otherwise appears to be a single unbroken surface. Barrell favoured the hypothesis that these benches were, at least finally, shaped by marine erosion, marking successively lower traces of the sea margin. He believed there were present in the area he studied, besides higher benches, eight that were developed in the Pliocene and Pleistocene periods. The method of projected profiles has yielded evidence also of accordance of summit-levels in strips bordering inner valleys in the Northern Appalachians sufficient, it is held, to indicate the former existence of high-level wide valleys, and to establish a succession of cycles in the development of the valleys as they exist to-day. Restoration of the composite valley-side slopes indicates their development in a "quickening series of uplifts".[1]

Ideally these multicycle effects would be produced by intermittent uniform uplift (or eustatic emergence), but gentle tilting or broad doming uplift is not precluded, for its effects would be nearly the same. Writing on the subject of uplift with "warping and gentle arching", or "undulatory" uplift, Andrews says:

No geologist conceives the Eastern Australian plateau as being raised to a uniform height. Such a structure would produce a series of towering precipices of uniform height at the place where the sea or the inland plains intersect them. As undulatory uplifts they reveal a gradual bending or warping in a general way from plateau summit to associated valley.[2]

Barrell's idea of the sequence of events in the Northern Appalachians was "progressive doming at an irregular rate combined

---

[1] Peneplains of successive ages with stair-like arrangement have been described from various regions. In Africa such are dated from late Jurassic onwards (F. Dixey, Physiographical Development of Central and Southern Africa, *Trans. Geol. Soc. S. Af.* 41, pp. 113–71 (1938)). The evidence relied on for their identification in the Rocky Mountain region by van Tuyl and Lovering (*Bull. Geol. Soc. Am.* 46, pp. 1291–1350 (1936)) has been strongly criticised by J. L. Rich (*ibid.* 46, pp. 2046–54 (1936); 49, pp. 1695–1722 (1938)).
[2] E. C. Andrews, Origin of Modern Mountain Ranges, *J. and Proc. Roy. Soc. N.S.W.* 67, p. 321 (1934).

with recurrent phases of emergence or submergence" (H. H. Robinson).[1]

In various eroded masses of ancient rocks forming mountain ranges in Europe, summit-levels have been observed to indicate the existence of benched profiles on the flanks of the mountain masses similar to those brought to light by the projected-profile studies of Barrell in North America. "Close observation reveals the new and surprising fact that the heights and slopes of the German mountains are not overstretched by a single peneplain, but that several peneplains are there repeated in step-like succession" (W. Penck, translated by Davis). Both in North America (according to Barrell) and in Germany (according to Penck) the older (higher) benches are somewhat more steeply inclined than the younger (lower), this relation contrasting, it may be noted, with that of the "concordant" succession of valley profiles recognised by Baulig. Associated with the peneplain benches in the German mountains traces have been noted of successive rejuvenations of rivers working upstream into the mountain masses.

The explanation advocated by W. Penck[2] of the "piedmont staircase", as he has termed the succession of down-stepping "piedmont" benches, and of the features associated with them, contrasts strongly with what one may call the American hypothesis of successive cycles of erosion developing during pauses in intermittent uplift.[3] Briefly it is as follows: the mountain area after having been reduced to low relief in an earlier period of erosion underwent *continuous* upheaval as an *expanding dome*—i.e. as a dome with continually increasing diameter at its base, so that outlying parts, after being for a long time unaffected by the upheaval that was already in progress, were eventually uplifted. It is a part of the theory also that the continuous uplift was of the *accelerated* kind (taking place at an increasingly rapid rate). "The step-like

---

[1] Intermittent uniform uplift is the verdict, however, of Meyerhoff and Hubbell (Erosional Landforms of... Vermont, 16 *Rep. Vermont State Geol.* (1928)).

[2] W. Penck, *Die morphologische Analyse*, pp. 162–86 (1924); Die Piedmontflächen des südlichen Schwartzwaldes, *Zeits. Ges. Erdk. Berlin*, pp. 82–108 (1925); see also G. Braun, Zum Problem der Piedmonttreppen, *Internat. Congr. Geog.* 2, pp. 125–32 (1938).

[3] C. Sauer (*Univ. Cal. Publ. Geog.* 3 (4), pp. 199–290 (1929)), who follows Penck in interpreting landscape convexities and concavities as migrating horizontally to their present locations, adopts the American hypothesis of intermittent uplift to explain other features.

succession of benchlands does not indicate in the least that the upheaval proceeds intermittently, but that it is continuously accelerated" (W. Penck).

One of the last tasks which the veteran geomorphologist Davis undertook was that of examining with an open mind this theory of W. Penck. He arrived at the conclusion that it must be rejected, but apart from this verdict his perfectly fair exposition of the theory is of great value, and may be referred to[1] in view of the importance of the questions raised. The theory as applied to the development of nicks in river profiles is summarised as follows:

The lower course of the river, having a larger volume and therefore also a greater erosive power than the upper course, will be the first to be able to overcome the increase of its gradient due to accelerated upheaval. Hence as upheaval becomes faster, the larger lower course cuts down faster than before, but the weaker upper course does not. Thus a convex nick is formed in the river profile [at some unspecified point] separating an upper and a lower segment of its graded course. The top of this nick, retrogressively eroded [by the locally steep-pitching stream], serves as a local base-level for the upper segment of the graded course, which is therefore no longer controlled by the more general base-level at the margin of the [expanding] dome. Moreover, the local base-level is, while working upstream, raised with the rise of the dome and therefore rises in relation to the upper segment of the graded course. Hence there the erosive power of the upper stream is weakened, and concave basal side slopes are developed below the higher convex slopes. [In the meantime, the lower segment below the nick continues to deepen its valley and to maintain its course at grade in the margin of the rising dome.] Continued acceleration of upheaval causes the production of a series of nicks, all working headward, in the stream profile.

As regards the "step-like succession of benchlands", the central part of the dome is upheaved sufficiently rapidly to cause its dissection, but its more slowly upheaved margin is worn down by erosion to a lowland *pari passu* with its uplift, and, as the dome expands, successively eroded marginal lowlands are converted into higher-standing benches undergoing dissection. Davis has pointed out that the process by which successive benches are differentiated during continuous uplift has not been explained; and in view of the systematic arrangement of the benches, their correlation on different parts of the mountain flanks, and their obvious relation to nicks

[1] W. M. Davis, Piedmont Benchlands and Primärrumpfe, *Bull. Geol. Soc. Am.* 43, pp. 399–440 (1932).

in the river profiles, all demonstrated by Penck's field studies, he has reached the conclusion that they can be explained only by assuming that they were developed during pauses in a discontinuous uplift. "How can serious students...ever have persuaded themselves that continuous upheaval would or could cause intermittent erosion?" (Davis).[1]

CHAPTER XXI

Block-faulted Landscapes

No attempt has been made in the foregoing chapters to describe landscape forms that are directly related to the outcrops of faults, though it has been necessary occasionally to refer to fault movements as occurring along with warping and folding in the deformations of the earth's crust and of its surface, not only those that initiate "first" cycles and cycles following long periods of still-stand, but also those that interrupt earlier cycles at some intermediate stage.

Faults, either in the body of the rocky crust, or looked at from the viewpoint of the effects of their outcropping edges as influencing surface relief, may occur sporadically, as though minor breaks or tears had been formed at places of exceptional stress accumulation during warping or folding; but, on the other hand, in some regions deformation of rocks and surface has taken place mainly by faulting, which has broken the superficial crust into differentially moved blocks; and a combination of large-scale faulting with strong warping is not unusual. Faults of recent occurrence have been responsible for the initiation of many impressive landscape features that may still be recognised as fault-made in the sequential forms they have assumed as a result of the ravages of erosion.

Complications of the structure of the underlying rocks due to the presence also of faults that are very ancient as compared with the date of origin of any existing surface forms are common in most regions in which folded and deformed rocks of any age are present. Subsequent erosion has resulted in certain circumstances in the development of striking landscape features along the lines

[1] Since this chapter was written Penck's theory has been vigorously attacked by H. Baulig (*Jour. Geom.* 2, pp. 281–304 (1939)).

of outcrop of such faults, and description of land forms in this category has been reserved for inclusion in this chapter because of their many points of resemblance to features resulting from recent faulting, and because of the necessity of a critical knowledge of details of both types of landscape form for their successful differentiation.

Where faulting has just taken place actual breaks of the land surface occur—sudden descents from the high-standing to the low-lying sides of the faults (Fig. 170). These are *fault scarps*. They

Fig. 170. The Wellington fault scarp, which forms one boundary of the otherwise down-warped (and drowned) basin of Port Nicholson, New Zealand.

are striking landscape features in the early stages of the cycle introduced by the movements associated with the faulting. In soft material, such as that immediately underlying a newly uplifted sea floor, they are very quickly destroyed by erosion, but they are much longer lived in cycles introduced by uplift and deformation of pre-existing land (generally composed of more resistant rocks), and also where newly uplifted marine or alluvial beds are thin and rest on resistant rocks, which are exposed in the initial scarps formed by faults of large displacement.

Geologists whose field experience has been confined to those recently stable regions, like western Europe and eastern North America, in which fault scarps, in common with all other features that may be produced by very recent and contemporaneous differential movements whether of block faulting or warping, are entirely absent[1] have been inclined to discount the importance, and even doubt the existence anywhere, of surface features resulting directly from fault movement. The argument has been resorted to that differential movements are essentially so slow that, even if it be granted that faults extend upward to the earth's surface, the development of scarps along their outcrops will be prevented by

[1] Douglas Johnson recognises "not a single true fault scarp" in the stable New England-Acadian region. *C.R. XV Internat. Geol. Cong.* 2, p. 357 (1929).

erosion, embryonic scarps being worn down as rapidly as fault surfaces emerge.[1] To refute this argument it will be sufficient to refer to the discussion of the similar proposition that peneplains in general develop as surfaces that are "old from birth" (p. 189). All students of recently disturbed regions, such as western North America,[2] Japan, Turkestan, China,[3] Macedonia, and New Zealand, are convinced of the reality of fault scarps.

W. M. Davis, after having adopted Gilbert's explanation of the origin of the basin ranges as fault-bounded blocks formed at the surface and demonstrated its correctness by his own critical analysis of the geomorphic evidence, thus disposing of other competitive theories,[4] welcomed a confirmation of his adopted and proved explanation that resulted from the work of Louderback,[5] who was able to demonstrate that lavas found on the back slopes of certain blocks were parts of a former continuous sheet. This had flowed out on a surface of small relief and the compound mass had afterwards been broken into blocks, so that these carried up on their backs the lava covering. Such lava-sheeted block mountains have been described by Davis as "louderbacked".

In block-faulted regions of tectonic relief faults commonly occur in groups, the members of a group being parallel to one another. There may be two intersecting systems of such fractures, which cut the landscape up into quadrilateral *blocks*. Commonly, however, the blocks that have risen or subsided (relatively), or assumed tilted attitudes independently of one another, are elongated, and their terminations may be either cross faults or warped surfaces, as represented in Figs. 171, 172. Such blocks may sink or rise uniformly (movement relative to adjacent blocks only being taken

---

[1] "Faults are rarely visible at the surface of the ground as a sharp difference of level, since the processes of erosion usually keep pace with the movement of a fault." Brown and Debenham, *Structure and Surface*, p. 68 (London, 1929).

[2] G. D. Louderback dates the beginning of the great displacements that formed the ranges of the Great Basin as late Pliocene or post-Pliocene (*Univ. Cal. Publ. Bull. Dep. Geol.* 15, p. 38 (1924)).

[3] "At several places in...Kansu young fault scarps dislocate the Pleistocene terraces....These pass close to villages that suffered heavily at the time of the earthquake of 1920." G. B. Barbour, *Bull. Geol. Soc. Am.* 44, pp. 1152–3 (1933).

[4] W. M. Davis, The Mountain Ranges of the Great Basin (1903), reprinted in *Geographical Essays*, pp. 725–72 (1909).

[5] G. D. Louderback, Basin Range Structure of the Humboldt Region, Nevada, *Bull. Geol. Soc. Am.* 15, pp. 289–346 (1904).

into account), becoming in the one case a trough (*G*, Fig. 172), or *graben*, or in the other an uplifted block (*H*), or *horst*, bounded on two long sides by fault scarps. Some (*T*), however, are *tilted blocks*, with one side uplifted and the other depressed (relatively). A tilted block is limited by a fault scarp on the uplifted side only, and from the crest-line of this scarp an inclined *back slope* (*S*) of tilted land surface descends, to abut generally against the base of the scarp of the next upland block in a *fault-angle depression* (*F*). Examples of

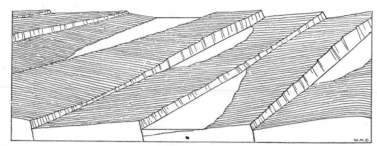

Fig. 171. Diversely tilted fault blocks, with lakes in fault-angle depressions. (After Davis.)

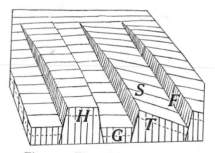

Fig. 172. Elongated fault blocks.

a horst, a tilted block, and a fault-angle depression, from the Otago block-faulted district of New Zealand are shown in Figs. 173, 174 and 175. In all these the smooth upland, or block surface, which contrasts with steep fault scarps, is either the extensively resurrected fossil peneplain of that region (pp. 208–14) or the peneplain that slightly bevels that surface in some places. Part or all of the stripping of the layer of weak covering beds from the fossil plain has taken place since the uplift with faulting occurred, but the blocks in their present state, though somewhat reduced in size by this erosion, retain almost perfectly the broad outlines of their original shape.

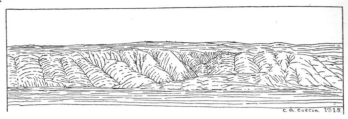

Fig. 173. Horst forming the Rock and Pillar Range, New Zealand; relief, 3000 ft.; slight north-westward tilt makes the upland plateau surface visible in this distant view.

Fig. 174. Small tilted block at Kurow, in the complex graben of the Waitaki Valley, New Zealand; relief, 1000 ft.

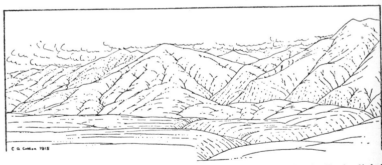

Fig. 175. Shag Valley fault-angle depression, New Zealand. A tilted, slightly dissected peneplain slopes down from the foreground to the base of a high fault scarp somewhat modified by erosion.

When some warping of the surface accompanies fault deformation, fault blocks grade into anticlinal uplifts, and tilted blocks especially, in New Zealand, have their place taken in some districts by asymmetrical anticlinal folds of the surface, with a reverse fault instead of an overturned limb on the steeper side.[1] Maturely dissected residuals of such uplifts form the Kaikoura Mountains (Figs. 82, 90) and also some smaller neighbouring ranges[2] (Fig. 176). Even normal faults, such as bound most of the great mountain blocks of the Great Basin province of North America, which

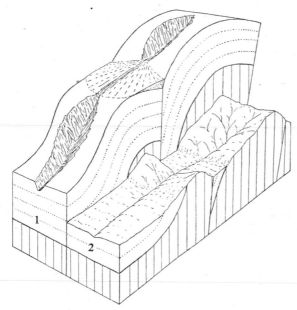

Fig. 176. Diagram illustrating a theory of origin of the Haldon Hills, New Zealand, and their remarkable drainage; 1, initial form; 2, present-day sequential form.

extends from the Sierra Nevada to Salt Lake, pass in places lengthwise into warped surfaces or sharp monoclinal flexures (Fig. 177), which are easily detected if the strata are elsewhere horizontal or nearly so, but which, as surface features, closely resemble fault scarps when the initial differences have been obliterated by erosion.

More gently inclined monoclinal scarps grade, however, into the warped and inclined surfaces of arched or domed uplifts, and are

[1] The "Saxonian" type of deformation.
[2] C. A. Cotton, The Physiography of the Middle Clarence Valley, N.Z., *Geog. Jour.* 42, pp. 226–46 (1913); The Haldon Hills Problem, *Jour. Geomorph.* 1, pp. 187–98 (1938).

recognisable owing to the presence of "bottle-neck" valleys dissecting them, separated by flat-iron shaped facets of the tilted surface (if it was formerly of small relief). A very large-scale example of a monoclinal scarp bounds the Blue Mountains of New South Wales on the eastern side, where the peneplain of the Blue Mountain plateau is sharply warped down towards the coast. It is divided into segments by the great escarpment-bounded bottleneck valleys of the Cox and Grose Rivers[1] (Fig. 79). Steeper

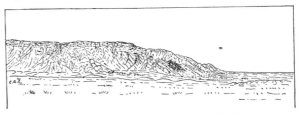

Fig. 177. Scarp developed by erosion on a monoclinal flexure of a resistant formation elsewhere horizontal, Coconino Point, Little Colorado Valley, Arizona. (Drawn from a photograph.)

monoclinal scarps dissected submaturely by numerous small bottleneck ravines occur in the Otago district of New Zealand. This type of valley, characteristic of the dissection of all smooth inclined surfaces, is seen, indeed, on all inclined parts of the peneplain (and resurrected fossil plain) of Otago (pp. 208, 217) whether they are steep enough to be described as monoclinal scarps or not (see Pl. XXXI, 2).

In regions deformed by compression, "thrust scarps", developed along the outcropping edges of low-angle or thrust fault surfaces, may perhaps be distinguishable in certain stages at least from scarps of normal or other nearly vertical faults. When maturely dissected they must be geomorphically indistinguishable, but, if formed by rapid dislocating movements, they may be expected to be, while fresh and young, characterised throughout their length by development (on a great scale, if the scarps formed are high) of landslide features, where the edges of diagonally upthrust blocks have crumbled. There may even be, it has been suggested, a separation as "splinters" of quite large landscape blocks that give way along normal gravity faults of the landslide type. "It is a fair question

[1] Griffith Taylor, The Australian Environment, Adv. Council Sci. and Ind. Mem. I, p. 150 (Melbourne, 1918).

whether fault splinters and normal-fault blocks,...attributed to rifting of the normal type, may not in some cases at least be the result of large-scale landslips on the imperfectly supported front of a thrust block."[1]

This explanation has been suggested to account for the appearance of gravity faulting along the boundaries of the Lake Albert graben, or "rift valley", in East Africa, though the main fractures determining the scarps may be thrusts (Wayland), but the suggestion has been adversely criticised. The hypothesis has been rejected for the origin of the young lava blocks, great and small, of southern Oregon, in favour of an explanation by normal faulting.[2] In Fig. 178, A (1, 2) represents separation of the first two of a long succession

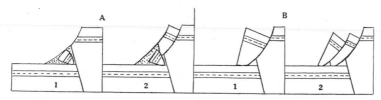

Fig. 178. Landsliding from a thrust scarp. (After Fuller and Waters.)

of small blocks or strips from an overhanging scarp as it emerges. These will fall and lie in all attitudes and be buried in the debris of crumbling. It has been argued that the development of step-faulted blocks of large size, B (1, 2), requires that a great overhanging scarp shall remain suspended and unsupported during its emergence until a large-scale landslide breaks away from it. It seems possible, however, that support might be afforded by an apron of detritus (A, 2) overridden by the emerging thrust scarp until landslide faulting on the required scale could take place.

In a cycle of erosion introduced by rapid earth movements in which faulting is prominent, the infantile surface is diversified by uplifted fault blocks (*block mountains*) and fault troughs and fault-angle depressions variously arranged in plan and probably presenting considerable variety of form. The usual features characteristic of landscape youth and river youth will be present, including

[1] Douglas Johnson, Geomorphologic Aspects of Rift Valleys, *C.R. XV Internat. Geol. Cong.* 2, p. 368 (1929).
[2] Fuller and Waters, The Nature and Origin of the Horst and Graben Structure of Southern Oregon, *Jour. Geol.* 37, pp. 204–39 (1929).

consequent lakes in troughs and on lowlying parts of tilted blocks, and consequent falls where new consequent and perhaps also pre-existing rivers descend steep fault scarps. Lakes may spill over from one tectonic basin to another (provided that the climate is sufficiently humid) forming integrated systems of consequent rivers that thread their way among and around the mountain blocks

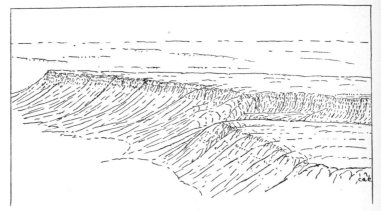

Fig. 179. Young lava horsts, Steens Mountain, Oregon. (Drawn from a photograph.)

in characteristic zigzags. The lakes are filled or drained, insequent and subsequent streams develop, stream profiles and the surface generally become graded, and the relief of the landscape is progressively reduced and destroyed as it is on other initially diversified surfaces such as have been discussed in earlier chapters.

The lava-covered region of southern Oregon and north-eastern California affords the best-known example of an extensive and very young block-faulted landscape (Figs. 179, 180) with consequent lakes on the lowest parts of the relatively down-faulted blocks and with very little modification of the initial forms by erosion.[1]

Southern Macedonia is another block-faulted region in which consequent lakes of considerable size still remain on the down-

[1] I. C. Russell, Geological Reconnaisance in Southern Oregon, *U.S. Geol. Surv. IV Ann. Rep.* pp. 431–64 (1885); Douglas Johnson, Geomorphologic Aspects of Rift Valleys, *C.R. XV Internat. Geol. Cong.* 2, p. 366 (1929); M. A. Peacock, The Modoc Lava Field, *Geog. Rev.* 21, pp. 259–75 (1931); R. E. Fuller, Geomorphology and Volcanic Sequence of Steens Mountain in S.E. Oregon, *Univ. Wash. Publ. Geol.* 3, pp. 1–130 (1931).

thrown blocks. These date from the "end of the Tertiary and beginning of the Quaternary periods, when the whole of the central Balkan Peninsula was convulsed....The entire rock base... became partitioned into blocks....The separate basins continued to hold water, and as the level of this gradually sank the lakes became isolated."[1]

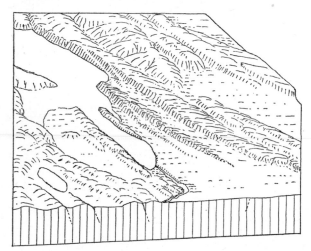

Fig. 180. Young fault-block landscape of narrow tilted lava blocks, forming eastern shore of Upper Klamath Lake, Oregon. (Copied from a block diagram of a larger area by Dr Erwin J. Raisz, in Johnson, *loc. cit.*)

In western North America the Colorado River, according to the interpretation of Blackwelder[2] (following up a suggestion of Newberry), came into existence very recently by taking a course as a consequent stream across and through a faulted and warped landscape comprising a string of large depressions of the surface, which became lakes that spilled over from one to another. The integration of drainage did not, however, immediately follow the deformation, for this occurred in a period of insufficient precipitation, but came later, when more water became available at the source of the river and the consequent lakes overflowed instead of being kept down to low levels by evaporation. "In time, enough

[1] A. G. Ogilvie, Physiography and Settlements in Southern Macedonia, *Geog. Rev.* 11, p. 174 (1921).
[2] Eliot Blackwelder, Origin of the Colorado River, *Bull. Geol. Soc. Am.* 45, pp. 551–66 (1934).

excess overflow may have developed to fill a series of basins all the way to the Gulf of California, thus forming a chain of lakes strung upon a river" (Blackwelder). Cutting down of the outlets as gorges (Fig. 24) has resulted in the drainage of all the lakes, and this has been followed by elimination from the landscape of lake-shores and erosion of lake-floor features.

It is probable that in many cases of uplift with fault deformation, whether affecting pre-existing landscapes or sea floors or other constructional surfaces, no consequent lakes have been formed, at any rate under humid conditions of climate. It would be, at least, unsafe to assume that in all cases deformation went on so rapidly that erosion accompanying the uplift of blocks might be ignored, and such erosion must cut gorges through blocks as they rise. Depending on the rate of deformation in relation to the rate at which rivers can deepen their valleys, however, there may commonly be some development of small temporary lakes, though far short of occupation of all rock-rimmed basins by water to their full un-eroded extent. Erosion also will be very active on all the steep slopes of rising blocks, supplying much waste, which will be deposited, temporarily at least, in the depressions, so that gravel-built basin plains may entirely or almost entirely take the place of consequent lakes.

The outflowing streams from a system or chain of lakes resulting from hypothetically instantaneous strong deformation, and also the integrated systems of valleys of which the lakes for a time formed a part, would be entirely consequent; and if the relief prior to the deformation were small, or the surface plane, even a small amount of instantaneous deformation would produce the same result. In the case of slow deformation, however, of a former land surface, antecedent rivers may be expected to persist in their courses to some extent, and to cut perhaps very deep gorges through uprising fault blocks.[1] The early development of such features is shown in Fig. 181.

The widely different stages of youth, maturity, and old age to which blocks in the North American Great Basin have attained as a result of erosion and degradation since their uplift indicates that in that extensive geomorphic province deformation by faulting

[1] Such a gorge, through the Canyon Range, Utah, is cited by Davis, *Cvijić recueil de travaux*, p. 321 (Belgrade, 1924).

has gone on intermittently throughout a long period. Though such extreme attenuation of the period of deformation need not be regarded as always associated with fault movements, it is probably never the case that all members of a group of blocks rise simultaneously and continuously until they assume their final elevations and attitudes. Even in the case of any single elongated block, it is extremely probable that some parts have risen before others. Thus

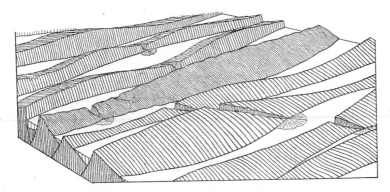

Fig. 181. "Little-modified potential surfaces of diversely tilted and warped blocks...in a humid region. The slope of the middle block is drawn to show its pre-faulting surface of low relief. The other block slopes are drawn as if the pre-faulting surface had been a plain. Consequent transverse gorges have been cut across sags in the crests of three background blocks by the outlets of consequent lakes. Oblique gorges have been cut in line through three foreground blocks, irrespective of their height and slant, by segments of a persistent antecedent river, the defeated work of which in three other blocks is indicated." (After W. M. Davis.)

some rivers that are strictly consequent on the earlier spasms of movement in a writhing uplift, and become fixed in gorges owing to their activity in downcutting, eventually do not occupy the lowest sags in the crests of blocks over or through which they flow. Such courses are anteconsequent (p. 109).

Across grabens[1] and along fault-angle depressions stream courses of a block-faulted landscape will be mainly consequent, and these reaches will be linked together by the gorges of transverse consequents, anteconsequents, and perhaps some true antecedents, though, of course, these last will not appear in a first-cycle landscape. The patterns of river systems thus made up will probably be

[1] Improvised English plural for a word of German origin.

irregular and zigzag, for consequent courses in the depressions may be very roundabout, where they skirt and avoid the higher blocks of the mosaic. The rivers of the southern and northern ends of the South Island of New Zealand afford good examples of such mainly consequent and rather roundabout courses on a block complex— for example, the Taieri (*T*, Fig. 182) and branches of the Clutha

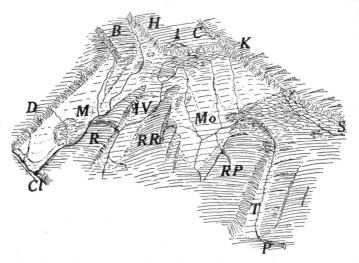

Fig. 182. Generalised diagram of the Central Otago district of large relatively depressed blocks traversed by consequent rivers, New Zealand. From the higher parts of some of the uplifted blocks adjoining these a thin cover has been stripped, but the main outlines of the initial blocks have been only slightly modified by erosion. Considerable erosion by lateral planation has taken place on soft covering strata in the Ida Valley (*IV*) and Maniototo (*Mo*) depressions; aggradation has been followed by dissection to the Clutha (*Cl*) local base-level in the Manuherikia (*M*) fault angle. *D*, fault scarp of Dunstan Range; *B*, *H*, *I*, *C*, *K*, tilted blocks and uplifted plateau of North Otago (northern highland); *R*, *RR*, Raggedy and Rough Ridge tilted blocks (cf. Figs. 152, 207); *RP*, Rock and Pillar horst (Fig. 173); *S*, Shag Valley fault angle (Fig. 175).

system (*Cl*, *M*). The south-eastward continuation of the Taieri is shown in Fig. 183.

Other very fine examples of rivers consequent on the slopes and fault angles in a mosaic of recently uplifted and tilted blocks are found in Japan, notably on the Boso Peninsula, near Tokyo (Fig. 184).

The tops and back slopes of horsts and tilted blocks that become block mountains may be eroded surfaces of an interrupted cycle of erosion, or may be plains of deposition, either uplifted portions of the sea floor or alluvial plains. In the former case rejuvenation will go on rapidly because of either tilting of the surface (Fig. 15) or the development of steep marginal slopes bounding a small uplifted area. Where the surfaces are initially smooth or nearly so

Fig. 183. Part of the block complex of Otago, New Zealand, showing the lower consequent and (?) anteconsequent course of the Taieri River. Both upper and lower blocks represent the present-day landscape. (Copied from a block diagram of a larger area by Professor W. N. Benson.)

—being parts either of plains or peneplains—the streams that drain them will be consequent on such slopes and corrugations as result from block uplift. Being relatively high-standing areas, they will be rapidly dissected with development of strong relief, and they will thereafter run through the usual stages of mature relief leading on to peneplanation. Block tilting of compound structures in which an undermass of resistant rocks with a planed surface carries on its back a weak-rock cover, affords ideal conditions for the resurrection of fossil plains, such as has taken place extensively in New Zealand (Fig. 182; see also Chapter XVIII). Whatever the structure, however, and whatever landscape reliefs may be developed at intermediate stages, a block-faulted region, like any other, must eventually

Fig. 184. Tilted blocks and consequent river courses in Japan. The steep slopes shown by heavy hachures are all scarped fronts of tilted blocks. After N. Yamasaki (Physiographic Studies of the South-eastern Part of Boso Peninsula, *Jour. Fac. Sci. Imp. Univ. Tokyo*, (2) 1, pp. 35–47 (1925)).

become a peneplain if subjected to erosion under normal humid conditions for a sufficiently long period uninterrupted by any renewal of earth movements.

CHAPTER XXII

Fault Scarps

THE characteristic features of faulted-block regions are the actual fault scarps that mark the outcroppings of fault surfaces continuing underground to a very great depth. It is very unusual to find any large uneroded part of an emergent fault surface, but there are records of the discovery of small areas of such surfaces bearing the slickenside markings that result from fault movement underground. In the infantile block-faulted lava district of Southern Oregon (p. 246), on a steep, undissected scarp facing Upper Klamath Lake (Fig. 180), "we have preserved that rare phenomenon, a portion of the actual fault-plane of a fault-block mountain".[1] The slopes of the majority even of very young fault scarps, if initially steep, have slumped or crumbled back considerably from the fault surface. At the base-line a nearly unbroken wall-like scarp may coincide approximately with the fault line (or surface trace of the fault), and yet slope back at a much gentler angle than does the fault surface—which is generally very steep, and may overhang. The common condition in the Great Basin fault scarps is intermediate between those shown as *a* and *b* in Fig. 185, but the slope of equilibrium in the diagram is of exaggerated steepness. It is recorded that observed slopes of undissected parts of fault scarps in that region are generally considerably gentler than observed dips of fault planes, which are commonly between 50 and 90°, and rarely

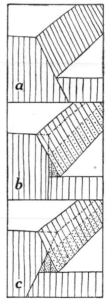

Fig. 185. Infantile forms of fault scarps on (*a*) backward-sloping, (*b*) vertical, and (*c*) overhanging faults.

[1] Douglas Johnson, Block Faulting in the Klamath Lakes Region, *Jour. Geol.* 26, p. 236 (1918).

less than 40°.[1] Overhanging fault surfaces seem to be the rule in New Zealand, as represented in *c*, Fig. 185. Further crumbling, if accompanied by erosional removal of talus material from the scarp base, or its engulfment on a sinking block, may result in retreat of such a scarp to the vicinity of the fault line before it is appreciably dissected.

It may be imagined that the spur-end facets...are really landslide surfaces of much less declivity than that of the true fault planes between the mountain blocks, and that great slabs of the steep-faced blocks slipped down these surfaces into the intermont depressions while the displacement was going on; for if the bounding fault of a mountain block be nearly vertical, and if upheaval of the block be relatively rapid, the upper edge of the block might not be able to sustain itself unsupported, and great slabs of it would therefore break off and slide down on the depressed block.[2]

Some very high, and still very young, fault scarps in central Washington were found by Russell to be completely mantled with the debris of landslides, which in their case accounted for "a very large portion of the details" of the relief.[3] In the stage of infancy, while the crest of a scarp has suffered as yet little or no dissection, large-scale landslides of the slump type may bite out amphitheatres, giving the scarp a scalloped outline. Such amphitheatre-shaped landslide scars break the line of the Wellington fault scarp, New Zealand (Fig. 186). In this case the landslides must have been engulfed below present sea-level in the Port Nicholson basin before it became partly filled with sediment.

Irregular or jagged fault surfaces are unknown. Faults are not far

[1] E. Blackwelder, The Recognition of Fault Scarps, *Jour. Geol.* 36, pp. 289–311 (1928).
[2] W. M. Davis, Faults, Underdrag, and Landslides of the Great Basin Ranges, *Bull. Geol. Soc. Am.* 33, p. 94 (1921). Compare, however, "The Basin Range Problem" (*Proc. Nat. Ac. Sci.* 11, pp. 387–92 (1925)), in which Davis returned to the opinion (originally Gilbert's) that fresh scarps present to view parts of the actual fault surface, even though they slope at only 30 to 40°. Examples of such supposed facets and strips of the fault surface were found in the rejuvenated basal parts of the scarps of large block mountains with total displacement of 5000–10,000 ft., and it was suggested that these might be the exposed deeper parts of fault surfaces that reached the originally dislocated land surface with very much steeper inclination. The mechanism of movement of broad block mountains on curved fault surfaces of such small radius is, however, difficult to imagine.
[3] I. C. Russell, A Geological Reconnaissance in Central Washington, *U.S. Geol. Surv. Bull.* 108, p. 40 (1893).

from plane, as a rule, but may be smoothly and broadly curved. Thus the lines traced by the bases of fault scarps must be "simple", either approximately straight or following broad sweeping curves. Occasionally abrupt salients, however, occur interrupting such lines, and some at least of these appear to be due not to irregularity of the main fault lines, but to the presence of minor faulted blocks or lagging portions of downthrown blocks clinging, as it were, to the fault surfaces, and having the appearance of buttressing the scarps. Such buttressing remnants have been termed *kernbuts* by Lawson.[1]

Fault scarps pass through a cycle of stages of dissection simultaneously with the dissection of the fault blocks of which they form part, and these present special interesting and diagnostic features

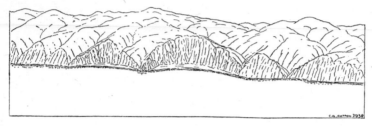

Fig. 186. Part of the Wellington fault scarp, showing amphitheatre-shaped scars due to landsliding.

of their own. Though a number of low scarps, or "scarplets", are known in an infantile condition, no high or large-scale fault scarps have been preserved in the form of continuous wall-like lines of cliff across the landscape, such as have been deduced above for the infantile stage. Even the scarp bounding the front of a backward-tilted block, though the catchment areas of the streams that flow (as consequents) down its slope are at first very small, is subject to rapid dissection because of its steepness; and a scarp that receives a considerable contribution of consequent (or other) drainage from an upland plateau or arched block surface above it, flowing in extended and consequent courses down the slope of the infantile scarp, must be dissected very rapidly indeed. Great contrasts are found between the stages of young and mature dissection exhibited by neighbouring scarps that may very well have been initiated almost

[1] A. C. Lawson, The Geomorphogeny of the Upper Kern Basin, *Univ. Cal. Publ. Bull. Dep. Geol.* 3, pp. 291–376 (p. 332), (1904).

simultaneously, and these can generally be correlated with the small or large part played in the dissection by streams fed from the surface above. Such contrast is found, for example, on opposite scarps of the slightly tilted Rock and Pillar horst (Figs. 173, 182).

In the simple case of the scarp of a backward-tilted block (Fig. 187), where the first-formed consequent streams on the scarp surface in its infantile condition, as prepared by landsliding in most cases, are alone responsible for the formation of dissecting ravines, these will extend back by headward erosion and rapidly develop notches in the crest-line (*B*), dividing it into segments, and these are rapidly reduced, as the ravines between them continue to

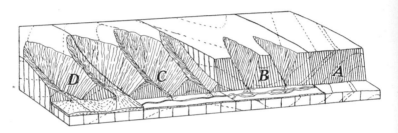

Fig. 187. Dissection of a fault scarp. *A*, initial (or infantile) form; *B*, *C*, *D*, sequential forms. Debris from dissection may be removed by a river, *B*, *C*; or accumulate as fans, *D*.

develop, to triangular *facets* bluntly truncating tapering spurs that descend from the upland above the scarp (*C* or *D*). The bases of these facets, or remnants of the infantile scarp, if not of the actual fault surface, are situated approximately at the fault, and so they trace a simple line (Figs. 187, 188).

In a humid climate spur-end facets become rounded at the edges even when the dissection of a scarp is still young (Pl. XXXV, 1), whereas under arid conditions they retain a sharp-edged character (Pl. XXXV, 2) in common with all forms resulting from rapid dissection.

As dissection advances towards maturity, general lowering of the land surface on the spurs and widening of the lower valleys of the dissecting streams gradually reduces the areas of the facets or blunt spur-ends until the spurs taper practically to points. These may still end in line, however, and very close to the fault trace, and as long as they do so dissection of the scarp has not passed beyond

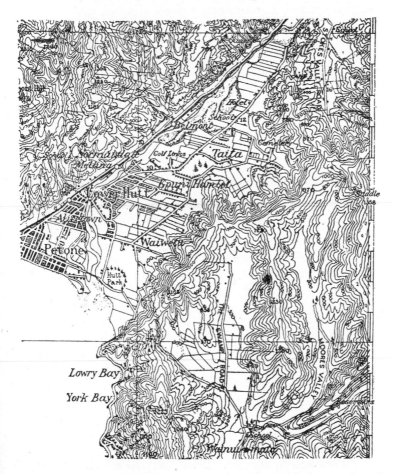

Fig. 188. The simple line traced by the somewhat dissected fault scarp along the north-western side of the Hutt Valley depression, Wellington, New Zealand. The eastern side, in contrast, is embayed, owing to down-warping and aggradation of a mature surface (cf. Fig. 165). Heads of valleys of the Wainui-o-mata system, aggraded owing to headward tilting, occupy the south-east corner of the area mapped (see p. 227). Scale: $\frac{3}{4}$ in. = 1 mile.

maturity (Pl. XXXV, 1, and Fig. 189). In old age of the fault scarp the much-reduced spurs will be worn back to varying distances from the fault line, all geomorphic traces of which will now be lost.

Scarps in course of dissection may or may not be modified by lateral stream corrasion. Under humid conditions of climate, consequent rivers traverse grabens and fault-angle depressions, developing eroded valleys in them, and removing perhaps all the debris of dissection of the fault scarps that flank them (Fig. 187, *B, C*). Where such is the case, they cannot fail to corrade the fault scarps themselves, truncating and faceting the spur-ends and cutting them back to alignments no longer related to the fault

Fig. 189. Maturely dissected southward-facing fault scarp of the Hawkdun Range (*H*, Fig. 182), part of the northern highland of Otago, New Zealand. Relief, 3000 ft. All the upper part of the scarp is undoubtedly a true fault scarp.

traces. The problem of recognition of fault scarps is thus complicated, and due allowance must be made for river work. A fault scarp descending to the sea may be similarly much obscured, or obliterated, by marine erosion, as has certainly occurred on parts of the coasts of New Zealand. Even wide lateral swinging of streams emerging from a fault scarp on to a bahada may be accompanied by a trimming back by lateral corrasion of the spurs beside them to the extent of developing an erosion scarp.[1] Fault scarps in arid regions have escaped such mutilation, except perhaps a certain amount due to the last-mentioned cause in the case of some scarps that have been dissected to full maturity. In arid and semi-arid regions, however, much waste accumulates on down-faulted blocks to form basin plains, and growing bahadas fringe fault-scarp bases (Fig. 187, *D*, and Pl. XXXVI, 1), burying them deeply, perhaps, while at maturity aggradation extends up the dissecting valleys.

It has been tacitly assumed in most of the foregoing discussion of fault scarps that deformation and uplift are so rapid that the

[1] Implied in Johnson's rock-fan theory (see p. 130).

effects of erosion accompanying uplift may be neglected. This is a simplified case only, however, and it must be recognised that much dissection may, and usually does, take place during a long period of intermittent movement, which, regarded broadly, may be considered to produce the same result as very slow continuous movement. While this is going on the spur-ends are always fresh and little modified—i.e. infantile—portions of the fault surface, and, as they are being actively cut down by ravines on each side as they rise, so that their edges cannot become rounded off, they present conspicuous sharp-edged facets. Thus, though circumstances may combine to preserve facets after movement has ceased, a con-

Fig. 190. Faceted fault scarp of the Wasatch Range, Utah. (After Davis.)

spicuous line of sharp-edged facets on the ends of numerous short spurs, especially where main spurs descending from a high block or range sprawl and are divided up by splitting ravines into minor spurs, can generally be taken as an indication of the presence of an "active" fault, or of a scarp that is still growing or has been growing until very recently. A classical example of such is the western scarp of the Wasatch Range, in Utah (Pl. XXXVI, 2, and Fig. 190), where "the mountain base is characterised by a series of basal spur facets, sloping at an angle of 38° or 40°.... The ridge or crest-line of the spurs slopes at angles that do not vary greatly from 25°" (Davis).

Some other features that are diagnostic of continued or, at least, of very recent movement are found in basins to which fault scarps descend, but are confined to scarps in arid regions. In an arid climate throughgoing rivers are not present to remove the debris of fault degradation, and this must, therefore, accumulate in front of scarps as bahadas and in the ephemeral lakes on basin floors.

Fault-scarp relief results from differential movement between blocks, and, where a fault is active, the movement that reveals a scarp may be wholly or in part a continuation of the subsidence or down-tilting of the block below the scarp. Continued degradation of a scarp after such fault movement has ceased is accompanied by such growth of the bahada in front of it that the axial line of the basin plain in the depression is pushed away from the fault, but frequent renewal or continuity of the down-tilting movement may keep the axial line close to the scarp base;[1] and the fans at the ravine mouths of a dissected scarp may seem "abnormally" small because

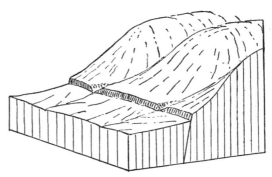

Fig. 191. A rejuvenated fault scarp. (Copied from a diagram by W. M. Davis illustrating a feature of the Lepini Mountains, Italy.)

the debris of early stages of dissection has been carried down by the sinking basin floor and is lost to view (Pl. XXXV, 2). Under such conditions alluvial deposits may have accumulated to an enormous thickness in front of a scarp, though surface forms will give no indication of this.[1]

Rejuvenated fault scarps have been freshened by renewed movement after some dissection in a period of rest (Fig. 191). The newer portion of the scarp may be nearly continuous, and steeper than the somewhat degraded spur-ends above it, joining these at a distinct shoulder; the dissecting streams, more or less completely graded farther upstream, will have steeper descents in their lower courses, and may plunge as falls over the edge of the new scarp. This is the case in all the small dissecting streams of the Wellington fault scarp (Fig. 170), New Zealand, which has been rejuvenated, though

[1] E. Blackwelder, The Recognition of Fault Scarps, *Jour. Geol.* 36, pp. 289-311 (1928).

several larger streams that debouch through the scarp are graded at their mouths. Sharp facets on the ends of some tapering spurs of this scarp are attributable to the same rejuvenation (Pl. XXXVII, 1). Even when the newer portion of a rejuvenated scarp itself becomes submaturely dissected, the spur-ends may retain a blunt or faceted form in contrast with the more subdued and tapering forms on higher parts of the same spurs, which may be regarded as parts of the earlier-formed and more thoroughly degraded scarp.

Numerous low scarps of rejuvenation so recently formed as to be as yet untouched by erosion are known in seismic regions of block

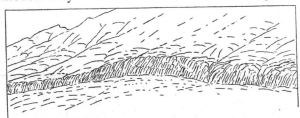

Fig. 192. Scarplet at Genoa, Nevada, which has appeared as a result of renewal of movement on a fault, the scarp of which bounds the Sierra Nevada on the east; described by Lawson (*Bull. Seism. Soc. Am.* 2, pp. 193–200 (1912)). (Drawn from a photograph.)

faulting, and the emergence of some such "scarplets", as Davis called them, has been definitely associated with the occurrence of earthquakes of tectonic origin (Fig. 192, and Pl. XXXVII, 2). The centres of origin of the earthquakes associated with the formation of these scarplets have been situated on great faults undergoing rejuvenation, but other scarplets associated with earthquakes appear sporadically in the landscape as though on the lines of small new dislocations.[1] The relation of some scarplets to deeply extending fault fissures is indicated by the association of hot springs with them—for example, with those at Genoa, Nevada, shown in Fig. 192.

In New Zealand a considerable number of long, continuous scarplets that have been described as "earthquake rents", closely parallel the base-lines of scarped ranges in such a way as to make it quite obvious that they are related to major faults. These

[1] A scarp 10 ft. high dislocated the main road between Westport and Murchison, New Zealand, in 1929; and numerous well-defined small scarps have been recorded as dislocating the landscape of southern Hawke's Bay, in addition to such disturbance of the surface as occurred during the Napier earthquake of 1931.

scarplets, however, face the main scarps to which they are so obviously related in such a way as to enclose between the scarps and scarplets shallow trenches (Pl. XXXVIII, 1), which are in places partly filled and converted into benches 20–30 ft. wide, and to indicate that the very recent movements that formed them have been reversals of the main movements on the faults. This suggests that great fault movements are not only discontinuous but are also frequently reversed, so that the total displacement evidenced by the uprise of a block mountain is the algebraic sum of many positive and negative movements. There appears to be no record of reverse-sloping scarplets outside New Zealand, with the exception of some mentioned by Blackwelder "southeast of Salt Lake, Utah, and in the northern part of the Panamint Valley of California", which traverse alluvial deposits and are suspected of being merely superficial features due to subsidence of unconsolidated material.[1]

Fig. 193. View southward along an "earthquake rent", the higher of two parallel "rents", along the eastern scarp of the Ruahine Range, North Island, New Zealand. (After Waghorn.)

The New Zealand "earthquake rents" trace simple lines like those of fault lines, some of them for great distances. One, for example, along the north-west side of the Awatere Valley tectonic depression, where it closely follows the line of a fault that is probably a high-angle thrust, is clearly marked for about 50 miles, a remarkable distance for any feature to be continuous in this land of assorted samples of land forms.[2] They never follow contour lines,

---

[1] *Loc. cit.* p. 304.

[2] Many "earthquake rents" have been reported in New Zealand. Actual descriptions accompanied by photographic illustrations of some of them have been made (among others) by R. J. Waghorn ("Earthquake Rents"...in Hawke's Bay, *N.Z. Jour. Sci. Tech.* 9, pp. 22–6 (1927)) and by R. Speight (Recent Faulting in the Southern Alps, *ibid.* 19, pp. 701–8 (1938)).

but ascend and descend as they cross bedrock spurs (Fig. 193), and are, therefore, not a result of local subsidence of alluvium, although they have been traced across fans also.[1]

Most tectonic earthquakes, as distinguished from those that are related to volcanic eruptions and are felt severely over a rather limited area, occur in regions of block faulting, and are directly caused by sudden movements on faults. Movement on the San Andreas fault, in California, such as resulted in the San Francisco earthquake of 1906, takes place horizontally, and, while it is not

Fig. 194. The Mino Owari fault scarp, formed in Japan in 1891. (Drawn from a photograph.)

uplifting block mountains, causes topographic complications that can be imagined. Such horizontal movement seems to be rather exceptional, and more usually the sudden jerks of movement on faults observed in association with earthquakes have been such as to produce vertical displacements, though some of the faults may be gravity faults and others thrusts. The formation of scarplets in association with such movements has already been referred to. A spectacular development of a scarp across the lines of valleys—the first development of a new scarp to be accurately recorded—took place in Japan in 1891 (Fig. 194).

The changes of level resulting from such upheavals produce the

R. Speight, *loc. cit.*

263

most striking results where they affect coastal areas. Very uniformly raised beaches emerged at Wellington, New Zealand, in 1855, and more irregular changes of level have since been recorded elsewhere —for example, at Yakutat Bay, Alaska, 1899, and in the vicinity of Tokyo, 1923. In New Zealand, in 1931, uplift took place on the north-west side of a line running north-eastward to the sea just south of Napier. The Napier wharves rose 6 ft. (Pl. XXXVIII, 2), and thousands of acres of tidal mud-flats were converted into a plain that has already become cultivated land.

Effects such as those just described are not the results of earthquakes, but are produced by earthquake-making earth movements. The actual earthquake shaking brings down landslides, large and small, the scars of which must be distinguished from fault scarps. Small scarps also, generally short and curved, and perhaps grouped in networks, develop owing to settling and subsidence of unconsolidated material, the surface of which may be thrown into irregular ridges and mounds without direct relation to underlying faults. Funnel-shaped pits, like small craters, are also formed, where fountains of water are ejected from sand or gravel deposits that settle as a result of agitation. Such minor features are formed in abundance in the severely shaken areas close to centres of earthquake origin.

CHAPTER XXIII

Erosional Features Related to Fault Lines

FAULTING, both recent and ancient, has frequently brought together weak and resistant rocks on opposite sides of a fault surface, or, in terms of a map, a fault-line, and removal of the weak rocks from one side by erosion leaves exposed a scarp of the more resistant rocks on the other side, and this persists in the landscape until it is degraded by erosion and obliterated. Such a scarp is a *fault-line scarp*,[1] and it is impossible to over-emphasise the importance of distinguishing with meticulous care between fault-line scarps and fault scarps, thus avoiding the possibility of introducing grave errors into interpretations of geological history from surface forms. Being exposed by differential erosion, "fault-line scarps develop best in the mature or post-mature stages of the erosion cycle. They may be non-existent in the very youthful stage, and theoretically they should be effaced before the end of the cycle.... They are most prominently brought out in relief during that long intermediate stage in the cycle which has been reached over the greatest areas of the continents" (Blackwelder). In contrast, therefore, with fault scarps, which are found only in seismic belts of contemporary earth movements, fault-line scarps are common the world over, being as widespread in their occurrence as the processes of differential erosion that produce them. In most parts of the world fault-line scarps have been developed as a result of a recent stimulation of erosion by a regional uplift dating long after the formation of the faults, and long after the fault scarps (if any) that marked initial breaks of the land surface in a long-past cycle have been obliterated by ancient erosion.

Fault-line scarps are of two kinds, *resequent* and *obsequent*,[2] according as they face in the direction the initial fault-scarp faced on the same line of fault or in the opposite direction. Thus a resequent scarp faces, or descends towards the structurally depressed (downthrown) side of the fault (Fig. 195, *A*, *c*), and an obsequent scarp towards the structurally uplifted (upthrown) side (*B*, *b*). Resequent fault-line scarps are commoner than obsequent, since it is true in a general way that the more deeply buried rocks, being older and having been subjected to greater pressure than those overlying them, are harder and more resistant to erosion. Exceptions to this rule are quite common in flat-lying sedimentary series, where limestones and sandstones are more resistant than other

[1] W. M. Davis, Nomenclature of Surface Forms on Faulted Structures, *Bull. Geol. Soc. Am.* 24, pp. 187–216 (1913). This term is well established, in spite of the obvious defect of not being fully self-explanatory to the extent of making clear the vital distinction between fault scarps and fault-line scarps—i.e. between tectonic features and those due to differential erosion. "'Fault-line erosion scarp' is less concise, but also less open to misinterpretation" (Johnson). The distinction has been overlooked by some writers (Brown and Debenham, *Structure and Surface*, p. 69 (1929)).

[2] W. M. Davis, *loc. cit.*

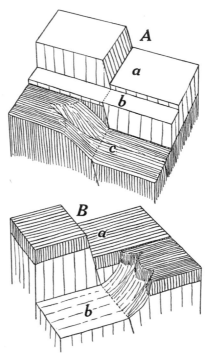

Fig. 195. Development of fault-line scarps, resequent (*A*, *c*) and obsequent (*B*, *b*); a hypothetical initial fault scarp is lettered *a* in each diagram.

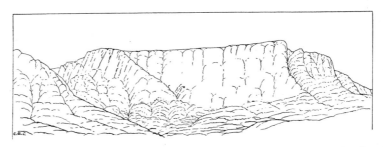

Fig. 196. Table Mountain, Cape Town, bounded by escarpments developed from obsequent fault-line scarps.

266

formations (shales, for example) on which they may rest, as also are lavas and intrusive sills; or older and more indurated rocks may overlie younger and softer rocks as a result of earth movements of overthrusting, as is the case along the eastern front of the northern Rocky Mountains. An example of a thick resistant formation extensively overlying weaker rocks is the Table Mountain sandstone of South Africa, and the escarpment of Table Mountain is an obsequent fault-line scarp developed at the boundary of a down-faulted block of the sandstone (Fig. 196).

A condition that leads readily to the development of an obsequent fault-line scarp from an ordinary ("consequent") fault scarp in a single cycle is the presence of a superficial sheet of lava lying on weaker materials before the fault movement takes place (Fig. 195, B). After the formation of the initial fault scarp, the lava on the upthrown block, being weakened by the presence of softer rock (exposed in the scarp) beneath it, is liable to be destroyed rapidly by erosion, but the lava on the downthrown side may survive much longer, its edge forming a fault-line scarp. Development of a resequent fault-line scarp in a single cycle is also obviously possible, and undoubtedly has very frequently occurred (Pl. XXXIX, 1), but the introduction of the middle strip b in Fig. 195, A, representing the surface at the end of a cycle introduced by the fault movement, makes the diagram fit the case of a great number of fault-line scarps in stable crustal regions, where a vast period of erosion, broken by uplifts of a regional character, may intervene between stages a and c. The New South Wales scarp (Pl. XXXIX, 2) serves as an example. A peneplain developed in such an intermediate cycle on soft rocks, so as to obliterate the last vestiges of the initial scarp (A, b), has been locally preserved in a well-known instance beneath a lava flow spread across the trace of the fault, where preservation of a mesa-like promontory of lava-capped shale on the downthrown side of a portion of the long scarp in Arizona known as the Hurricane "Ledge" (Fig. 197) proves this portion to be a resequent fault-line scarp.[1]

Where a fault-line scarp, either resequent or obsequent, is exposed owing to rapid removal of very soft material in an early stage of its emergence, it may exhibit an almost continuous wall-like

---

[1] W. M. Davis, An Excursion to the Plateau Province of Utah and Arizona, *Bull. Mus. Comp. Zool. Harv.* 42, pp. 27–9 (1903).

form, and the later dissection and degradation of this may simulate the stages of young and mature dissection of a fault scarp. Relative steepness of spur-ends, which may for a time even assume the form of facets, does not, therefore, serve to distinguish fault-line scarps from fault scarps. "Some fault-line scarps that have been identified by critical study are as high and as abrupt as most true fault scarps. The only necessary condition is an unusually massive and resistant formation exposed to erosion along a fault contact

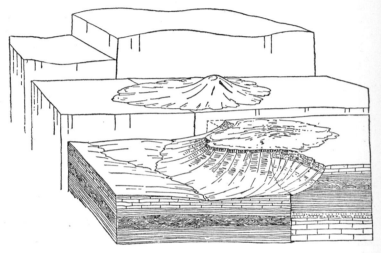

Fig. 197. Erosional ("fault-line") character of the scarp of the Hurricane fault, in Arizona, demonstrated by local preservation beneath lava of weak beds elsewhere removed by differential erosion from the downthrown side of the fault. (After Davis.)

with a very easily eroded formation. The latter may be reduced to a plain before the former has lost the aspect of youth."[1]

In disturbed regions, where fault scarps are found, many combinations of fault-scarp relief with erosional fault-line relief are possible (Fig. 198). One combination which forces itself on the attention of observers in New Zealand is that to which the name *composite fault scarp* has been applied. It must be of common occurrence in any recently deformed block-faulted region in which a cover of weak strata lies upon a resistant undermass. Fault scarps

[1] E. Blackwelder, The Recognition of Fault Scarps. *Jour. Geol.* 36, p. 294 (1928).

on this compound structure may degenerate into fault-line scarps in a single cycle, and will do so if the vertical displacement on the fault is of smaller measure than the thickness of the covering strata. Where, however, as in much of the southern part of New Zealand,

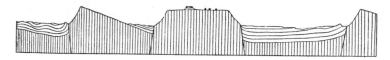

Fig. 198. Combination of fault relief and erosional relief, of the New Zealand types.

the thickness of the cover is considerably less than the displacements on the major faults, erosion even to the stage of late maturity will not wholly destroy the true fault scarps, though removal of the weak cover from downthrown blocks will frequently expose fault-line scarps below the base-lines of the fault scarps. In such a case the whole scarp, as it exists at the present day, is composite.[1] The

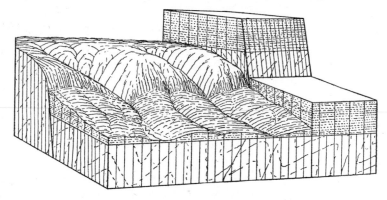

Fig. 199. Development of a composite fault scarp.

lower part of a composite fault scarp (Fig. 199), having been recently stripped, may be expected to retain something of the wall-like form of the fault surface (Pl. XL, 1), or may display blunt or faceted spur-ends (Fig. 199) resembling those of a rejuvenated fault scarp. If removal of the cover has been somewhat long

[1] C. A. Cotton, Block Mountains in New Zealand, *Am. Jour. Sci.* 44, p. 261 (1917).

delayed, blunt or faceted spur-ends may persist after the fault scarp above has been so thoroughly dissected that its spurs, if not thus extended downward, would taper to points.

Composite fault scarps, resequent fault-line scarps, and similar erosion scarps developed on monoclinal flexures have often hog-backs of resistant strata close to and parallel with their fronts. These are developed on the outcropping edges of beds formerly horizontal, and commonly members of the covering strata (if the structure is compound), which have been uptilted by the drag of the uplift (Fig. 200).

Fig. 200. Prominent high scarp at Takaka, New Zealand, with a hogback along the base of a scarp on the outcrop of a limestone stratum of the "cover" upturned by drag close to the fault that determines the scarp.

In another scarp combination, which has also unfortunately been called "composite" (Johnson), a fault-line scarp has been freshened by the development of a true fault scarp along its base as a result of renewal of movement on the ancient fault. An example cited is "that part of the Hurricane Ledge just south of the Virgin River in Arizona".[1]

Yet another variety of scarp to a certain extent resembling the resequent type of fault-line scarp, but not to be confused with it, is the *resurrected fault scarp*.[1] The "impressive escarpment" west of Clermont-Ferrand, in the Central Plateau of France, has been selected (by Johnson) as the type of resurrected fault scarps (Fig. 201). As in the case of the fault-line scarp of the Hurricane Ledge a lava flow across the fault-line at a time when it had no expression as a surface feature has preserved in the form of a promontory (Montagne de la Serre) a considerable remnant of the

[1] Douglas Johnson, Geomorphologic Aspect of Rift Valleys, *C.R. XV Internat. Geol. Cong.* 2, pp. 354–73 (1929).

weak superficial formations that elsewhere have been removed from the low side of the scarp, but in this case the weak materials consist of alluvium that accumulated in front of and during the growth of a rather ancient (Oligocene) fault. In general, resurrected fault scarps are those that have been re-exposed by erosion after having been buried, while fresh, beneath the bahada deposits which accumulate along block fronts in cases where the debris of their destruction is not removed by rivers. Resurrected fault-line scarps are also theoretically possible.

Fig. 201. The resurrected fault scarp at the Montagne de la Serre, near Clermont-Ferrand. (After a drawing by W. M. Davis.)

In Central France a resurrected graben is also recognised. In the case of some of the fault-bounded tectonic intermont basins of New Zealand, it is quite probable that the grabens and the fault scarps that enclose them are in part resurrected. The Hanmer Basin (Fig. 83) is an example. The outlet gorge (Pl. XL, 2), through a bounding scarp, is bordered by terraces, and of the alternative explanations, alluvial filling re-excavated, and very recent renewal of fault movements accompanied by redeepening in antecedent fashion of the outlet gorge, the former seems preferable.

Structural grabens excavated between fault-line scarps by differential erosion to form resequent lowlands are of common occurrence as broad landscape features—for example, the Scottish lowland, and the valley of the Rhine between the Vosges and the Schwarzwald. Many valleys also have been developed by headward erosion along fault lines, or rather along the belts of shattered and very much weakened rocks that are developed to a considerable breadth along the surfaces of displacement of great faults when, as is often the case, the fault is not a clean break but is "distributed" (Pl. V, 1). Such valleys, being wholly produced by erosion, and, in many cases, cycles later than the obliteration by ancient erosion of any consequent features on the same lines, are *fault-line valleys*[1] in the strict sense of the term. There is probably no such thing as

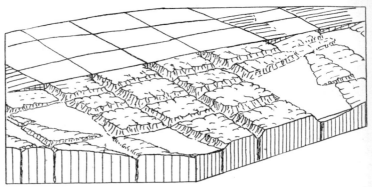

Fig. 202. Fault-line valleys of central Sweden. (After Davis.) After "a broad uplift without faulting, and in the cycle of erosion thus introduced and still current, many narrow fault-line valleys have been eroded along the shattered zone of the faults in the area of the resistant crystallines, and broad lowlands have been excavated, partly by aid of glacial erosion, in the large patches of covering strata" (Davis).

a true "fault" valley, in the sense of a gaping fissure that guides consequent drainage, at any rate on such a scale as to make it of any importance; but consequent rivers that are guided by fault-angle depressions are "fault" features rather than "fault-line" features, even though they may have deepened their valleys along the fault lines. Fault-line valleys are termed *résequent* and *subsequent* (Davis) according as they do or do not follow lines of former consequents related to the same faults, but as it is generally impossible to come to a decision on this point, the distinction is of little value.

The stream pattern of central Sweden results from the circumstance that the streams have been developed by headward erosion

---

[1] W. M. Davis, Nomenclature of Surface Forms on Faulted Structures, *Bull. Geol. Soc. Am.* 24, pp. 187–216 (1913).

on an ancient rectangular or rhomboidal fault network (Fig. 202); and a neat example of an isolated fault-line valley is that occupied by the upper course of the Kaiwarra stream, Wellington, New Zealand (Fig. 54), where rapid headward erosion along a fault line has resulted in capture of a stream that had earlier discovered and extended headward along an adjacent segment of the fault-line.

With the object of distinguishing where necessary between such features and consequent valleys in narrow grabens (so-called "rift

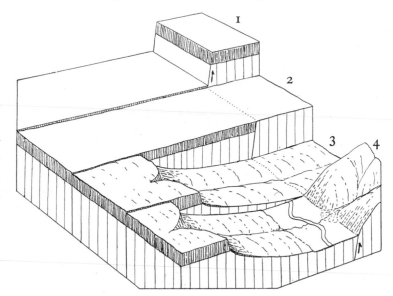

Fig. 203. Successive stages in the development of an "obsequent-consequent" pseudo-graben valley.

valleys") Johnson has deduced the forms of graben-like valleys that may be developed by a combination of fault-line erosion and renewed faulting along single faults[1] (Fig. 203). Such a valley will be enclosed between an obsequent fault-line scarp and a fault scarp.

Intermediate in character between faults that are clean breaks and those that are distributed through a fault-zone or shatter-belt of crushed rock are *step faults* and *splintered faults*. In the former the dislocated land surface, or that revealed by erosion in the case of

[1] Douglas Johnson, *loc. cit.* p. 369.

fault-line scarps, descends in a step-like series of low scarps, which in some large-scale examples remain separate, but which, if small and numerous, tend to merge into a single scarp as degradation proceeds,[1] though even at a stage of maturity of dissection of the compound scarp they may be traced as jogs in the crest-lines of the spurs that descend from the face of a block mountain. In the case of a splintered fault, while the displacement on the whole fault system remains reasonably constant, dwindling displacement on one line (such as *ab*, Fig. 204) is compensated by the development

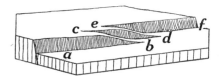

Fig. 204. A splintered fault dislocating a plane surface.

parallel to it of another line of fault (*cd*) with increasing displacement, and this may occur more than once (*ef*); so that discontinuous faults *en échelon* separating successive splinters form the complex boundary between adjacent relatively upthrown and downthrown blocks. It is as though faulting had followed pre-existing lines of weakness—lines of least resistance—running diagonally across the boundary between two tectonic blocks.

Both fault scarps and fault-line scarps may exhibit splintered features. They are common on the infantile fault-scarps of southern Oregon (Figs. 180, 205). Fig. 206 is a copy of Davis's drawing of the great splinter of the Hurricane fault in southern Utah. Several very well-defined splinters diversify the line of the composite scarp separating the resurrected fossil plain (or peneplain) of South Canterbury, New Zealand, from the graben occupied by the valley of the Waitaki River. That figured (Pl. XLI, 1) forms a broad ramp, or gangway, descending 1000 ft. from the upland plateau, with which it is continuous at one end. In Central Otago two splinters with the dimensions of subsidiary fault blocks descend ramp-like from the scarp of Rough Ridge (Fig. 207).

So important is the distinction of true fault scarps, or features of a first post-faulting cycle, from those produced by differential

[1] G. D. Louderback, Morphologic Features of Basin Range Displacements, *Univ. Cal. Publ. Bull. Dep. Geol.* 16, pp. 1–42 (1926).

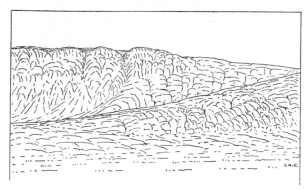

Fig. 205. Splinter, or "inclined step-fault block" (Fuller), on the young fault scarp of Northern Steens Mountain, Oregon. (Drawn from a photograph.)

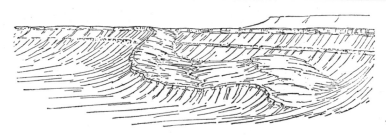

Fig. 206. Rock splinter on the Hurricane fault. (After Davis.)

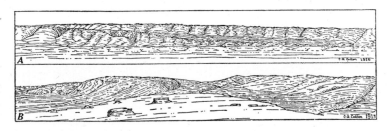

Fig. 207. Two views of the splintered scarp of Rough Ridge, New Zealand. A, view looking north-west; B, view looking south-west along the splinter shown in view A.

erosion, that it would be desirable, if it were possible, to set out clear-cut rules for their differentiation in the field. In practice, however, difficulties arise. Some criteria that have been relied on are merely proofs of the presence of faults so closely parallel to scarps as to have obviously some causal relationship to them, but the distinction between fault scarps and fault-line scarps remains to be made. The most easily applied test is the purely artificial and unscientific one that in many large regions, indeed in all parts of the world except certain definitely limited regions, no true fault scarps have ever been reliably identified.[1] In seismic regions of recent faulting, however, the problem of fault-scarp identification retains its importance. Here the isolation of fault scarps must be tackled in two stages. Scarps related to faults may first be distinguished from other features more or less resembling them, and then tests may be applied to prove or disprove fault-scarp character, and so to determine whether the features of the landscape are tectonic or residual.

The commonest of the landscape forms from which features related to faults and fault-lines must be distinguished are: (1) valley sides cut back to lines of bluffs by lateral stream planation; (2) trough walls straightened and steepened by glacial erosion; (3) lines of sea cliffs formed where marine erosion is cutting back a coast; (4) steep mountain fronts that are receding as a result of long-continued erosion under arid conditions; and (5) structural escarpments.

Except in the very exceptional case of undissected scarps of equal height facing each other across a narrow graben, the distinction from (1) and (2) is easily made. In all ordinary cases fault scarps do not occur in matched pairs, and in the very common case of a fault-angle depression that may become a river valley, the cross-section is highly asymmetrical. For the Hutt River valley, Wellington, N.Z., this asymmetry is brought out strongly by the contoured map (Fig. 188), which shows a fault scarp forming a straight wall on the north-west side, while the opposite valley side is embayed, with extensions of the flat valley floor in the embayments.

---

[1] " I know of no feature in the whole of France that can be confidently accepted as a true fault scarp" (H. Baulig, *The Changing Sea-Level*, p. 34 (1935)). See also footnote, p. 239.

A useful point of distinction from a wave-cut coast is the absence at the base of a fault scarp facet of a recognisable broad abraded rock platform that might indicate the plan of former coastal salients cut back by marine erosion, and would be cut in the same kind of rocks as those exposed in the cliffs. A plain strip at the base of a fault scarp would, on the other hand, be a bahada underlain by the waste resulting from degradation of the scarp, or, in the case of a young fault scarp descending into the sea, there would be at first, as a rule, deep water close to the shore, and in early sequential stages an apron of marine sediments separated from the cliff base by a *narrow* strip of marine-cut platform. Along the base of the Wellington fault scarp, for example, which descends to the north-west shore-line of Port Nicholson, New Zealand (Fig. 208), absence of reefs of rock and the presence of deep water close to the cliff base are good indications of the occurrence of recent fault movement. In the case of marine erosion developing a fault-line scarp, outlying reefs cut down by wave action would consist of rocks distinctly different from and weaker than those in the scarp; but a shore-line of submergence localised on

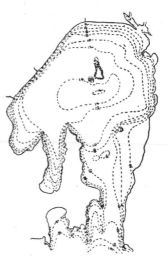

Fig. 208. Bathymetric contour map of Port Nicholson, N.Z. (contour interval, 2 fathoms). Deep water is present along the north-west straight shore-line, which is the line of the Wellington fault.

either a young fault scarp or a fault-line scarp[1] would resemble a fault scarp descending initially into the sea.

In front of a scarp of desert erosion there is a complementary rock-cut sloping plain, or "pediment", veneered only thinly with discontinuous alluvial gravels, whereas a young fault scarp under similar conditions of climate has at its base only a narrow bahada, and this, together with any alluvial or lake-formed plain in front of it may be underlain by alluvial deposits to a great depth, as has been indicated in some cases by well-drilling.

As regards the distinction of fault scarps from structural escarp-

[1] Douglas Johnson, *The New England–Acadian Shore-line*, pp. 32–4 (1925).

ments, a fault scarp can, of course, be formed in rock formations the structure of which favours the development of escarpments, and fault-line scarps also can originate in strata with such structure suitably faulted. Thus many fault scarps and fault-line scarps, as they are worn back by erosion from the faults, are also escarpments. The distinction of such scarps from simple escarpments does not generally present difficulties, however, for in rock formations with simple escarpment-making structure, the presence or absence of great faults is generally obvious. In contrast with the necessary parallel relation of rock strike and outcrops with scarp trend in structural escarpments, there is obviously no necessary correspondence between the strike of strata or fold axes and the trends of scarps—especially true fault scarps—related to the lines of faults. Thus the outcrops of inclined or folded strata commonly run obliquely up and down scarp faces, as is well illustrated in Pl. XLI, 2.

Some special features of fault scarps that may be relied on, where they are developed, to make a distinction from fault-line scarps have been listed by Blackwelder.[1] Among these the following may be noted:

(1) "Poor correlation between rock resistance and surface form" contrasting with "close" correlation in the case of fault-line scarps. Definitely development of a fault-line scarp depends on a strong contrast in the resistance offered to erosion by rocks on one side of the fault as compared with those on the other.

(2) Alluvial deposits on the downthrown block thickest near the fault-line.

(3) Lake, or "sink", close to the scarp base.

(4) Alluvial fans abnormally small (Pl. XXXV, 2).

Criteria (2), (3) and (4) are not always available in humid regions, where throughgoing rivers of considerable size in the depressed areas of a fault mosaic may either carry away all the detritus resulting from fault-scarp degradation, or redistribute it in such a way as to mask deep basin-plain filling. So also one of Blackwelder's indicators of fault-line scarps, "little or no alluvial deposit on the downthrown block", cannot be applied to distinguish them in humid regions. He remarks, moreover, that "a sheet of alluvial

[1] E. Blackwelder, The Recognition of Fault Scarps, *Jour. Geol.* 36, pp. 289–311 (1928).

materials 200 ft. to 400 ft. thick may be the result of a mere climatic change".

(5) Frequent severe earthquakes. These indicate that "movement is actively going on; and it is only such relatively frequent dislocations that outstrip the erosional processes and produce notable fault scarps".

(6) Basal scarplets. Association of the emergence of these with earthquakes is well known.

(7) Displacement of an older topographic surface. It is almost too optimistic to hope to find a landscape surface dislocated by faulting but in such a state of preservation that the parts below and above the fault may be neatly fitted together again. Remnants or

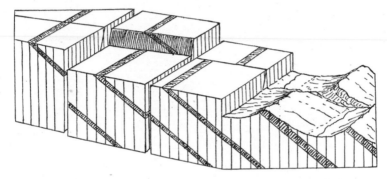

Fig. 209. Development of homoclinal ridges offset by a fault.

traces of a prefaulting surface thus dislocated may sometimes, however, be tentatively correlated. Too often the land surface of a downthrown block has been deeply buried under extensive bahada or basin-plain deposits; or it may have been ruthlessly and rapidly cut to pieces by river corrasion.

In contrast with the foregoing, positive evidence leading to a decision that a scarp is a fault-line erosional feature is available where an exceptional local cause has led (as in the case of the Hurricane Ledge example, referred to earlier in this chapter) to preservation up to a high level of uneroded rock formations that have elsewhere been stripped away to expose the scarp. Definitely proved occurrence of superposed drainage across the scarped area is equally decisive. Of this Blackwelder has cited examples.[1]

[1] *Loc. cit.* p. 308.

In case horizontal offsetting of the outcrops of inclined strata, and of homoclinal relief features developed on some of these where they are intersected by faults, should be mistakenly accepted as a proof of the occurrence of horizontal longitudinal movement of the San Andreas type along the faults, it is well to bear in mind that such offsetting is commonly a result of ancient faulting in the vertical direction followed by homoclinal shifting (p. 98) during the lowering of corresponding surface features to a common level on opposite sides of the fault. Small fault-line scarps, resequent and obsequent, are developed on the dislocated ends of strata left standing in relief as homoclinal ridges by differential erosion during this process (Fig. 209).

CHAPTER XXIV

Limestone Landscapes

ALTHOUGH chemical weathering is accompanied by the removal in solution of some of the products of decay from most wasting land surfaces, during young and early mature stages of the cycle of erosion mechanical corrasion is so active that it overshadows chemical corrosion, and only when old age approaches is more than an almost negligible proportion of the total lowering of a land surface to be ascribed to this process, except in terrains of soluble rocks. In these, however, the effects of corrosion by solution assume importance in earlier stages of the cycle also, and in some regions the normal cycle of erosion is even superseded by a special "limestone" cycle. Limestone and the closely related dolomite and magnesian limestone are the only soluble rocks that occur commonly in sufficiently large masses to produce important landscape effects.

Well-drained upland surfaces of limestone are often completely bare of soil, and the effects of solution by rain water are visible in remarkable small-scale relief forms of the bare-rock surfaces of such "limestone deserts". Among these are deep flutings (lapiés), due to development of parallel furrows by solution where rain water runs down steep rock faces (Pl. XLIV, 2). (Such flutings, though rare, are not unknown on rocks other than limestone, e.g. being seen on basalt undergoing chemical weathering in Hawaii.[1]) A miniature mature landscape of close-set ridges separated by vertical-sided furrows several feet deep (*karrenfeld*) may develop (Pl. XLII, 1). A somewhat similar irregular rock surface is formed where limestone is weathering beneath a residual soil, and it has been suggested that the karrenfeld is such a surface stripped of its soil in recent times after deforestation of the land,[2] but it is highly probable that some, if not most, karren features are developed without much soil cover. They occur under jungle vegetation on the limestone surfaces of raised coral reefs on Pacific islands—for example, forming the "makatea" of Mangaia.[3]

Solution underground, resulting in enlargement of fissures, is responsible for the development of larger landscape features that characterise a limestone landscape, or *karst* landscape, as it is frequently termed, the name having been taken from the Karst, or Carso, a district in the Dinaric limestone region east of the Adriatic Sea. Enlargement of underground water channels by solution leads in most cases to a drastic reduction of surface run-off, for rain water is swallowed by the ground and sinks at once to join the ground water. When fissures are so enlarged that they become open passages or strings of caverns, they offer infinitely less resistance to the flow of water through them than do the minute passages between the grains, or the narrow joint crevices, in other rocks; and so there is little or no heaping of water under interfluves of the land. Rain water descends at once to join a deep-lying body of ground water with an approximately horizontal surface, or water table, the level of which is controlled by that of the lowest available outlet; and through this the water gushes out as a ready-made river, or joins one of the few main streams draining the region in

---

[1] H. S. Palmer, Lapiés in Hawaiian Basalts, *Geog. Rev.* 17, pp. 627–31 (1927).
[2] W. M. Davis, An excursion in Bosnia, etc., *Bull. Geog. Soc. Phil.* 3, p. 32 (1901).
[3] "The surface is formed entirely of hard splintery limestone projecting everywhere in sharp serrated pinnacles 10–15 ft. in height, and is trenched by numerous crevices with vertical or even overhanging sides, many of them expanding into caves of irregular form and extent. The whole Makatea structure is riddled with chasms, while vertical pinnacles and palisades with needle-like projections and razor edges are found everywhere in extravagant profusion. And this intricate rocky maze is covered with a tangle of interlacing vegetation, making a surface almost impossible to traverse" (P. Marshall, Geology of Mangaia, *Bishop Mus. Bull.* 36, p. 20 (Honolulu, 1927)).

the bottom of its deeply cut valley (Pl. XLII, 2). Thus small surface streams, such as occur in branching systems on other terrains and dissect the land surface, are non-existent or very rare, though some may be present that are related to "perched" ground water held up by local intercalations of impermeable rock. Where, owing to the nature of the relief, the ground water is not at a very great depth, seasonal fluctuations of the ground-water level may cause a few streams to flow intermittently, as in the case of some on the English Chalk.[1] In the absence of surface streams there can be little or no valley development by mechanical corrasion or normal dissection of the surface. There is very wide spacing of valleys and the texture

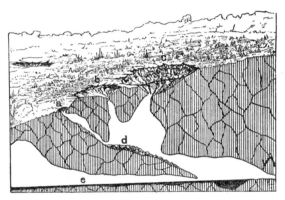

Fig. 210. Relation of sinkholes (*a, b, c*) to caverns and underground drainage (*d, e*) in limestone. (After Cvijić, by courtesy of the *Geographical Review*.)

of normal dissection is very coarse, but the place of dissection by minor streams is taken by a pitting that results from development of features related to underground solution, and a "fine-textured" surface of a special kind may result (Pl. XLIII, 1).

Funnel-shaped, or occasionally precipitous-sided, sinks (*sinkholes, swallow holes*, or, in the Dinaric karst region, *dolines*) varying in diameter from a yard or two to about a thousand yards, are related to enlarged fissures below ground, which lead water down into caverns and open galleries that are underground stream courses (Fig. 210). They do not, as a rule, remain as open pits of great depth, but are partly choked by debris fallen from the sides and washed in from the surface; and they may thus hold water for

[1] Wooldridge and Morgan, *The Physical Basis of Geography*, Chapter XI (1937).

a time after heavy rains, forming temporary lakes in the case of the larger dolines.

Where the level of ground water is sinking, as new outlets are opened at lower levels, caverns and shafts formerly filled with ground water are abandoned, and several tiers or stories of caverns may be thus left—as at Jenolan Caves, in New South Wales—the higher caverns being afterwards partly filled with calcite redeposited as stalactites and stalagmites. Anciently enlarged caverns and underground stream courses may be found in a more or less ruined and unroofed condition, and, if still traversed by streams of water, may become river gorges, with perhaps occasional remnants of the roofs forming "natural bridges". Arches that have originated in this way appear in Pl. XLIV, 1. An alternative explanation that has been offered for some natural bridges in soluble rocks is that rivers have abandoned courses over falls of the Niagara type, making their way along fissures enlarged by solution so as to issue below the edges of their former falls.[1] Celebrated natural bridges in limestone formations are the great Natural Bridge of Virginia, near Lexington,[1] and that in the gorge of the Rummel, at Constantine, in Algeria, figured by de Martonne.[2]

Large sinkholes may be arranged in line in such a way as to indicate the presence of an underground river. (One of such a series is figured in Pl. XLIII, 2.) They may be aligned along the bottom of the valley of a former surface stream that has ceased to flow owing to lowering of the ground-water level, or, on the other hand, may be the first stage in the unroofing of an underground water-course in process of transformation into a gorge (Fig. 211).

Where, in the Dinaric karst region, a surface stream plunges into an open vertical shaft that has been enlarged by solution, this is termed a *ponor*, or the place of these more or less circular shafts may be taken by narrow, elongated chasms (*bogaz*). Where a stream flowing in a valley is thus swallowed into the ground, the abruptly terminated valley is termed "blind". Valleys occupied by surface streams issuing from caverns may have a similar form at the head.

The last residuals of a limestone stratum that is wasting away by solution where it rests upon non-calcareous rocks are *hums* (Pl.

[1] C. D. Walcott, The Natural Bridge of Virginia, *Nat. Geog. Mag.* 5, pp. 59–62 (1893).
[2] E. de Martonne, *Traité de Géographie physique*, 5th ed., p. 661 (1935).

XLIV, 2), but the term is applied also to any small "monadnocks" of limestone in the Dinaric karst region. Small residual mesas, or "hums", of limestone, riddled with caverns, remnants of a sheet formerly continuous over the now resurrected fossil plain of the plateaux of northern Nelson, New Zealand, have been referred to on p. 211.

The various features mentioned and described without system in the foregoing pages as characteristic of the erosion of limestone

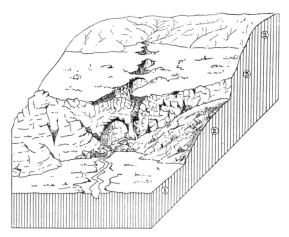

Fig. 211. Transformation of a cavern into a gorge in a tributary of the Danube in eastern Serbia; 3, limestone intercalated between sandstone layers, 2. (After Cvijić, by courtesy of the *Geographical Review*.)

may be present sporadically throughout parts of a limestone terrain that is undergoing normal erosion and exhibits elsewhere typical mechanically eroded valley forms. They interfere in such cases only locally with the development and progress of a landscape through the normal stage of maturity. In other cases, however, these special forms are developed in such profusion as to diversify the surface to the exclusion of features of normal stream origin. Other conditions being favourable, such replacement depends very largely on the presence of open joint fissures in the limestone, which are the initial channels sequentially enlarged by solution. Some limestones, on the other hand (e.g. the Amuri limestone, where it occurs extensively in a thick mass in the Marlborough district of New Zealand), though they have been thoroughly shattered by earth movements, have had their joint fissures completely healed by deposition of calcite veins below water-level.

To a certain extent the development of features related to underground solution is independent of climate, but a seasonal variation of rainfall may result in a considerable seasonal change in the level of the water table (level of saturation) in the underground rocks. Where this occurs to an appreciable extent it leads to alternation of normal erosion by surface streams with erosion by underground solution in parts of the districts affected, and this may be a reason for the particularly full development of the "limestone" or "karst" cycle, or cycle of erosion by solution, in the extensive Dinaric limestone region.

Where the relation of a mass of limestone rocks to general base-level and to associated relatively impermeable formations determines that the water table shall not descend to such a depth as to rob surface channels of their streams, erosion on limestone follows the same course as on other terrains—that is to say, normal systems of valleys are eroded. Should the water-level sink, however, after some development of valley features has taken place, the normal landscape may be abandoned by the streams that have eroded it, all, or all but the largest, of them taking to underground courses. All valleys at higher levels become "dry" valleys, and only a few of the larger and deeper valleys, into which the underground streams discharge as springs, remain occupied by rivers and continue their normal development. If the cycle of erosion be not far advanced, these may continue to deepen their valleys as steep-walled trenches, causing the water-level to descend still deeper, while the valley systems of their former tributaries will be left stranded on a dry upland landscape, perhaps approximating to a limestone-desert plateau, like that traversed by the deep trench of the Rhone in the south of France.

Such is believed to be the origin of a landscape of dry valleys on the Chalk terrain of south-eastern England, where retreat of a Chalk escarpment, accompanied by development of valleys to progressively deeper levels in the underlying impermeable formation as it was uncovered, has lowered the water-level.[1] In some other regions such abandonment of the surface by normal super-

[1] See Wooldridge and Morgan, *The Physical Basis of Geography*, Chapter XI (1937), and authorities there cited.

ficial drainage has been followed by a more complete replacement of valley forms by the irregularly pitted karst landscape that results when all surface water is swallowed into underground channels.

In the Dinaric limestone region, as interpreted by Cvijić,[1] the history of karst development begins with uplift of a peneplain extending over a region of intensely deformed thick limestone strata with intercalations of impermeable formations, on areas of which, forming the surface in some districts, normal mature stream-eroded landscapes are to be found at the present day. The uplift of the peneplain was irregular, being accompanied by block faulting, or possibly subsidence of elongated grabens may have followed uplift. Thus a tectonic origin is ascribed to the larger of many mountain-rimmed basins, some without surface outlets, that characterise the region and are termed *poljes*. As the Jugoslav term *polje* is applied to basins of various sizes and various origins, it may be as well to distinguish those initiated by earth movements as "tectonic poljes".[2]

In an early stage of landscape youth tectonic poljes would be connected by gorges, and the drainage of the whole region might for a time be superficial, but this condition must soon have given place to one in which the enlargement of fissures by solution had lowered the water table to such an extent that much drainage was led off through underground channels. Thus some (though not all) tectonic poljes are now without outlet gorges. Some normal valleys also, after being opened out by stream erosion to a considerable size on easily eroded formations, have had their drainage diverted to underground channels and have become poljes—for example, the polje of Kostan, near Novi-Bazar. This can take place as a result of a sinking of the water table, which, in a region of open underground channels, can be brought about by lowering of local base-levels due to progressive valley deepening in a neighbouring river system.

---

[1] J. Cvijić, Hydrographie souterraine et évolution morphologique du Karst, *Rec. Trav. Inst. Géogr. Alpine*, 6, pp. 375–426 (Grenoble, 1918); E. M. Sanders, The Cycle of Erosion in a Karst Region (after Cvijić), *Geog. Rev.* 11, pp. 593–604 (1921); see also A. Penck, Über das Karstphänomen, *Vort. Ver. Verbr. naturw. Kenntn. Wien*, 44, pp. 1–38 (1904).

[2] W. M. Davis was of the opinion in 1901 that warping might account for the initiation of some poljes, but he apparently had not then examined the hypothesis of block faulting (An Excursion in Bosnia, Hercegovina, etc., *Bull. Geog. Soc. Phil.* 3, pp. 21–50 (1901)).

The whole landscape (on limestone terrain) that is sufficiently above ground-water level to be without surface streams is now subject to complete disintegration of existing normal surface forms and their replacement by dolines, which grow in size to form larger funnels and collapsed areas (termed *uvalas*) with a diameter of a kilometre or more. Further coalescence of uvalas may even result in the formation of basins of this solution origin that are sufficiently large to be classed among the "poljes".

On the floors of large poljes ground-water level reaches to the surface in the wet season, so that the ground is saturated and even locally flooded, surface streams can flow, and there is a local base-level of erosion. Thus extensive and nearly level floors, which are

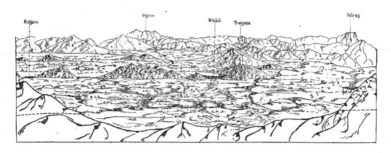

Fig. 212. The polje of Nikšić, in Montenegro. (After Cvijić, by courtesy of the *Geographical Review*.)

found in many of the large poljes, are regarded as having been reduced to small relief by a process of erosion akin to peneplanation. There are in places flat floors "of truncated limestone" (Davis), but in places the floors are aggraded with a layer of silt, while unconsumed monadnock-like hills of limestone (referred to as "hums") remain here and there. As an example of a large polje of tectonic origin greatly modified by erosion, so that it has now a great area of level floor diversified by residual hills, Cvijić figures that of Nikšić, in Montenegro (Fig. 212). Davis has described similar features as follows:

Among the many poljes that have no outlet gorge, one of the simplest examples that we saw occupied a depression in the uplands west of Mostar; it is known as the Mostarsko blato. Its floor...is of oval outline, with axes measuring about seven and two miles.... The surface of the polje is smoothly aggraded with fine silt. The uplands are pasture grounds; the polje is laid out in fields, largely submerged in winter, still partly submerged...late in May, but dry enough for cultivation or pasturage in the late summer, although a small lake remains even then in the south-eastern part of the plain. The drainage is effected at time of high water by discharge into an ugly cavernous hole, known as a ponor, at the rim of the polje plain, and at all times by underground percolation. The waters reappear after a subterranean passage of two miles in a great spring, which fed a good-sized branch of the Narenta....A much larger enclosed basin was that of the Nevesinje, fifteen miles long and three or four wide...from which several streams find underground escape through different ponors. Here the floor of the basin was gently rolling. Much of the underground water from this gathering-ground reappears ten miles away...in the great Buna spring...from which a vigorous stream runs to the Narenta.[1]

Certain poljes seem to have been developed in two stages, an inner floor being excavated to a level considerably lower than that indicated by terrace-forming remnants of an earlier floor, which probably means that the local base-level, governed by the water table, has sunk from an old to a new fixed level. In two examples about twenty miles north of Trebinje, Davis has described the poljes as "the lower compartments of a double-floored basin, the lower floors lying about 200 metres beneath the rimming remnants of what must have been once a much larger upper floor. Both floors were about horizontal, and both truncated the strongly inclined limestone strata."

A positive check to the lowering of local base-levels that results from progressive sinking of the water table is given by exposure of relatively impermeable formations beneath the limestone. Where the conditions of structure make this possible, the eventual removal by erosion of the limestone cover from an area thus floored with non-calcareous rocks is regarded as marking the "old-age" stage in a variety of the karst cycle specially related to this type of structure. When such "old age" is reached, only isolated hums of cavern-riddled limestone remain scattered over a landscape developed (or developing) on the underlying rocks. This is the stage that has been reached in the removal of a sheet of limestone from the plateaux of the Nelson province of New Zealand, with exposure of an underlying fossil plain (Fig. 213). The limestone residuals, referred to in Chapter XVIII as mesas, are in reality hums (see also

[1] W. M. Davis, *loc. cit.* pp. 40–1.

Pl. XXXI, 1). Cvijić's diagram (Fig. 214, 4) of this "old-age" stage of the karst cycle shows that it is not necessarily a stable or long-enduring type of landscape, and is, therefore, not truly senile or at all comparable with a peneplain. It is instead merely the ephemeral

Fig. 213. Bush-covered limestone hums, the last residuals of a sheet of limestone formerly covering a fossil plain that has been resurrected to form the Gouland Downs, Nelson province, New Zealand.

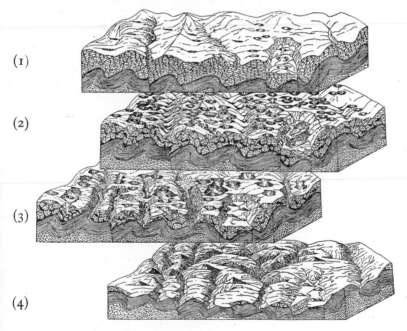

(1)

(2)

(3)

(4)

Fig. 214. Cvijić's diagram of four stages in a karst cycle.
(By courtesy of the *Geographical Review*.)

stage of partial exposure of the underlying rocks, which are from now on subject to dissection and gradation by the normal processes of erosion.

Stages in the karst erosion of the thick limestone cover pictured by Cvijić as leading up to the "old-age" stage, or (4) in Fig. 214, are (1) "youth", (2) "maturity", and (3) "late maturity". In (1) some karst features, which result from sinking of the water table, are making their appearance as modifications of an initial surface that has been prepared for "karsting" by removal of overlying non-calcareous, and presumably very weak, overlying strata so as to expose an undulating structural plateau of limestone varied by superposition on it of some streams from normal valley systems of the now vanished cover. At stage (2) all surface water is swallowed by abundant dolines and uvalas, which have developed to the extent of becoming the dominant features of the relief. At stage (3) new open valleys appear along the lines of the main underground stream courses of the previous stage, exposed now by foundering of their roofs, and carrying permanent streams of water because they have been cut down through the limestone into the underlying rocks.

The conditions of structure making possible the development of a landscape through the well-known "mature" stages of the karst to the ideal "old age" of this cycle—i.e. presence of a floor of impervious rocks below the limestone and above sea-level—are found only locally in the Dinaric limestone region, as is shown in Cvijić's large and beautifully designed generalised diagram of karst structures and relief.[1] Local reduction of the floors of poljes to small relief in relation to local base-levels is seen also to be merely an episode in the general reduction of the relief of the region in relation to a general base-level, which is sea-level.

As regards constructional forms peculiar to limestone regions, above-ground deposition of calcium carbonate from lime-saturated water is occasionally responsible for the development of features of some importance. Where such water emerges from underground channels as springs, or is broken by cascades where flowing in open courses, deposits of calcareous tufa in the compact form of travertine may be formed. Thus falls may grow forward instead of retreating by headward erosion as they do in other rocks. The beautiful cascades at Tivoli, near Rome, are advancing in this way,

---

[1] E. M. Sanders, The Cycle of Erosion in a Karst Region (after Cvijić), *Geog. Rev.* 11, Fig. 11, p. 603 (1921).

and so also are many in the Dinaric limestone region. Travertine bars built in river valleys where they are entered by springs emerging from caverns have ponded rivers in Dalmatia, forming lakes. A notable example is the Kerka River, dammed by travertine to form a large lake, the overflow falls from which supply a coastal town with power. An Australian example of a large river that leaps over "constructive" waterfalls formed by travertine bars is the Gregory (as Daneš has described), which is fed by ground water from a vast reservoir under the great limestone plateau south-west of the Gulf of Carpentaria.[1]

[1] J. V. Daneš, Physiography of some Limestone Areas in Queensland, *Proc. Roy. Soc. Q.* 23, p. 82 (1910).

PLATE I

. Rockfall from the side of a young gorge, Porter River, New Zealand.

Slump and earth-flow, Motunau, New Zealand.

PLATE II

1. Backward-tilted strips giving a terraced effect on a slumped hillside, North Auckland, New Zealand.

2. The Whitecliffs landslide, West Nelson, New Zealand.

PLATE III

Landslide near Tinui, New Zealand.

A concourse of hillocks, the cores of which are heaps of lava boulders believed to have been brought down from Ruapehu volcano (New Zealand) by a mudflow. View looking south up the slope of the volcano.

PLATE IV

1. Soil-creep carrying trees and fence-posts downhill, Mangapakeha Valley, New Zealand.

2. Sheep tracks, near Wellington, New Zealand.

PLATE V

. Bad-land forms developed on brecciated rock in a fault-zone affected by recent movement, Palliser Bay, New Zealand.

. Excavation exposing sub-surface weathering, with development of spheroidal cores, in basalt, near Mosgiel, New Zealand.

PLATE VI

1. Residual boulders of granite forming tors, New South Wales.

2. Horizontal "earth-fingers" cut by wind-driven rain, Wellington, New Zealand.

PLATE VII

2. Parallel-walled young valley, Gorner Gorge, Switzerland.

1. Earth pillars near Bozen (Bolzano), South Tyrol.

PLATE VIII

1. V-shaped young valley of the Ngahauranga, Wellington, New Zealand.

2. Winding valley forms in the young Ngahauranga Valley, Wellington, New Zealand, where curves have been enlarged by lateral corrasion accompanying incision of the valley. At the right the neck of a valley-side spur is narrowed, and almost cut through, by intersection of undercut slopes.

PLATE IX

1. A stream infantile in the post-Glacial cycle of normal erosion plunges at the Stirling Falls from the lip of a hanging valley, dropping 500 ft. into a fiord, Milford Sound, New Zealand.

2. Halawa Falls, Molokai, Hawaiian Islands, illustrating plunge-pool back-scour.

PLATE X

1. The Wairua Falls, North Auckland, New Zealand.

2. Stoneybyres Falls, Lanark, Scotland, showing development
of a canyon below the falls.

PLATE XI

1. Lakelets on an ice-scoured upland in Switzerland.

2. The English Lake Ullswater, of Glacial origin.

PLATE XII

Waikaremoana, a landslide lake. The outlet gorge (left) through a homoclinal ridge of sandstone, the escarpment of which defines the skyline, has been blocked by an enormous rock slide, and this dams the lake to a high level in a branching valley-system.

PLATE XIII

1. Lake Rotoaira, New Zealand, impounded by the more distant lava-flows descending northward (right to left in this view) from the volcano Tongariro.

2. A small lake in a valley blocked by a wandering dune, near Auckland, New Zealand.

PLATE XIV

1. Youthful dissection of an uplifted peneplain, Southern Tableland, New South Wales ("Shoalhaven Lookover").

2. Consequent drainage on a volcanic "shower" deposit spread over a hilly surface near Lake Rotomahana, New Zealand, by the explosive eruption of 1886.

PLATE XV

1. Homoclinal ridge, Marlborough, New Zealand, showing contrast between escarpment and dip-slope.

2. Full-face view of the escarpment in a continuation of the ridge shown in Fig. 1.

PLATE XVI

1. Serrate hogback ridges, Marlborough, New Zealand.

2. A rapidly retreating escarpment of limestone in the Broken River
intermont basin, New Zealand.

PLATE XVII

A scalloped escarpment of the Carboniferous limestone, Eglwyseg Mountain, Denbighshire.

Butte near Ficksburg, Orange Free State.

PLATE XVIII

1. The Vermilion Cliffs escarpment separating broad structural benches, in the Colorado Plateau province of the Western United States.

2. Structural terraces and dissected valley-side spurs projecting into the Grand Canyon of the Colorado River, Arizona.

PLATE XIX

1. The Rakaia Gorge, Canterbury, New Zealand.

Lodore Canyon, the gorge of the Green River through the Uinta Mountains, formerly regarded as of antecedent origin, but now explained as superposed.

PLATE XX

1. Flood-plain scrolls, an early stage of flood-plain development, in the valley of the Waimana River, Urewera, New Zealand.

1. The Rainbow Natural Bridge, Utah.

PLATE XXI

1. Meanders on a continuous flood plain in the upper valley of the Cobb River, Nelson, New Zealand.

2. Valley-floor features in the beheaded valley of the Karori stream, Wellington, New Zealand, which is now occupied only by an underfit rivulet.

PLATE XXII

1. Braided channels of the Waimakariri River, New Zealand.

2. "Rock terrace", Wairoa River, Nelson, New Zealand.

PLATE XXIII

1. Terraces of the Waikato River, North Island of New Zealand, cut in weak alluvial valley-filling and defended at a point where the river is confined in a gorge as a result of its being superposed on a buried valley-side spur.

2. A valley constriction in resistant rocks protects terraces in soft rocks where terraces of the Broken River, New Zealand, converge on the outlet gorge of an intermont basin.

PLATE XXIV

1. Terraces at the point of emergence from a gorge, Waimakariri River, New Zealand.

2. Submaturely dissected valley-plain terrace in the Makara Valley, Wellington, New Zealand.

PLATE XXV

Ungraded rocky slopes and early maturity of dissection in mountains sculptured by normal erosion, the Seaward Kaikoura Range, New Zealand, viewed from the north-west.

PLATE XXVI

1. Exfoliation dome of granitic rock, Stewart Island, New Zealand.

2. Talus slopes (the smooth grey areas) on a mountain-side, Hooker Valley, New Zealand.

PLATE XXVII

1. Soil-erosion and incipient gullying on deforested spurs near Wellington, New Zealand.

2. Incipient gullying where a protective cover of grassland vegetation has been weakened by burning and grazing, North Canterbury, New Zealand.

PLATE XXVIII

1. Aggradation in progress in the glaciated trough of the Rangitata Valley, New Zealand.

2. Truncated fans of the Paekakariki coast, New Zealand. The fans slope to the left; at the right a steeper small fan overlaps the main fan. After trimming the fronts of the fans to a line of cliffs the sea has withdrawn leaving a strand-plain (foreground).

PLATE XXIX

1. A rapidly-built delta which has filled an embayment of Lake Tarawera, New Zealand. The material deposited in the delta has been derived by erosion from a volcanic "shower" spread over the surrounding country by the eruption of 1886.

2. Fore-set and top-set beds of a delta of gravel built into Lake Wakatipu, New Zealand, at a former high level of the lake and subsequently trenched by erosion.

PLATE XXX

1. An aggraded valley-plain, which is an up-valley extension of the delta of the Clarence River, New Zealand.

2. Horizontal sky-line of a level-topped block mountain, Mount Pisa, Otago, New Zealand, which may be a remnant of an extensive late-Tertiary peneplain.

PLATE XXXI

1. The Gouland Downs plateau, New Zealand. The plateau is a resurrected fossil plain, and the same surface, slightly dissected, is warped up over the mountains at the rear.

2. A narrow tilted strip of resurrected fossil plain, showing the bottle-neck valleys of superposed consequent streams incised to a shallow depth below the surface, near St Bathans, New Zealand.

PLATE XXXII

1. Sarsen stones lying on the little-dissected tilted surface of Rough Ridge, New Zealand.

2. Dissected margin of the undulating plateau of south-eastern Otago, at Hillend, New Zealand.

PLATE XXXIII

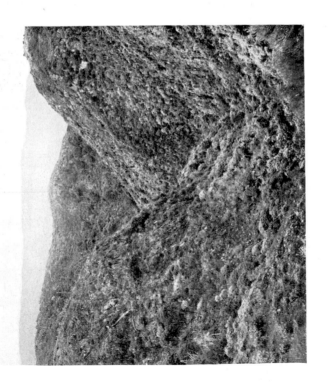

2. Valley-in-valley form of the Shotover Valley, New Zealand.

1. Shoulders separating fully mature upper valley-side slopes from steep young lower slopes, Haywards, Wellington, New Zealand.

PLATE XXXIV

1. Incised ("ingrown") meanders in a rejuvenated landscape, Hawke's Bay, New Zealand.

2. Headwater tributaries of the Wainui-o-mata system aggraded so as to form extensive swampy flats as a result of strong headward tilting, Wellington, New Zealand.

PLATE XXXV

1. Youthfully dissected fault scarp, with blunt-ended spurs strictly in line, Wellington, New Zealand.

2. Young fault scarp of a granitic mountain block south-east of Deep Springs Valley, eastern California. " Narrow **V**-shaped canyons have abnormally small alluvial fans at their mouths. Also the lowest part of the valley...is situated at the base of the scarp instead of in the middle of the basin " (Blackwelder).

Plate XXXVI

1. Maturely-dissected fault scarp of the Inyo Mountains (of Palaeozoic rocks with granite intrusions) north of Lone Pine, California.

2. Facetted spur-ends along part of the western base of the Wasatch Range, Utah.

PLATE XXXVII

1. Facets of the Wellington fault scarp at Petone, New Zealand.

2. Scarplet along the west base of the Sonoma Range, Nevada, formed at the time of the earthquake of 1915. It extends for about 40 miles across both spur-ends and alluvial fans, and is from 10 ft. to 20 ft. high.

PLATE XXXVIII

1. "Earthquake rent" tracing the line of outcrop of a great thrust fault which bounds the tectonic block of the Seaward Kaikoura Range, New Zealand, on the south-east side.

2. Wharf at Napier, New Zealand, uplifted 6 ft. in 1931. Former and present high-water marks are at the upper edges of two dark bands of marine growth on the piles.

PLATE XXXIX

1. Fault-line scarp. Ruakokopatuna Valley, Wairarapa district, New Zealand. Deformed Mesozoic rocks are separated by a fault at the base of the scarp from Pliocene limestone (foreground), from above which a great thickness of weak beds has been eroded.

2. West base of the Baldwin Range, New South Wales, which, as described by W. N. Benson, is a fault-line scarp exposed by the removal of soft mudstone of late Upper Devonian age along a fault contact with resistant agglomerate beds (early Upper Devonian). Relief, 1000 ft.

PLATE XL

1. Fault-line or composite scarp, Cave, South Canterbury, New Zealand. Subdued forms developed by erosion on soft covering strata are seen in front of the scarp.

2. Rejuvenated outlet gorge from the Hanmer intermont basin, New Zealand, which has been in part re-excavated, with resurrection of fault scarp bounding it.

PLATE XLI

1. Splinter of the scarp forming the north wall of the Waitaki Valley graben, New Zealand.

2. A fault scarp facing Death Valley, California, showing structural bands of rock-outcrops running obliquely down the scarp.

PLATE XLII

1. Karrenfeld, Punakaiki, New Zealand.

2. A stream emerges at water-level from an underground course through a tunnel due to solution of limestone, Broken River, New Zealand.

PLATE XLIII

1. Sinkholes in a limestone surface, South Canterbury, New Zealand.

2. One of a series of sinkholes aligned along an underground drainage channel, Nelson province, New Zealand.

PLATE XLIV

2. A wasting outcrop (a small "hum") of limestone, showing lapiés, Whangarei district, New Zealand.

1. Limestone arches, Jenolan Caves, New South Wales.

INDEX

CAMBRIDGE: PRINTED BY
WALTER LEWIS, M.A.
AT THE UNIVERSITY PRESS